SOLUTION KEY

Geometry

Ray C. Jurgensen
Richard G. Brown
John W. Jurgensen

HOUGHTON MIFFLIN COMPANY • BOSTON

Atlanta   Dallas   Geneva, Ill.   Lawrenceville, N.J.   Palo Alto   Toronto

1988 Impression

Copyright © 1985 by Houghton Mifflin Company

All rights reserved. No part of this work may be reproduced or transmitted in any form or by any means, electronic or mechanical, including photocopying and recording, or by any information storage or retrieval system, except as may be expressly permitted by the 1976 Copyright Act or in writing by the Publisher. Requests for permission should be addressed in writing to: Permissions, Houghton Mifflin Company, One Beacon Street, Boston, Massachusetts 02108.

Printed in U.S.A.

ISBN: 0-395-43062-3

ABCDEFGHIJ-A-943210/8987

CONTENTS

Pages 4-5 · WRITTEN EXERCISES

A 1. true   2. true   3. true   4. false   5. true   6. true

   7. true   8. false   9. false   10. true

  11. Sketches may vary.

  a.
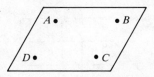

  b.
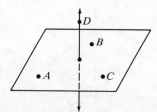

  12. VRS, VST, VTW, VWR, WRS   13. no   14. $\overleftrightarrow{RW}$, $\overleftrightarrow{RV}$, $\overleftrightarrow{RS}$ 15. WRS, VST

  16. VRS, VST, WRS   17-18. Answers may vary.   17. $\overleftrightarrow{VS}$, WRS   18. $\overleftrightarrow{WR}$, WRS

  19. Check students' drawings.   20. RFG, GFB   21. $\overleftrightarrow{ER}$, $\overleftrightarrow{EA}$, $\overleftrightarrow{EH}$

  22. EAB, FBC, DAB   23. a. no   b. yes   24. a. yes   b. no

  25. a. EAB, HDC   b. EAD, FBC

B 26. a. no   b. yes   27-34. Sketches may vary.

  27.
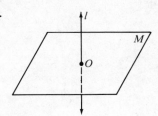

  28.
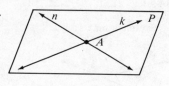

  29.
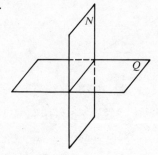

  30.
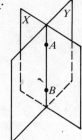

1

<u>C</u> <u>31</u>.

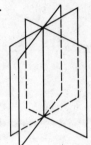

<u>32</u>.

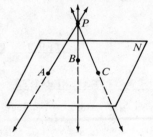

<u>33</u>.

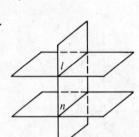

<u>34</u>.

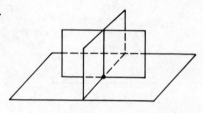

Pages 8-10 · WRITTEN EXERCISES

<u>A</u> <u>1</u>. 15   <u>2</u>. 14   <u>3</u>. 4.5   <u>4</u>. 7.1   <u>5</u>. true   <u>6</u>. false   <u>7</u>. true

<u>8</u>. true   <u>9</u>. false   <u>10</u>. true   <u>11</u>. false   <u>12</u>. true   <u>13</u>. true

<u>14</u>. false   <u>15</u>. true   <u>16</u>. false   <u>17</u>. B   <u>18</u>. F   <u>19</u>. C, G

<u>20</u>. $\overrightarrow{BA}$ <u>21</u>. D   <u>22</u>. -1   <u>23</u>. -1   <u>24</u>. $\overline{BG}$

<u>25-28</u>. Sketches may vary.

<u>25</u>.

<u>26</u>.

<u>27</u>.

<u>28</u>.

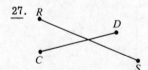

<u>B</u> <u>29</u>. a. 5   b. 10   c. 10   d. 6   <u>30</u>. -7; 5; 8   <u>31</u>. x = 6   <u>32</u>. x = 11

<u>33</u>. x = 3   <u>34</u>. x = 7   <u>35</u>. y = 6   <u>36</u>. y = 7   <u>37</u>. z = 8; GE = 10;

EH = 10; yes   <u>38</u>. z = 5; GE = 5; EH = 6; no   <u>39</u>. a. one   b. two

<u>C</u> <u>40</u>. If AB < 10, there is one; otherwise there are two.   <u>41</u>. $\overline{HN}$ <u>42</u>. $\overrightarrow{MH}$ $(\overrightarrow{MG})$

43. M   44. $\overleftrightarrow{MN}$ (or any other suitable name for $\overleftrightarrow{MN}$)   45. $\overline{GT}$ 46. x ≥ 0

47. -2 ≤ x ≤ 8   48. x > 2

49. a. C = $\frac{5}{9}$(98.6 - 32) = 37, 98.6° F = 37° C; C = $\frac{5}{9}$(-40 - 32) = -40; -40° F = -40° C

    b. C = $\frac{5}{9}$(F - 32); F - 32 = $\frac{9}{5}$C; F = $\frac{9}{5}$C + 32

    c. F = $\frac{9}{5}$(100) + 32 = 212, 100° C = 212° F; F = $\frac{9}{5}$(-10) + 32 = 14; -10° C = 14° F

Pages 14-15 · WRITTEN EXERCISES

A   1. E   2. $\overrightarrow{AT}$, $\overrightarrow{AS}$ 3-8. Answers may vary.   3. ∠ELS   4. ∠LAT

    5. ∠AEL   6. ∠2 or ∠ALE   7. ∠7 or ∠ASL   8. ∠6 or ∠DES

    9. acute   10. acute   11. right   12. acute   13. straight

    14. obtuse   15. LKP   16. 3   17. $\overrightarrow{KN}$; ∠LKP   18. m∠2 = m∠3

    19. m∠LNP = 180   20. 3; 1, 2, 3

    21.   22.   23.   24.

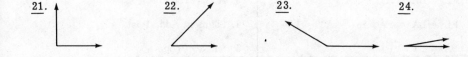

B   25. Yes; 180 (Check students' drawings.)   26. a. 90; 90; 90   b. 87; 93; 87

    c. 180 - x; x; 180 - x   27. ∠KZJ, ∠KZL, ∠JZM, ∠LZM   28. ∠KJZ, ∠JKZ,

    ∠ZKL, ∠ZLK, ∠KJM, ∠ZJM, ∠ZMJ, ∠ZLM, ∠ZML   29. ∠JKL, 100; ∠KLM, 120;

    ∠LMJ, 100   30. ∠JKL, ∠JML

    31. Sketches may vary.

    32. 99   33. 31   34. x = 35   35. x = 30   36. x = 3   37. x = 6

    38. x = 11

C   39. a. 6; 10   ' b. 15   c. $\frac{n(n - 1)}{2}$

Pages 20-22 · WRITTEN EXERCISES

A   1. Given; Add. Prop. of =; Div. Prop. of =

    2. Given; Mult. Prop. of =; Div. Prop. of =

<u>3</u>. Given; Mult. Prop. of =; Subtr. Prop. of =

<u>4</u>. Given; Add. Prop. of =; Subtr. Prop. of =; Div. Prop. of =

<u>5</u>. Given; Mult. Prop. of =; Dist. Prop.; Add. Prop. of =; Div. Prop. of =

<u>6</u>. Given; Mult. Prop. of =; Dist. Prop.; Subtr. Prop. of =; Add. Prop. of =;

Div. Prop. of =

<u>7</u>.

Statements	Reasons
1. $m\angle AOD = m\angle AOC + m\angle 3$	1. Angle Add. Post.
2. $m\angle AOC = m\angle 1 + m\angle 2$	2. Angle Add. Post.
3. $m\angle AOD = m\angle 1 + m\angle 2 + m\angle 3$	3. Subst. Prop.

<u>8</u>.

Statements	Reasons
1. FL = AT	1. Given
2. LA = LA	2. Refl. Prop.
3. FL + LA = AT + LA	3. Add. Prop. of =
4. FL + LA = FA; LA + AT = LT	4. Segment Add. Post.
5. FA = LT	5. Subst. Prop.

<u>9</u>.

Statements	Reasons
1. DW = ON	1. Given
2. DW = DO + OW; ON = OW + WN	2. Segment Add. Post.
3. DO + OW = OW + WN	3. Subst. Prop.
4. OW = OW	4. Refl. Prop.
5. DO = WN	5. Subtr. Prop. of =

B <u>10</u>.

Statements	Reasons
1. $m\angle 4 + m\angle 6 = 180$	1. Given
2. $m\angle 4 + m\angle 5 = 180$	2. Angle Add. Post.
3. $m\angle 4 + m\angle 5 = m\angle 4 + m\angle 6$	3. Subst. Prop.
4. $m\angle 4 = m\angle 4$	4. Refl. Prop.
5. $m\angle 5 = m\angle 6$	5. Subtr. Prop. of =

<u>11</u>. 1. $m\angle 1 = m\angle 2$; $m\angle 3 = m\angle 4$ (Given)   2. $m\angle 1 + m\angle 3 = m\angle 2 + m\angle 4$ (Add.

Prop. of =)   3. $m\angle 1 + m\angle 3 = m\angle SRT$; $m\angle 2 + m\angle 4 = m\angle STR$ (Angle Add.

Post.)   4. $m\angle SRT = m\angle STR$ (Subst. Prop.)

12. 1. RP = TQ; PS = QS (Given)   2. RP + PS = TQ + QS (Add. Prop. of =)

    3. RP + PS = RS; TQ + QS = TS (Seg. Add. Post.)   4. RS = TS (Subst. Prop.)

13. 1. RQ = TP; ZQ = ZP (Given)   2. RZ + ZQ = RQ; TZ + ZP = TP (Seg. Add.

    Post.)   3. RZ + ZQ = TZ + ZP (Subst. Prop.)   4. RZ = TZ (Subtr. Prop. of =)

14. 1. m∠SRT = m∠STR (Given)   2. m∠1 + m∠3 = m∠SRT; m∠2 + m∠4 = m∠STR

    (Angle Add. Post.)   3. m∠1 + m∠3 = m∠2 + m∠4 (Subst. Prop.)

    4. m∠3 = m∠4 (Given)   5. m∠1 = m∠2 (Subtr. Prop. of =)

15. b

Pages 26-28 · WRITTEN EXERCISES

A 1. Def. of midpoint   2. Def. of angle bisector   3. Angle bisector Thm.

   4. Angle Add. Post.   5. Def. of midpoint   6. Midpoint Thm.

   7. Angle Add. Post.   8. Segment Add. Post.   9. Def. of angle bisector

10. 60   11. 75   12. 70   13. 8.5   14. 15   15. -20   16. 5

17. 38   18. -16

B 19. a. $\overline{LM} \cong \overline{MK}$; $\overline{GN} \cong \overline{NH}$ b. Answers may vary. For example, LK = GH

20. a. ∠RSV ≅ ∠VST; ∠SRU ≅ ∠URT

    b. Answers may vary. For example, ∠RSU ≅ ∠SRV

21. AC = DB   22. AE = EC = DE = EB and AC = DB.

23. L   Y   N   X   a. 12   b. 6   c. 22   d. 28
    •——————•——————•———————————•
    16   40

24. a. 18   b. 54

25. 1. Given   2. Ruler Post.   3. Given   4. Def. of midpoint   5. Subst. Prop.

    6. a + b; Add. Prop. of =   7. Div. Prop. of =

26. By the Protractor Post., m∠POX = p - x and m∠XOQ = x - q. By the def. of

    angle bisector, p - x = x - q. Then 2x = p + q and x = $\frac{p + q}{2}$.

27. a. x = 45   b. 0 < x < 45   c. 45 < x < 90

28. 1. $\overrightarrow{AC}$ bisects ∠DAB; $\overrightarrow{CA}$ bisects ∠BCD. (Given)   2. m∠1 = $\frac{1}{2}$m∠DAB;

    m∠3 = $\frac{1}{2}$m∠DCB (Angle Bisector Thm.)   3. m∠1 = m∠3 (Given)

    4. $\frac{1}{2}$m∠DAB = $\frac{1}{2}$m∠DCB (Subst. Prop.)   5. m∠DAB = m∠DCB (Mult. Prop. of =)

29. 1. M is the midpoint of $\overline{LK}$; N is the midpoint of $\overline{GH}$. (Given)   2. MK = $\frac{1}{2}$LK;

NH = $\frac{1}{2}$GH (Midpoint Thm.)   3. LK = GH (Given)   4. $\frac{1}{2}$LK = $\frac{1}{2}$GH (Mult. Prop.

of =)   5. MK = NH (Subst. Prop.)

<u>C</u> 30.

m∠1 + m∠2 + m∠3 + m∠4 = 180; m∠1 = m∠2;

m∠3 = m∠4; 2m∠2 + 2m∠3 = 180;

m∠2 + m∠3 = 90

<u>31.</u> If WT = y, ZS = x + y and TS = 2x + y. RT = 2y, so 2y = 2x + y or y = 2x.

<u>a</u>. 2x   <u>b</u>. 3x   <u>c</u>. 8x   <u>d</u>. 3x

Page 29 · COMPUTER KEY-IN

<u>1.</u> The coordinates seem to be approaching $.\overline{6}$; $\frac{2}{3}$

<u>3.</u> $1 - \frac{1}{3} + \frac{1}{9} - \frac{1}{27} + \cdots + (-\frac{1}{3})^{n-1}$; Line 50 becomes

50 P(N) = P(N - 1) + $(-\frac{1}{3})$ ↑ (N - 1); $\frac{3}{4}$

<u>4.</u> 50 P(N) = P(N - 1) + $(-\frac{1}{4})$ ↑ (N - 1); $\frac{4}{5}$

Pages 32-35 · WRITTEN EXERCISES

<u>A</u> <u>1.</u> 35; 125   <u>2.</u> 89; 179   <u>3.</u> 17.5; 107.5   <u>4.</u> 90 - 3x; 180 - 3x   <u>5.</u> 45

<u>6.</u> 90   <u>7.</u> ∠LAE   <u>8.</u> ∠LAE, ∠KAE

<u>9.</u> ∠LAN, ∠NAK; ∠BAE, ∠EAN; ∠LAB, ∠BAK; ∠LAB, ∠LAN; ∠NAK, ∠KAB

<u>10.</u> ∠LBA, ∠ABE   <u>11.</u> ∠LAB, ∠BAE (or ∠BAE, ∠NAK)

<u>12.</u> ∠LAB, ∠NAK; ∠LAN, ∠BAK   <u>13.</u> 35   <u>14.</u> 155   <u>15.</u> 25   <u>16.</u> 120

<u>17.</u> 60   <u>18.</u> 85   <u>19.</u> 3x - 5 = 70; 3x = 75; x = 25

<u>20.</u> 4x + 8 = 6x - 22; 2x = 30; x = 15

<u>21.</u> $x^2 = 64 + 36$; $x^2 = 100$; x = 10 (x > 0)

<u>22.</u> a. m∠1 + m∠2 = 180; m∠2 + 27 = 180; m∠2 = 153. Similarly, m∠4 = 153.

b. m∠1 + m∠2 = 180; m∠2 + x = 180; m∠2 = 180 - x. Similarly,

m∠4 = 180 - x.   <u>c</u>. yes

<u>B</u> <u>23.</u> m∠A + m∠B = 180; 2x + x - 15 = 180; 3x = 195; x = 65; m∠A = 2x = 130;

m∠B = x - 15 = 50

<u>24.</u> m∠A + m∠B = 180; x + 16 + 2x - 16 = 180; 3x = 180; x = 60; m∠A =

x + 16 = 76; m∠B = 2x - 16 = 104

25. $m\angle C + m\angle D = 90$; $3y + 5 + 2y = 90$; $5y = 85$; $y = 17$; $m\angle C = 3y + 5 = 56$;

$m\angle D = 2y = 34$

26. $m\angle C + m\angle D = 90$; $y - 8 + 3y + 2 = 90$; $4y = 96$; $y = 24$; $m\angle C = y - 8 = 16$;

$m\angle D = 3y + 2 = 74$

27. $180 - x = 2x$; $3x = 180$; $x = 60$; $2x = 120$; 60 and 120

28. $90 - x = 5x$; $6x = 90$; $x = 15$; $5x = 75$; 15 and 75

29. $90 - x = 2x - 6$; $3x = 96$; $x = 32$; $90 - x = 58$; 32 and 58

30. $(180 - x) - x = 42$; $180 - 2x = 42$; $2x = 138$; $x = 69$; $180 - x = 111$; 69 and 111

31. $180 - x = 6(90 - x)$; $180 - x = 540 - 6x$; $5x = 360$; $x = 72$; $90 - x = 18$;

$180 - x = 108$; 72, 18, and 108

32. $3(180 - x) = 8(90 - x)$; $540 - 3x = 720 - 8x$; $5x = 180$; $x = 36$; $90 - x = 54$;

$180 - x = 144$; 36, 54, and 144

33. 1. Vert. $\angle$ are $\cong$.   2. Given   3. Vert. $\angle$ are $\cong$.   4. $\angle 1 \cong \angle 4$

34. 1. $\angle 1 \cong \angle 2$ (Vert. $\angle$ are $\cong$.)   2. $\angle 2 \cong \angle 3$ (Given)   3. $\angle 3 \cong \angle 4$ (Vert. $\angle$ are $\cong$.)

4. $\angle 1 \cong \angle 4$ (Trans. Prop. of $\cong$)

35. $x + 3x - 8 = 180$; $4x = 188$; $x = 47$; $2y - 17 = 3x - 8$; $2y - 17 = 133$;

$2y = 150$; $y = 75$

36. $2x - 16 = 50$; $2x = 66$; $x = 33$; $x = 3x - y$; $33 = 99 - y$; $y = 66$

C 37. $x = 2y + 5$ and $x + y = 95$; $(2y + 5) + y = 95$; $3y + 5 = 95$; $3y = 90$; $y = 30$;

$x = 2y + 5 = 65$

38. $x + 2y = 40$; $x = 40 - 2y$; $4x - y + 110 = 180$; $4x - y = 70$; $4(40 - 2y) - y = 70$;

$160 - 8y - y = 70$; $160 - 9y = 70$; $9y = 90$; $y = 10$; $x = 40 - 2y = 20$

39. Let x be the measure of an angle and suppose the measure of its complement is exactly

half the measure of its supplement.   Then $90 - x = \frac{1}{2}(180 - x) = 90 - \frac{1}{2}x$ and

$x = \frac{1}{2}x$.   That cannot be true since $x > 0$.

40. All $\angle$ whose measure is less than or equal to 90; that is, all $\angle$ which have both a

complement and a supplement.

Pages 37-39 · WRITTEN EXERCISES

A 1. $\perp$ lines are 2 lines that form rt. $\angle$.   2. A rt. $\angle$ is an $\angle$ with measure 90.

3. If the ext. sides of 2 adj. acute $\angle$ are $\perp$, then the $\angle$ are comp.

4. If 2 lines form $\cong$ adj. $\angle$, then the lines are $\perp$.

5. A rt. ∠ is an ∠ with measure 90.   6. Adj. ∕s formed by ⊥ lines are ≅.

7. ⊥ lines are lines that form 2 rt. ∕s.

8. Comp. ∕s are ∕s whose measures have the sum 90.

9. 1. Angle Add. Post.   2. Given   3. Subst. Prop.   4. m∠1 = 90

   5. Def. of rt. ∠   6. a ⊥ b (Def. of ⊥ lines)

10. 1. Given   2. ∠ABD is a rt. ∠.   3. Def. of rt. ∠   4. Angle Add. Post.

    5. m∠ABC + m∠CBD = 90   6. ∠ABC and ∠CBD are comp. ∕s.

B 11. 1. $\overline{SW} \perp \overline{RT}$ (Given)   2. m∠1 = m∠2 (Adj. ∕s formed by ⊥ lines are ≅.)

12. 1. m∠1 = m∠2 (Given)   2. $\overline{SW} \perp \overline{RT}$ (If 2 lines form ≅ adj. ∕s, then the lines

    are ⊥.)

13. 90 + x   14. 180 - y   15. x + y   16. 90 - (x + y)   17. yes

18. no   19. no   20. no   21. no   22. yes   23. yes   24. no

25-28. Answers may vary.

25. ∠RSX and ∠YST are comp.   26. ∠XSY is a rt. ∠, $\overrightarrow{SX} \perp \overrightarrow{SY}$

27. $\overrightarrow{AD} \perp \overleftrightarrow{AC}$ and $\overrightarrow{CE} \perp \overleftrightarrow{AC}$ 28. m∠2 = m∠3

C 29. 1. ∠1 and ∠2 are comp. ∕s. (Given)   2. m∠1 + m∠2 = 90 (Def. of comp. ∕s).

    3. m∠1 + m∠2 = m∠AOC (Angle Add. Post.)   4. m∠AOC = 90 (Subst. Prop.)

    5. ∠AOC is a rt. ∠. (Def. of rt. ∠)   6. $\overleftrightarrow{AO} \perp \overleftrightarrow{CO}$ (Def. of ⊥ lines)

30. 1. $\overleftrightarrow{AO} \perp \overleftrightarrow{CO}$ (Given)   2. ∠1 and ∠2 are comp. ∕s. (If the ext. sides of 2 adj. acute

    ∕s are ⊥, then the ∕s are comp.)   3. m∠1 + m∠2 = 90 (Def. of comp. ∕s)

    4. m∠2 = m∠3 (Vert. ∕s are ≅.)   5. m∠1 + m∠3 = 90 (Subst. Prop.)

    6. ∠1 and ∠3 are comp. ∕s. (Def. of comp. ∕s)

Pages 43-45 · WRITTEN EXERCISES

A 1. a. ∠1   b. ∠4   c. Angle Add. Post.   d. If 2 ∕s are supp. of ≅ ∕s, then the

      2 ∕s are ≅.

2. a. ∠1   b. ∠4   c. If the ext. sides of 2 adj. acute ∕s are ⊥, then the 2 ∕s are comp.

   d. If 2 ∕s are comp. of ≅ ∕s, then the 2 ∕s are ≅.

3. Segment Add. Post.   4. Angle Add. Post.

5. Add. Prop. of =   6. Vert. ∕s are ≅

7. Def. of ∠ bisector   8. Def. of midpoint

9. Def. of ⊥ lines, Def. of rt. ∠   10. Angle Add. Post.

11. Def. of comp. ∠.   12. Def. of supp. ∠.

13. Midpoint Thm.   14. Def. of ∠ bisector

15. Adj. ∠ formed by ⊥ lines are ≅.

16. If 2 ∠ are comp. of the same ∠, then the 2 ∠ are ≅.

17. Def. of rt. ∠, ⊥ lines

18. If 2 lines form ≅ adj. ∠, then the lines are ⊥.

19. a. 1. Given   2. If the ext. sides of 2 adj. acute ∠ are ⊥, then the ∠ are comp.

    3. Given   4. If 2 ∠ are comp. of ≅ ∠, then the 2 ∠ are ≅.

    b. ∠3 and ∠6 are supp. of ∠2 and ∠5, resp.; since they are supp. of ≅ ∠, ∠3 ≅ ∠6.

20. a. ∠2; ∠2 and ∠4 are vert. ∠.   b. ∠2 as in part (a); ∠6 and ∠8, since ∠6 and

    ∠8 are also supp. of ∠5.

B 21. 1. ∠2 ≅ ∠3 (Given)   2. ∠1 and ∠2 are supp. ∠; ∠3 and ∠4 are supp. ∠ (Angle

    Add. Post.; Def. of supp. ∠)   3. ∠1 ≅ ∠4 (If 2 ∠ are supp. of ≅ ∠, then the

    2 ∠ are ≅.)

22. 1. $\overline{AC}$ ⊥ $\overline{BC}$ (Given)   2. ∠2 is comp. to ∠1. (If the ext. sides of 2 adj. acute ∠

    are ⊥, then the 2 ∠ are comp.)   3. ∠3 is comp. to ∠1. (Given)   4. ∠3 ≅ ∠2

    (If 2 ∠ are comp. of the same ∠, then the 2 ∠ are ≅.)

23. Given: ∠1 and ∠2 are comp.;

        ∠3 and ∠4 are comp.;

        ∠2 ≅ ∠4 (or m∠2 = m∠4)

    Prove: ∠1 ≅ ∠3 (or m∠1 = m∠3)

    Proof: 1. ∠1 and ∠2 are comp.; ∠3 and ∠4 are comp. (Given)

    2. m∠1 + m∠2 = 90; m∠3 + m∠4 = 90 (Def. of comp. ∠)   3. m∠1 + m∠2 =

    m∠3 + m∠4 (Subst. Prop.)   4. m∠2 = m∠4 (Given)   5. m∠1 = m∠3

    (Subtr. Prop. of =)

24. 1. m∠1 + m∠3 = 180; m∠2 + m∠3 = 180 (Angle Add. Post.)   2. ∠1 and ∠3 are

    supp. ∠; ∠2 and ∠3 are supp. ∠. (Def. of supp. ∠)   3. ∠1 ≅ ∠2 (If 2 ∠ are

    supp. of the same ∠, then the 2 ∠ are ≅.)

25. a. 3   b. 4   c. 7   d. 8

26. 1. m∠5 + m∠6 = 180 (Angle Add. Post.)   2. ∠5 is supp. to ∠6. (Def. of supp. ∠)

    3. ∠4 is supp. to ∠6. (Given)   4. ∠4 ≅ ∠5 (If 2 ∠ are supp. of the same ∠, then the

    2 ∠ are ≅.)   5. ∠3 ≅ ∠4 (Vert. ∠ are ≅.)   6. ∠3 ≅ ∠5 (Trans. Prop.)

<u>27</u>. 1. $\angle 1 \cong \angle 2$ (Vert. $\angle$s are $\cong$.)   2. $\angle 2 \cong \angle 3$ (Given)   3. $\angle 1 \cong \angle 3$ (Trans. Prop.)

4. $\angle 3 \cong \angle 4$ (Vert. $\angle$s are $\cong$.)   5. $\angle 1 \cong \angle 4$ (Trans. Prop.)   6. $\angle 4 \cong \angle 5$ (Given)

7. $\angle 1 \cong \angle 5$ (Trans. Prop.)   8. $m\angle 5 + m\angle 6 = 180$ (Angle Add. Post.)

9. $m\angle 1 + m\angle 6 = 180$ (Subst. Prop.)   10. $\angle 1$ is supp. to $\angle 6$. (Def. of supp. $\angle$s)

<u>28</u>. 1. $m\angle 1 = m\angle 2$; $m\angle 3 = m\angle 4$ (Given)   2. $m\angle 1 + m\angle 3 = m\angle 2 + m\angle 4$ (Add.

Prop. of =)   3. $m\angle AOC = m\angle 1 + m\angle 3$; $m\angle EOC = m\angle 2 + m\angle 4$ (Angle Add.

Post.)   4. $m\angle AOC = m\angle EOC$ (Subst. Prop.)   5. $\overrightarrow{OC} \perp \overleftrightarrow{AE}$ (If 2 lines form $\cong$

adj. $\angle$s, then the lines are $\perp$.)

<u>29</u>. 1. $\overrightarrow{OC} \perp \overleftrightarrow{AE}$ (Given)   2. $\angle AOC \cong \angle EOC$ (Adj. $\angle$s formed by $\perp$ lines are $\cong$.)

3. $m\angle AOC = m\angle 1 + m\angle 3$; $m\angle EOC = m\angle 2 + m\angle 4$ (Angle Add. Post.)

4. $m\angle 1 + m\angle 3 = m\angle 2 + m\angle 4$ (Subst. Prop.)   5. $\overrightarrow{OC}$ bisects $\angle BOD$. (Given)

6. $m\angle 1 = m\angle 2$ (Def. of $\angle$ bis.)   7. $m\angle 3 = m\angle 4$ (Subtr. Prop. of =)

<u>C</u> <u>30</u>. $\overrightarrow{OY}$ bisects $\angle COD$.   Proof: 1. $\overrightarrow{OX}$ bisects $\angle AOB$. (Given)   2. $m\angle 1 = m\angle 2$ (Def.

of $\angle$ bis.)   3. $m\angle 2 = m\angle 3$ (Vert. $\angle$s are $\cong$)   4. $m\angle 1 = m\angle 3$ (Trans. Prop.)

5. $m\angle 1 = m\angle 4$ (Vert. $\angle$s are $\cong$.)   6. $m\angle 3 = m\angle 4$ (Trans. Prop.)

7. $\overrightarrow{OY}$ bisects $\angle COD$. (Def. of $\angle$ bis.)

<u>31</u>.   1. $\overrightarrow{QX}$ bisects $\angle PQR$ (Given)   2. $\angle 1 \cong \angle 2$ (Def. of

$\angle$ bis.)   3. $\angle PQY$ is supp. to $\angle 1$; $\angle RQY$ is supp. to

$\angle 2$. (Angle Add. Post.; Def. of supp. $\angle$s.)

4. $\angle PQY \cong \angle RQY$ (If 2 $\angle$s are supp. of $\cong$ $\angle$s, then

the 2 $\angle$s are $\cong$.)

<u>32</u>. 1. $m\angle DBA = 45$; $m\angle DEB = 45$ (Given)   2. $\angle DBA \cong \angle DEB$ (Def. of $\cong$ $\angle$s)

3. $\angle FEB$ is supp. to $\angle DEB$; $\angle DBC$ is supp. to $\angle DBA$. (Angle Add. Post.; Def. of

supp. $\angle$s)   4. $\angle DBC \cong \angle FEB$ (If 2 $\angle$s are supp. of $\cong$ $\angle$s, then the 2 $\angle$s are $\cong$.)

Pages 48-49 · WRITTEN EXERCISES

<u>A</u> <u>1</u>. always   <u>2</u>. sometimes   <u>3</u>. sometimes   <u>4</u>. never   <u>5</u>. sometimes

<u>6</u>. never   <u>7</u>. always   <u>8</u>. sometimes   <u>9</u>. always   <u>10</u>. never

<u>11</u>. never   <u>12</u>. always

<u>B</u> <u>13</u>. Every angle has at least one bisector; an angle has no more than one bisector.

14.   Given: Lines j and k intersect.

Prove: j and k intersect in exactly one point, P.

15. a. Through any 3 points, there is at least one plane.   b. If 2 points are in a plane, then the line that contains the points is in that plane.   c. Through any two points there is exactly one line.   d. If 2 points are in a plane, then the line that contains the points is in that plane.

16. a. Through any 3 points there is at least one plane.   b. According to the Ruler Postulate the points on $\overleftrightarrow{AD}$ and $\overleftrightarrow{AC}$ can be paired with the real numbers.   Between any 2 real numbers there is another real number.   So there must exist a point P between A and D and a point Q between A and C.   c. Through any 3 points there is at least one plane.   d. There are an infinite number of points Q on $\overleftrightarrow{AC}$.   For each Q there exists a plane BPQ.   Therefore, there are an infinite number of planes through P.

C 17. a. 3   b. 6   c. 10   d. 15   e. 21   f. $\dfrac{n(n-1)}{2}$

Pages 50-52 · CHAPTER REVIEW

1.
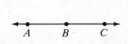

2.
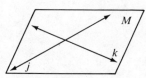

3.
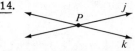

4. U or V

5. a. RS = 3; ST = 3   b. ≅   6. x = 9

7. ∠1, ∠2, ∠ADC; ∠1 and ∠2

8. a. 92   b. Angle Add. Post.   c. obtuse

9. 5x - 3 = x + 25; 4x = 28; x = 7   10. Trans. Prop. of ≅

11. Add. Prop. of =   12. Subst. Prop.

13. Midpoint Thm.   14. Def. of ∠ bis.

15. Angle Bis. Thm.   16. x + x = 90; 2x = 90; x = 45

17. 90; Vert. ∠ are ≅.

18. Answers may vary.   ∠1 and ∠2; ∠PXQ and ∠QXT

19. Adj. $\angle\!\!\!\angle$ formed by $\perp$ lines are $\cong$.

20. If 2 lines form $\cong$ adj. $\angle\!\!\!\angle$, then the lines are $\perp$.

21. $4t - 13 + 2t + 19 = 90$; $6t = 84$; $t = 14$

22-24. Answers may vary.

22. $\overleftrightarrow{GI} \perp \overleftrightarrow{GF}$ 23. $\angle 2 \cong \angle 4$ 24. $\angle 4 \cong \angle 6$

25. false   26. false   27. false   28. true

Page 52 · CHAPTER TEST

1. A, X, and C; or D, X, and B   2. A   3. Segment Add. Post.

4. $\overline{DX}$, $\overline{XB}$ 5. X; $\overrightarrow{XD}$ and $\overrightarrow{XA}$ 6. $\angle DAB$

7. Answers may vary. $\angle DXC$, $\angle CXB$ 8. $\angle DAX$, $\angle XAB$ 9. Trans. Prop. of $\cong$

10. AC   11. $m\angle DXC = 134$; $m\angle CXB = 46$ 12. 20   13. 3   14. never

15. always   16. $6x - 30 = \frac{1}{2}(5x + 24)$; $12x - 60 = 5x + 24$; $7x = 84$; $x = 12$

17. a. Angle Add. Post.   b. Mult. Prop. of =   c. Adj. $\angle\!\!\!\angle$ formed by $\perp$ lines are $\cong$.

18. 1. $m\angle 3 + m\angle 4 = 180$ (Angle Add. Post.)   2. $\angle 3$ and $\angle 4$ are supp. $\angle\!\!\!\angle$. (Def. of

supp. $\angle\!\!\!\angle$.)   3. $\angle 2$ and $\angle 4$ are supp. $\angle\!\!\!\angle$. (Given)   4. $\angle 2 \cong \angle 3$ (If 2 $\angle\!\!\!\angle$ are supp.

of the same $\angle$, then the 2 $\angle\!\!\!\angle$ are $\cong$.)

Page 53 · ALGEBRA REVIEW

1. $5a - 22 = 8$; $5a = 30$; $a = 6$ 2. $2z = 5z + 12$; $-3z = 12$; $z = -4$

3. $3x - 4 = 2x + 4$; $x = 8$

4. $3(9 - t) = 5 + t$; $27 - 3t = 5 + t$; $22 = 4t$; $t = 5\frac{1}{2}$

5. $4(90 - x) = 180 - x$; $360 - 4x = 180 - x$; $180 = 3x$; $x = 60$

6. $90 - y = 3 + 2y$; $87 = 3y$; $y = 29$

7. $(n - 2)180 = 160n$; $180n - 360 = 160n$; $20n = 360$; $n = 18$

8. $b(b - 3) = b^2 + 12$; $b^2 - 3b = b^2 + 12$; $-3b = 12$; $b = -4$

9. $2k(k - 1) = k(2k + 1)$; $2k^2 - 2k = 2k^2 + k$; $-2k = k$; $0 = 3k$; $k = 0$

10. $5(2d + 1) = 3(5d - 5)$; $10d + 5 = 15d - 15$; $-5d = -20$; $d = 4$

11. $5 + 1.6m = 1$; $1.6m = -4$; $m = -2.5$

12. $0.3q - 8 = 6 + q$; $-0.7q = 14$; $q = -20$

13. $2x - 3y = -2$
    $\underline{5x + 3y = 37}$
    $7x \quad\quad = 35$; $x = 5$; $2x - 3y = -2$; $10 - 3y = -2$; $-3y = -12$; $y = 4$

<u>14</u>. $-4x + 7y = 2$

    $4x - 5y = 10$

           $2y = 12$; $y = 6$; $-4x + 7y = 2$; $-4x + 42 = 2$; $-4x = -40$; $x = 10$

<u>15</u>. $2x - 5y = 0$

    $x - 5y = 10$

    $x \qquad = -10$; $2x - 5y = 0$; $-20 - 5y = 0$; $-5y = 20$; $y = -4$

<u>16</u>. $y = 5x - 3$ $5x - y = 3$

      $8x - y = 9$; $8x - y = 9$

                  $-3x \qquad = -6$; $x = 2$; $y = 5x - 3 = 7$

<u>17</u>. $y = x - 8$ $x - y = 8$

    $x - 4y = 5$; $x - 4y = 5$

                  $3y = 3$; $y = 1$; $y = x - 8$; $1 = x - 8$; $x = 9$

<u>18</u>. $4x + 3y = -9$ $4x + 3y = -9$

    $2x - y = 3$; $4x - 2y = 6$

               $5y = -15$; $y = -3$; $2x - y = 3$; $2x + 3 = 3$; $2x = 0$; $x = 0$

<u>19</u>. $5x + y = 29$ $15x + 3y = 87$

    $2x - 3y = 32$; $2x - 3y = 32$

             $17x \qquad = 119$; $x = 7$; $5x + y = 29$; $35 + y = 29$; $y = -6$

<u>20</u>. $x + 4y = 7$ $x + 4y = 7$

    $2x - y = -1$; $8x - 4y = -4$

           $9x \qquad = 3$; $x = \dfrac{1}{3}$; $x + 4y = 7$; $\dfrac{1}{3} + 4y = 7$; $4y = 6\dfrac{2}{3}$; $y = 1\dfrac{2}{3}$

<u>21</u>. $2x - 3y = 21$ $8x - 12y = 84$

    $8x + 5y = -1$; $8x + 5y = -1$

             $-17y = 85$; $y = -5$; $2x - 3y = 21$; $2x + 15 = 21$; $2x = 6$; $x = 3$

<u>22</u>. $8x - 9y = 14$ $8x - 9y = 14$

    $5x + 3y = 26$; $15x + 9y = 78$

           $23x \qquad = 92$; $x = 4$; $8x - 9y = 14$; $32 - 9y = 14$; $-9y = -18$; $y = 2$

<u>23</u>. $7x + 4y = 2$ $14x + 8y = 4$

    $3x - 8y = 13$; $3x - 8y = 13$

           $17x \qquad = 17$; $x = 1$; $7x + 4y = 2$; $7 + 4y = 2$; $4y = -5$; $y = -\dfrac{5}{4}$

<u>24</u>. $12x - 7y = -6$ $12x - 7y = -6$

    $4x - 9y = -2$; $12x - 27y = -6$

             $20y = 0$; $y = 0$; $12x - 7y = -6$; $12x = -6$; $x = -\dfrac{1}{2}$

14

$\underline{25}$. $\begin{aligned} 4x - 5y &= 0 \\ 3x + 2y &= -46 \end{aligned}$; $\begin{aligned} 8x - 10y &= 0 \\ 15x + 10y &= -230 \end{aligned}$

$23x = -230$; $x = -10$; $4x - 5y = 0$; $-40 - 5y = 0$;

$-5y = 40$; $y = -8$

$\underline{26}$. $\begin{aligned} 3x + 7y &= 1 \\ 4x + 11y &= 8 \end{aligned}$; $\begin{aligned} 12x + 28y &= 4 \\ 12x + 33y &= 24 \end{aligned}$

$-5y = -20$; $y = 4$; $3x + 7y = 1$; $3x + 28 = 1$; $3x = -27$; $x = -9$

$\underline{27}$. $\begin{aligned} 13x + 11y &= -1 \\ 2x - 3y &= 28 \end{aligned}$; $\begin{aligned} 39x + 33y &= -3 \\ 22x - 33y &= 308 \end{aligned}$

$61x = 305$; $x = 5$; $13x + 11y = -1$; $65 + 11y = -1$;

$11y = -66$; $y = -6$

$\underline{28}$. $\begin{aligned} 4x + 5y &= -9 \\ 5x - 2y &= 8 \end{aligned}$; $\begin{aligned} 8x + 10y &= -18 \\ 25x - 10y &= 40 \end{aligned}$

$33x = 22$; $x = \dfrac{2}{3}$; $4x + 5y = -9$; $\dfrac{8}{3} + 5y = -9$; $5y = -\dfrac{35}{3}$;

$y = -\dfrac{7}{3}$

$\underline{29}$. $\begin{aligned} 2x &= 7(1 - y) \\ 3x + 8y &= -2 \end{aligned}$; $\begin{aligned} 2x &= 7 - 7y \\ 3x + 8y &= -2 \end{aligned}$; $\begin{aligned} 2x + 7y &= 7 \\ 3x + 8y &= -2 \end{aligned}$; $\begin{aligned} 6x + 21y &= 21 \\ 6x + 16y &= -4 \end{aligned}$

$5y = 25$; $y = 5$;

$2x = 7(1 - y) = 7(1 - 5) = -28$; $x = -14$

$\underline{30}$. $\begin{aligned} 3(2x - 5) &= y \\ 5x - y &= 11 \end{aligned}$; $\begin{aligned} 6x - 15 &= y \\ 5x - y &= 11 \end{aligned}$; $\begin{aligned} 6x - y &= 15 \\ 5x - y &= 11 \end{aligned}$

$x = 4$; $3(2x - 5) = y$; $3(8 - 5) = y$; $9 = y$

CHAPTER 2 · Parallel Lines and Planes

Pages 58-59 · WRITTEN EXERCISES

A 1. alt. int.   2. corr.   3. s.-s. int.   4. alt. int.   5. corr.

6. corr.   7. $\overleftrightarrow{PQ}$ and $\overleftrightarrow{SR}$; $\overleftrightarrow{SQ}$ 8. $\overleftrightarrow{PS}$ and $\overleftrightarrow{QR}$; $\overleftrightarrow{SQ}$ 9. $\overleftrightarrow{PQ}$ and $\overleftrightarrow{SR}$; $\overleftrightarrow{PS}$

10. $\overleftrightarrow{SK}$ and $\overleftrightarrow{AT}$; $\overleftrightarrow{AK}$ 11. $\overleftrightarrow{SK}$ and $\overleftrightarrow{AN}$; $\overleftrightarrow{RN}$ 12. $\overleftrightarrow{HA}$ and $\overleftrightarrow{RN}$; $\overleftrightarrow{AN}$ 13. corr.

14. corr.   15. alt. int.   16. s.-s. int.   17. s.-s. int.   18. corr.

19.   20. Corresponding ∠ are ≅.

21. Alternate interior ∠ are ≅.

22. Same side interior ∠ are supplementary.

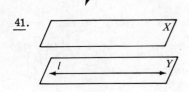

B 23. Check students' drawings.   24. $\overleftrightarrow{BH}$, $\overleftrightarrow{CI}$, $\overleftrightarrow{DJ}$, $\overleftrightarrow{EK}$, $\overleftrightarrow{FL}$ 25. $\overleftrightarrow{GH}$, $\overleftrightarrow{ED}$, $\overleftrightarrow{KJ}$

26. Answers may vary. $\overleftrightarrow{FL}$, $\overleftrightarrow{GL}$, $\overleftrightarrow{CI}$, $\overleftrightarrow{DJ}$, $\overleftrightarrow{EK}$, $\overleftrightarrow{LK}$, $\overleftrightarrow{IJ}$, $\overleftrightarrow{HI}$ 27. DCIJ, GHIJKL

28. ABHG, CBHI, DCIJ, DEKJ   29. 4

30. If the top and bottom lie in ∥ planes, then $\overline{CD}$ and $\overline{IJ}$ are the lines of intersection of DCIJ with two ∥ planes, and are therefore ∥.

31. always   32. never   33. sometimes   34. sometimes   35. sometimes

36. always   37. sometimes   38. sometimes

C 39-41. Sketches may vary.

39.   40.

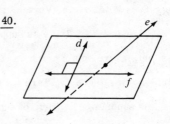

41.

15

Pages 62-64 · WRITTEN EXERCISES

A **1**. ∠3, ∠6, ∠8   **2**. ∠6, ∠9, ∠14   **3**. ∠2, ∠5, ∠7, ∠10, ∠12, ∠13, ∠15

   4. ∠1, ∠3, ∠6, ∠8, ∠9, ∠11, ∠14, ∠16   **5**. 50; 130   **6**. 180 - x; 180 - x

   7. x = 60; y = 61   **8**. 5y + 4y = 180; 9y = 180; y = 20; 3x + 90 = 180; 3x = 90;

   x = 30   **9**. x = 180 - 120 = 60; 3y + 6 = x = 60; 3y = 54; y = 18

   10. x + 140 = 180; x = 40; y = x = 40   **11**. x = 65; y = 65 + 40 = 105

   12. 4x = 52; x = 13; 4x + 3y + 5 + 90 = 180; 52 + 3y + 5 + 90 = 180; 3y = 33;

   y = 11   **13**. 1. Given   2. If 2 ∥ lines are cut by a trans., then corr. ∠ are ≅.

   3. Angle Add. Post.   4. Subst. Prop.   5. Def. of supp. ∠

B **14**. **a**. $\overline{ST}$ ∥ $\overline{QR}$ and $\overline{PQ}$ ⊥ $\overline{QR}$ so $\overline{PQ}$ ⊥ $\overline{ST}$.   Then m∠QST = 90. $\overrightarrow{QT}$ bisects ∠PQR

      and m∠PQR = 90, so m∠SQT = 45.   ∠STQ and ∠TQR are alt. int. ∠, and

      ∠TQR ≅ ∠SQT, so m∠STQ = 45.

      b. m∠STQ = 45 and m∠PTS = m∠R (Corr. ∠) = 60.   Since m∠PTS + m∠STQ +

      m∠QTR = 180, m∠QTR = 75.

   15. **a**. m∠DAB = 180 - 116 = 64; m∠KAB = $\frac{1}{2}$m∠DAB = 32; m∠DKA = m∠KAB = 32

      b. More information is needed.

   16. 2x + y + 120 = 180; y = 60 - 2x; 2x - y + 140 = 180; y = -40 + 2x;

      60 - 2x = -40 + 2x; 4x = 100; x = 25; y = 60 - 2x = 10

   17. 1. k ∥ ℓ (Given)   2. ∠5 ≅ ∠7 (If 2 ∥ lines are cut by a trans., then corr. ∠

      are ≅.)   3. ∠2 ≅ ∠5 (Vert. ∠ are ≅.)   4. ∠2 ≅ ∠7 (Trans. Prop.)

   18. 1. k ∥ ℓ (Given)   2. ∠1 is supp. to ∠4. (If 2 ∥ lines are cut by a trans., then

      s.-s. int. ∠ are supp.)   3. m∠1 + m∠4 = 180 (Def. of supp. ∠)

      4. m∠4 = m∠7 (Vert. ∠ are ≅.)   5. m∠1 + m∠7 = 180 (Subst. Prop.)

      6. ∠1 is supp. to ∠7. (Def. of supp. ∠)

   19. 1. m∠4 + m∠2 = 180 (Angle Add. Post.)   2. k ∥ m (Given)   3. m∠1 = m∠2

      (If 2 ∥ lines are cut by a trans., then alt. int. ∠ are ≅.)   4. m∠4 + m∠1 = 180

      (Subst. Prop.)   5. ∠1 is supp. to ∠4. (Def. of supp. ∠)

   20. **a**. 1. $\overline{AB}$ ∥ $\overline{DC}$; $\overline{AD}$ ∥ $\overline{BC}$ (Given)   2. ∠A is supp. to ∠B; ∠C is supp. to ∠B.

      (If 2 ∥ lines are cut by a trans., then s.-s. int. ∠ are supp.)   3. ∠A ≅ ∠C (If

      2 ∠ are supp. of the same ∠, then the 2 ∠ are ≅.)

      b. yes, by a similar proof

C 21. 1. $\overline{AS}$ || $\overline{BT}$ (Given)   2. m∠1 = m∠4 (If 2 || lines are cut by a trans., then corr.

∠ are ≅.)   3. m∠4 = m∠5 (Given)   4. m∠1 = m∠5 (Subst. Prop.)

5. m∠2 = m∠5 (If 2 || lines are cut by a trans., then alt. int. ∠ are ≅.)

6. m∠1 = m∠2 (Subst. Prop.)   7. $\overrightarrow{SA}$ bisects ∠BSR (Def. of ∠ bis.)

22. 1. $\overline{AS}$ || $\overline{BT}$ (Given)   2. m∠1 = m∠4 (If 2 || lines are cut by a trans., then

corr. ∠ are ≅.)   3. m∠2 = m∠5 (If 2 || lines are cut by a trans., then alt.

int. ∠ are ≅.)   4. m∠4 = m∠5 (Given)   5. m∠1 = m∠2 (Subst. Prop.)

6. $\overrightarrow{SB}$ bisects ∠AST (Given)   7. m∠2 = m∠3 (Def. of ∠ bis.)

8. m∠1 + m∠2 + m∠3 = 180 (Angle Add. Post.)   9. 3m∠1 = 180 (Subst. Prop.)

10. m∠1 = 60 (Div. Prop. of =)

Pages 68-70 · WRITTEN EXERCISES

A 1. $\overline{RU}$ || $\overline{AT}$ 2. none   3. none   4. $\overline{AU}$ || $\overline{NT}$ 5. $\overline{AU}$ || $\overline{NT}$

6. none   7. $\overline{RU}$ || $\overline{AT}$, $\overline{RN}$ || $\overline{OT}$ 8. $\overline{AU}$ || $\overline{NT}$ 9. none

10. $\overline{AU}$ || $\overline{NT}$, $\overline{RU}$ || $\overline{AT}$

11. 1. Given   2. Vert. ∠ are ≅.   3. Given   4. Trans. Prop.   5. If 2 lines are

cut by a trans., and corr. ∠ are ≅, then the lines are ||.

12. Through a point outside a line there is at least one line ⊥ to the given line.   Through

a point outside a line there is at most one line ⊥ to the given line.

13-14. Reasons may vary.

13. $\overleftrightarrow{FD}$ || $\overleftrightarrow{AC}$ (∠D and ∠DCA are supp.); $\overleftrightarrow{AG}$ || $\overleftrightarrow{DL}$ (∠BAG ≅ ∠ACL)

14. $\overleftrightarrow{HS}$ || $\overleftrightarrow{YO}$ (∠HSO ≅ ∠YOP); $\overleftrightarrow{SN}$ || $\overleftrightarrow{XO}$ (∠NSO ≅ ∠XOS)

B 15. x - 40 + x + 40 = 180; 2x = 180; x = 90; x - 40 + y = 180;

90 - 40 + y = 180; y = 130

16. 3x = 105; x = 35; x + 2y + 105 = 180; 35 + 2y = 75; y = 20

17. $\overline{PQ}$ || $\overline{RS}$ (∠1 ≅ ∠2 (Given); ∠2 ≅ ∠5 (Vert. ∠ are ≅.) ∠5 ≅ ∠4 (Given);

∠1 ≅ ∠4 (Trans. Prop.); $\overline{PQ}$ || $\overline{RS}$ (If 2 lines are cut by a trans. and alt. int. ∠

are ≅, then the lines are ||.)

18. ∠1 ≅ ∠4 (∠3 ≅ ∠6 (Given)); $\overline{PQ}$ || $\overline{RS}$ (If 2 lines are cut by a trans. and alt. int. ∠

are ≅, then the lines are ||.); ∠1 ≅ ∠4 (If 2 || lines are cut by a trans., then alt.

int. ∠ are ≅.)   Also, ∠2 ≅ ∠5 (Vert. ∠ are ≅.)

<u>19.</u> 1. Trans. t cuts lines k and n; ∠1 is supp. to ∠2. (Given)   2. ∠2 is supp. to ∠3
(Angle Add. Post., Def. of supp. ⓔ)   3. ∠1 ≅ ∠3 (If 2 ⓔ are supp. of the same ∠,
then the 2 ⓔ are ≅.)   4. k ∥ n (If 2 lines are cut by a trans. and alt. int. ⓔ are ≅,
then the lines are ∥.)

<u>20.</u> 1. k ⊥ t; n ⊥ t (Given)   2. m∠1 = 90; m∠2 = 90 (Def. of ⊥ lines)
3. m∠1 = m∠2 (Subst. Prop.)   4. k ∥ n (If 2 lines are cut by a trans. and
corr. ⓔ are ≅, then the lines are ∥.)

<u>21.</u> 1. $\overline{BE}$ ⊥ $\overline{DA}$; $\overline{CD}$ ⊥ $\overline{DA}$ (Given)   2. $\overline{CD}$ ∥ $\overline{BE}$ (In a plane, 2 lines ⊥ to the same
line are ∥.)   3. ∠1 ≅ ∠2 (If 2 ∥ lines are cut by a trans., then alt. int. ⓔ are ≅.)

<u>22.</u> 1. ∠C ≅ ∠3 (Given)   2. $\overline{CD}$ ∥ $\overline{BE}$ (If 2 lines are cut by a trans. and corr. ⓔ are ≅,
then the lines are ∥.)   3. $\overline{BE}$ ⊥ $\overline{DA}$ (Given)   4. $\overline{CD}$ ⊥ $\overline{DA}$ (If a trans. is ⊥ to 1
of 2 ∥ lines, then it is ⊥ to the other.)

<u>23.</u> Let $\overleftrightarrow{SZ}$ be the ∥ to $\overleftrightarrow{RX}$ through S; then $\overleftrightarrow{SZ}$ ∥ $\overleftrightarrow{TY}$ (2 lines ∥ to a third line are ∥ to
each other).   m∠R + m∠RSZ = 180; m∠RSZ = 180 - 120 = 60; m∠ZST + m∠T =
180; m∠ZST = 180 - 160 = 20; m∠RST = m∠RSZ + m∠ZST = 80

<u>24.</u> Let $\overleftrightarrow{SZ}$ be the ∥ to $\overleftrightarrow{XR}$ through S; then $\overleftrightarrow{SZ}$ ∥ $\overleftrightarrow{YT}$. (2 lines ∥ to a third line are ∥ to
each other.)   m∠RSZ = 60; m∠ZST = 50; m∠RST = m∠RSZ + m∠ZST = 110

<u>25.</u> 1. m∠1 = m∠4 (Given)   2. $\overline{BC}$ ∥ $\overline{ED}$ (Given)   3. m∠2 = m∠3 (If 2 ∥ lines are
cut by a trans., then alt. int. ⓔ are ≅.)   4. m∠1 + m∠2 = m∠3 + m∠4 (Add.
Prop. of =)   5. m∠ABD = m∠1 + m∠2; m∠BDF = m∠3 + m∠4 (Angle Add.
Post.)   6. m∠ABD = m∠BDF (Subst. Prop.)   7. $\overline{AB}$ ∥ $\overline{DF}$ (If 2 lines are cut
by a trans. and alt. int. ⓔ are ≅, then the lines are ∥.)

<u>26.</u> 1. m∠ABD = m∠1 + m∠2; m∠FDB = m∠3 + m∠4 (Angle Add. Post.)
2. m∠ABD = m∠FDB (Given)   3. m∠1 + m∠2 = m∠3 + m∠4 (Subst. Prop.)
4. m∠1 = m∠4 (Given)   5. m∠2 = m∠3 (Subtr. Prop. of =)   6. $\overline{BC}$ ∥ $\overline{ED}$
(If 2 lines are cut by a trans. and alt. int. ⓔ are ≅, then the lines are ∥.)

<u>27.</u> x - y = 30; x = y + 30; 2x = 5y; 2y + 60 = 5y; 3y = 60; y = 20; x = y + 30 = 50

<u>C</u> <u>28.</u> The bisectors appear to be ∥.

Given: $\overleftrightarrow{BD}$ ∥ $\overleftrightarrow{CF}$; $\overrightarrow{BG}$ bisects ∠ABD;

$\overrightarrow{CH}$ bisects ∠BCF

Prove: $\overrightarrow{BG}$ ∥ $\overrightarrow{CH}$

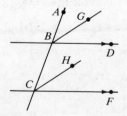

Proof: 1. $\overleftrightarrow{BD} \parallel \overleftrightarrow{CF}$ (Given)   2. $m\angle ABD = m\angle BCF$ (If 2 $\parallel$ lines are cut by a trans.,

then corr. $\angle$ are $\cong$.)   3. $\frac{1}{2}m\angle ABD = \frac{1}{2}m\angle BCF$ (Mult. Prop. of =)   4. $\overrightarrow{BG}$

bisects $\angle ABD$; $\overrightarrow{CH}$ bisects $\angle BCF$ (Given)   5. $m\angle ABG = \frac{1}{2}m\angle ABD$; $m\angle BCH =$

$\frac{1}{2}m\angle BCF$ (Angle Bis. Thm.)   6. $m\angle ABG = m\angle BCH$ (Subst. Prop.)   7. $\overrightarrow{BG} \parallel \overrightarrow{CH}$

(If 2 lines are cut by a trans. and corr. $\angle$ are $\cong$, then the lines are $\parallel$.)

<u>29.</u> $x^2 + 3x = 180$; $x^2 + 3x - 180 = 0$; $(x + 15)(x - 12) = 0$; $x + 15 = 0$ or $x - 12 = 0$;

   $x = -15$ (reject) or $x = 12$; $x = 12$

Pages 76-78 · WRITTEN EXERCISES

<u>A</u> <u>1.</u> <u>a.</u>   <u>b.</u>   <u>c.</u>

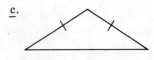

<u>2.</u> <u>a.</u>   <u>b.</u> not possible   <u>c.</u>

   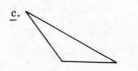

<u>3.</u> not possible   <u>4.</u> not possible   <u>5.</u> 100   <u>6.</u> 115   <u>7.</u> 115

<u>8.</u> 75   <u>9.</u> 80

<u>10.</u> $m\angle 6 = m\angle 1 + m\angle 2$; $120 = x + x + 10$; $2x = 110$; $x = 55$

<u>11.</u> $m\angle 4 = m\angle 2 + m\angle 3$; $140 = 2x - 5 + 3x + 10$; $5x = 135$; $x = 27$

<u>12.</u> $m\angle 4 + m\angle 5 + m\angle 6 = (180 - m\angle 1) + (180 - m\angle 2) + (180 - m\angle 3) =$

   $540 - (m\angle 1 + m\angle 2 + m\angle 3) = 540 - 180 = 360$

<u>13.</u> $x = 30$; $y = x + 45 = 75$

<u>14.</u> $x + 50 = 90$; $x = 40$; $x + y + 100 = 180$; $y = 80 - x = 40$

<u>15.</u> $x = 130$; $y + 70 = x$; $y = 130 - 70 = 60$

<u>16.</u> $y + 40 = 90$; $y = 50$; $x + y = 90$; $x = 40$

<u>17.</u> $x = 65 + 25 = 90$; $y + 65 = 90$; $y = 25$

<u>18.</u> $x = 40$; $x + y + 20 = 90$; $y = 30$

<u>B</u> <u>19.</u> Yes; $4n = 2n + 10$; $2n = 10$; $n = 5$; $4n = 7n - 15$; $15 = 3n$; $n = 5$;

   $2n + 10 = 7n - 15$; $25 = 5n$; $n = 5$

<u>20.</u> Let x be the measure of the smallest angle; the others are 2x and 3x;

   $x + 2x + 3x = 180$; $6x = 180$; $x = 30$; $2x = 60$; $3x = 90$

21. $m\angle C = 180 - (m\angle A + m\angle B) = 180 - 60 - m\angle B = 120 - m\angle B$; since
$m\angle B < 60$, $m\angle C > 60$.

22. $m\angle T = 180 - (m\angle R + m\angle S) = 180 - 90 - m\angle S = 90 - m\angle S$; since $m\angle S > 20$,
$m\angle T < 70$.

23. a. 22   b. 23   c. $\angle C$ and $\angle ABD$ are both complements of $\angle A$.

24. a. 130   b. 130   c. Let $m\angle IFG = x$. Then $m\angle EFG = 2x$; $m\angle EGF = 100 - 2x$;
$m\angle IGF = 50 - x$; $m\angle FIG = 180 - x - (50 - x) = 130$.

25. 1. $\angle A \cong \angle A$ (Refl. Prop. of $\cong$)   2. $\angle ABD \cong \angle AED$ (Given)   3. $\angle C \cong \angle F$ (If
2 $\angle$ of one $\triangle$ are $\cong$ to 2 $\angle$ of another $\triangle$, then the third $\angle$ are $\cong$.)

26. 1. Draw a ray, $\overrightarrow{CD}$, through C $\parallel$ to $\overleftrightarrow{AB}$. (Through a pt. outside a line there is exactly
one line $\parallel$ to the given line.)   2. $\angle 2 \cong \angle 5$ (If 2 $\parallel$ lines are cut by a trans., then
alt. int. $\angle$ are $\cong$.)   3. $\angle 1 \cong \angle 4$ (If 2 $\parallel$ lines are cut by a trans., then corr. $\angle$
are $\cong$.)   4. $m\angle 4 + m\angle 5 + m\angle 3 = 180$ (Angle Add. Post.)
5. $m\angle 1 + m\angle 2 + m\angle 3 = 180$ (Subst. Prop.)

27.   28.   29.

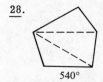

360°   540°   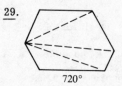720°

30. $m\angle MTR = 180 - 85 = 95$; $m\angle STR = 55$; $m\angle 1 = 35$; $m\angle NRS = 90$; $m\angle NRT = 55$;
$m\angle 2 = 180 - 55 = 125$.

31. 1. $m\angle JGI = m\angle H + m\angle I$ (The meas. of an ext. $\angle$ of a $\triangle$ = the sum of the meas. of
the 2 remote int. $\angle$.)   2. $m\angle H = m\angle I$ (Given)   3. $m\angle JGI = 2m\angle H$ (Subst. Prop.)
4. $\frac{1}{2} m\angle JGI = m\angle H$ (Mult. Prop. of =)   5. $\overrightarrow{GK}$ bisects $\angle JGI$ (Given)
6. $m\angle 1 = \frac{1}{2} m\angle JGI$ (Angle Bis. Thm.)   7. $m\angle 1 = m\angle H$ (Subst. Prop.)
8. $\overline{GK} \parallel \overline{HI}$ (If 2 lines are cut by a trans. and corr. $\angle$ are $\cong$, then the lines are $\parallel$.)

32. $2x + y = 180 - 125 = 55$; $y = 55 - 2x$; $x + 2y = 90 - 55 = 35$;
$x + 2(55 - 2x) = 35$; $x + 110 - 4x = 35$; $-3x = -75$; $x = 25$; $y = 55 - 2x = 5$

33. $10x + 100 = 180$; $10x = 80$; $x = 8$; $2x + y = 5x - y$; $2y = 3x = 24$; $y = 12$

34. $\angle 1, \angle 2, \angle 5$; $\angle 3, \angle 4, \angle 6$ 35. $\angle 7, \angle 8$; $\angle 11, \angle 12$

36. a-b.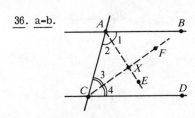

c. The angle measures 90, so the bisectors are $\perp$.   d. Given: $\overleftrightarrow{AB} \parallel \overleftrightarrow{CD}$; $\overrightarrow{AE}$ bisects $\angle BAC$; $\overrightarrow{CF}$ bisects $\angle ACD$ Prove: $\overleftrightarrow{AE} \perp \overleftrightarrow{CF}$ Proof:

1. $\overleftrightarrow{AB} \parallel \overleftrightarrow{CD}$ (Given)   2. $m\angle BAC + m\angle ACD = 180$ (If 2 $\parallel$ lines are cut by a trans., then s.-s. int. $\angle\!\!\!\angle$ are supp.; def. of supp. $\angle\!\!\!\angle$)   3. $\frac{1}{2}m\angle BAC + \frac{1}{2}m\angle ACD = 90$ (Mult. Prop. of =)   4. $\overrightarrow{AE}$ bisects $\angle BAC$; $\overrightarrow{CF}$ bisects $\angle ACD$. (Given)   5. $m\angle 2 = \frac{1}{2}m\angle BAC$; $m\angle 3 = \frac{1}{2}m\angle ACD$. (Angle Bis. Thm.)   6. $m\angle 2 + m\angle 3 = 90$ (Subst. Prop.)   7. $m\angle AXF = m\angle 2 + m\angle 3$ (The meas. of an ext. $\angle$ of a $\triangle$ is = to the sum of the meas. of the 2 remote int. $\angle\!\!\!\angle$.)   8. $m\angle AXF = 90$ (Subst. Prop.)   9. $\overleftrightarrow{AE} \perp \overleftrightarrow{CF}$ (Def. of $\perp$ lines)

37. Since $(3x)°$ and $(3y)°$ are the meas. of s.-s. int. $\angle\!\!\!\angle$, $3x + 3y = 180$; $x + y = 60$. Then $m\angle D = 180 - (x + y) = 120$. $\angle B$ is the third $\angle$ of a $\triangle$ with $\angle\!\!\!\angle$ of meas. $2x$ and $2y$, so $m\angle B = 180 - (2x + 2y) = 180 - 120 = 60$. $\angle C$ is an ext. $\angle$ of a $\triangle$ with remote int. $\angle\!\!\!\angle$ of meas. $2x$ and y, so $m\angle C = 2x + y$. Similarly, $m\angle A = 2y + x$. Then $m\angle A + m\angle C = 3x + 3y = 180$, and the opp. $\angle\!\!\!\angle$ of ABCD are supp.

Page 79 · APPLICATION

1. That allows them the greatest margin of safety.   **2.** north   **3.** Ray   **4.** right

Pages 83-84 · WRITTEN EXERCISES

A   **1.** a. $(5 - 2)180 = 540$ b. 360   **2.** a. $(6 - 2)180 = 720$ b. 360

3. a. $(4 - 2)180 = 360$ b. 360   **4.** a. $(8 - 2)180 = 1080$ b. 360

5. a. $(10 - 2)180 = 1440$ b. 360   **6.** a. $(n - 2)180$ b. 360

7.

No. of sides	9	15	30	60	45	24	180
Meas. of each ext. $\angle$	40	24	12	6	8	15	2
Meas. of each int. $\angle$	140	156	168	174	172	165	178

8. Let x = meas. of each of the 2 $\cong$ $\angle\!\!\!\angle$. $2x + 270 = (5 - 2)180$; $2x + 270 = 540$; $2x = 270$; $x = 135$

<u>9.</u> 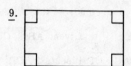   <u>10.</u> 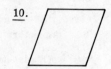   <u>11.</u>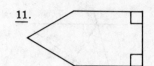

<u>12.</u> not possible   <u>13.</u> not possible (An ext. ∠ would have meas. 70, and 360 is not a multiple of 70.)   <u>14.</u> 120

<u>B</u> <u>15.</u> Let n = number of sides; (n - 2)180 = 4(360); 180n - 360 = 1440; 180n = 1800; n = 10

<u>16.</u> Let n = number of sides; $\frac{(n - 2)180}{n} = \frac{8(360)}{n}$; 180n - 360 = 2880; 180n = 3240; n = 18

<u>17.</u>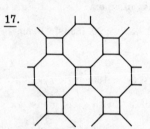

<u>18.</u> a. 108   b. no (360 is not a multiple of 108.)

<u>19.</u> a. yes   b.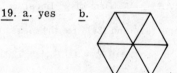

<u>20.</u> The sum of the meas. of the int. ∠ of 2 hexagons and 1 pentagon at any common vertex is 120 + 120 + 108 = 348.   A sum of 360 is necessary to tile a plane.

<u>21.</u> ∠KBC and ∠KCB are exterior angles of a regular decagon, so m∠KBC = m∠KCB = $\frac{360}{10}$ = 36.   m∠K = 180 - (m∠KBC + m∠KCB) = 180 - 72 = 108.

<u>22.</u> x + 2x + 3x + 4x = (4 - 2)180; 10x = 360; x = 36; m∠A = 36; m∠B = 72; m∠C = 108; m∠D = 144; $\overline{AB}$ ∥ $\overline{CD}$ (If 2 lines are cut by a trans. and s.-s. int. ∠ are supp., then the lines are ∥.)

<u>23.</u> <u>a.</u> Let m∠R = x; then m∠S = m∠T = 2x; 90 + 150 + x + 2x + 2x = (5 - 2)180; 5x + 240 = 540; 5x = 300; x = 60; m∠R = 60; m∠S = m∠T = 120   <u>b.</u> $\overline{QR}$ ∥ $\overline{TS}$ (If 2 lines are cut by a trans. and s.-s. int. ∠ are supp., then the lines are ∥.)

<u>24.</u> 2500 < (n - 2)180 < 2600; 13.$\overline{8}$ < n - 2 < 14.$\overline{4}$; 15.8 < n < 16.$\overline{4}$; n = 16

<u>25.</u> There are 5 small △ each with one of the letters as one vertex.   The other two ∠ of each of the △ are ext. ∠ of a pentagon.   There are 2 complete sets of ext. ∠ of the pentagon, with each set having total meas. 360.   Then m∠A + m∠B + m∠C + m∠D + m∠E + 360 + 360 = 5(180) = 900 and m∠A + m∠B + m∠C + m∠D + m∠E = 180.

<u>C</u> <u>26</u>. <u>a</u>. Since S = (n - 2)180, [(n + 1) - 2]180 = [(n - 2) + 1]180 = (n - 2)180 + 180 =

S + 180   <u>b</u>. (2n - 2)180 = 2(n - 1)180 = 2[(n - 2) + 1]180 = 2(S + 180) =

2S + 360

<u>27</u>. <u>a</u>. Sketches will vary.

<u>b</u>. yes

Page 85 · COMPUTER KEY-IN

Modification of long program lines may be necessary on some computers.

Results will vary.   Sample RUN's are given.

```
RUN
HERE ARE THE MEASURES OF ALL BUT ONE OF
THE INTERIOR ANGLES OF A POLYGON.
53
29
- - - - -
WHAT IS THE MEASURE OF THE MISSING ANGLE
? 98
YOU ARE CORRECT
RUN
HERE ARE THE MEASURES OF ALL BUT ONE OF
THE INTERIOR ANGLES OF A POLYGON.
120
175
38
- - - - -
WHAT IS THE MEASURE OF THE MISSING ANGLE
? 37
SORRY, THE MISSING ANGLE HAS MEASURE 27
```

Pages 89-91 · WRITTEN EXERCISES

<u>A</u> <u>1</u>. <u>a</u>. 3x - 7 = 32   <u>b</u>. x = 13   <u>c</u>. If x = 13, then 3x - 7 = 32

<u>2</u>. <u>a</u>. $\overline{AB} \perp \overline{BC}$ <u>b</u>. m∠ABC = 90   <u>c</u>. If m∠ABC = 90, then $\overline{AB} \perp \overline{BC}$

<u>3</u>. <u>a</u>. You will (try)   <u>b</u>. I'll try   <u>c</u>. If I try, then you'll try.

<u>4</u>. <u>a</u>. I'm not tired   <u>b</u>. I can't sleep   <u>c</u>. If I can't sleep, then I'm not tired.

<u>5</u>. <u>a</u>. |x| = 0   <u>b</u>. x = 0   <u>c</u>. If x = 0, then |x| = 0.

<u>6</u>. <u>a</u>. a + b = a   <u>b</u>. b = 0   <u>c</u>. If b = 0, then a + b = a

<u>7</u>. <u>a</u>. If a person is an Olympic competitor, then he or she is an athlete; true.

<u>b</u>. If a person is an athlete, then he or she is an Olympic competitor; false.

<u>8</u>. <u>a</u>. If a number is positive, then it has two square roots; true.

<u>b</u>. If a number has two square roots, then it is positive; true

9. a. If $x^2 = 0$, then $x = 0$; true   b. If $x = 0$, then $x^2 = 0$; true.

10. a. If $x = 4$, then $x^2 = 16$; true   b. If $x^2 = 16$, then $x = 4$; false.

11. a. If two integers are odd, then their product is odd; true.

    b. If the product of two integers is odd, then the integers are odd; true

12. a. If two integers are even, then their sum is even; true.

    b. If the sum of two integers is even, then the integers are even; false

13. a. If $-2x < 2$, then $x > -1$; true.   b. If $x > -1$, then $-2x < 2$; true

14. a. If $\triangle XYZ$ is obtuse, then $\angle XYZ$ is obtuse; false

    b. If $\angle XYZ$ is obtuse, then $\triangle XYZ$ is obtuse; true

15. a. If a polygon is regular, then it is equiangular; true

    b. If a polygon is equiangular, then it is regular; false

16. a. If an integer is even, then it is divisible by 4; false

    b. If an integer is divisible by 4, then it is even; true

17. If 2 ∠ are ≅, then their meas. are =.   If the meas. of 2 ∠ are =, then the ∠ are ≅.

18. If 2 ∠ are supp., then the sum of their meas. is 180.   If the sum of the meas. of

    2 ∠ is 180, then the ∠ are supp.

19. If $ab > 0$, then a and b are both positive or both negative.   If a and b are both positive

    or both negative, then $ab > 0$.

20. If $(x - 4)(x + 6) = 0$, then $x = 4$ or $x = -6$.   If $x = 4$ or $x = -6$, then

    $(x - 4)(x + 6) = 0$.

21. If corr. ∠ formed by 2 lines and a trans. are ≅, then the 2 lines are ∥; yes.

22. If 2 lines are ∥, then alt. int. ∠ formed by the 2 lines and a trans. are ≅; yes.

23. a. If $a - c = b - d$, then $a = b$ and $c = d$.

    b. Answers may vary.   Let $a = 4$, $c = 2$, $b = 7$, and $d = 5$.

24. True

Given: $\overline{AB} \cong \overline{AC}$

Prove: $\angle B \cong \angle C$

25. True

Given: $\angle E \cong \angle F$

Prove: $\overline{DE} \cong \overline{DF}$

26. False

27. True

Given: ABCDE is a reg. pent.

Prove: $\overline{AC} \cong \overline{AD} \cong \overline{BD} \cong \overline{BE} \cong \overline{CE}$

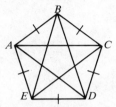

28. True

Given: $\overline{PQ} \parallel \overline{SR}$; $\overline{PS} \parallel \overline{QR}$

Prove: $\overline{PQ} \cong \overline{SR}$; $\overline{PS} \cong \overline{QR}$

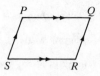

29. False

30. False

31. True

Given: ABCD is equilateral.

Prove: $\overline{AC} \perp \overline{BD}$

C 32. sufficient   33. necessary and sufficient   34. necessary   35. sufficient

36. necessary   37. necessary and sufficient

38. a. 1. $\overline{AB} \parallel \overline{DC}$; $\overline{AD} \parallel \overline{BC}$ (Given)   2. ∠A and ∠D are supp.; ∠C and ∠D are supp.;

∠A and ∠B are supp. (If 2 ∥ lines are cut by a trans., then s.-s. int. ⦤ are supp.)

3. ∠A ≅ ∠C; ∠B ≅ ∠D (If 2 ⦤ are supp. of ≅ ⦤, then the 2 ⦤ are ≅.)

b. Given: ∠A ≅ ∠C; ∠B ≅ ∠D; Prove: $\overline{AB} \parallel \overline{DC}$; $\overline{AD} \parallel \overline{BC}$

Proof: 1. m∠A + m∠B + m∠C + m∠D = (4 - 2)180 = 360 (The sum of the meas.

of the ⦤ of a convex polygon with n sides is (n - 2)180.)   2. m∠A = m∠C;

m∠B = m∠D (Given)   3. 2m∠A + 2m∠B = 360; 2m∠A + 2m∠D = 360

(Subst. Prop.)   4. m∠A + m∠B = 180; m∠A + m∠D = 180 (Div. Prop. of =)

5. ∠A and ∠B are supp.; ∠A and ∠D are supp. (Def. of supp. ⦤)

6. $\overline{AD} \parallel \overline{BC}$; $\overline{AB} \parallel \overline{DC}$ (If 2 lines are cut by a trans. and s.-s. int. ⦤ are supp.,

then the lines are ∥.)

c. $\overline{AB} \parallel \overline{DC}$ and $\overline{AD} \parallel \overline{BC}$ if and only if ∠A ≅ ∠C and ∠B ≅ ∠D.

Pages 94-96 · WRITTEN EXERCISES

A 1. a. If 5n - 5 ≠ 100, then n ≠ 21.   b. If 5n - 5 = 100, then n = 21.

c. If n ≠ 21, then 5n - 5 ≠ 100

2. a. If this is not white, then that is not red.   b. If this is white, then that is red.

   c. If that is not red, then this is not white.

3. a. If x + 1 is odd, then x is even.   b. If x + 1 is not odd, then x is not even.

   c. If x is even, then x + 1 is odd.

4. a. If Gregory is well, then he is here.   b. If Gregory is not well, then he is not here.

   c. If Gregory is here, then he is well.

5.

6.
Equilateral triangles

Equiangular triangles

7.
cheese likers

mice

8.
musicians   noise likers

9.	Statement	If $\angle 1 \cong \angle 2$, then $\angle 1$ and $\angle 2$ are vert. $\angle$.	False
	Contrapositive	If $\angle 1$ and $\angle 2$ are not vert. $\angle$, then $\angle 1$ is not $\cong$ to $\angle 2$.	False
	Converse	If $\angle 1$ and $\angle 2$ are vert. $\angle$, then $\angle 1 \cong \angle 2$.	True
	Inverse	If $\angle 1$ is not $\cong$ to $\angle 2$, then $\angle 1$ and $\angle 2$ are not vert. $\angle$.	True

10.	Statement	If $x > 6$, then $x = 5$.	False
	Contrapositive	If $x \neq 5$, then $x \leq 6$.	False
	Converse	If $x = 5$, then $x > 6$.	False
	Inverse	If $x \leq 6$, then $x \neq 5$.	False

B 11.	Statement	If AM = MB, then M is the midpoint of $\overline{AB}$.	False
	Contrapositive	If M is not the midpoint of $\overline{AB}$, then AM $\neq$ MB.	False
	Converse	If M is the midpoint of $\overline{AB}$, then AM = MB.	True
	Inverse	If AM $\neq$ MB, then M is not the midpoint of $\overline{AB}$.	True

12.

Statement	If $x^2 - 1 = 99$, then $x = 10$.	False
Contrapositive	If $x \neq 10$, then $x^2 - 1 \neq 99$.	False
Converse	If $x = 10$, then $x^2 - 1 = 99$.	True
Inverse	If $x^2 - 1 \neq 99$, then $x \neq 10$.	True

13.

Statement	If a is not negative, then $|a| = a$.	True
Contrapositive	If $|a| \neq a$, then a is negative.	True
Converse	If $|a| = a$, then a is not negative.	True
Inverse	If a is negative, then $|a| \neq a$.	True

14.

Statement	If $-3a > -6$, then $a < 2$.	True
Contrapositive	If $a \geq 2$, then $-3a \leq -6$.	True
Converse	If $a < 2$, then $-3a > -6$.	True
Inverse	If $-3a \leq -6$, then $a \geq 2$.	True

15.

Statement	If $x^2 > y^2$, then $x > y$.	False
Contrapositive	If $x \leq y$, then $x^2 \leq y^2$.	False
Converse	If $x > y$, then $x^2 > y^2$.	False
Inverse	If $x^2 \leq y^2$, then $x \leq y$.	False

16. a. If someone is a senator, then he or she is at least 30 years old.

b.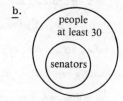

c. (1) No conclusion is possible.   (2) She is at least 30 years old.   (3) No conclusion is possible.   (4) He is not a senator.

17. a. $\overline{AC} \cong \overline{BD}$ b. No conclusion is possible.   c. No conclusion is possible.

d. EFGH is not equiangular.

18. a. It is raining.   b. I am happy.   c. No conclusion is possible.

d. No conclusion is possible.

19. a. Stu loves geometry.   b. No conclusion is possible.   c. No conclusion is possible.   d. George is not my student.

20. a. $\angle B \cong \angle C$ b. $\overline{ED}$ is not $\cong$ to $\overline{EF}$.   c. No conclusion is possible.

d. No conclusion is possible.

C 21. a. No conclusion is possible.   b. No conclusion is possible.   c. At least one of
       p and q is false.   d. No conclusion is possible.

22. a.   b. Yes; a point not inside p is not inside q.

                                c. The converse and inverse are logically equivalent.

23. Given: m∠1 + m∠2 + m∠3 = 180   Prove: $\ell \parallel$ k

    Proof: 1. m∠1 + m∠2 + m∠3 = 180 (Given)   2. m∠3 = 180 - m∠1 - m∠2
    (Subtr. Prop. of =)   3. m∠1 + m∠2 + m∠4 = 180 (The sum of the meas. of
    the ∠ of a △ is 180.)   4. m∠4 = 180 - m∠1 - m∠2 (Subtr. Prop. of =)
    5. m∠3 = m∠4 (Subst. Prop.)   6. $\ell \parallel$ k (If 2 lines are cut by a trans. and
    corr. ∠ are ≅, the lines are $\parallel$.)

24. Given: n is even   Prove: n^2 is even
    Proof: 1. n is even. (Given)   2. For some integer k, n = 2k. (Def. of even)
    3. n^2 = (2k)(2k) (Subst. Prop.)   4. $n^2 = 2(2k^2)$ (Comm. and Assoc. Prop. of Mult.)
    5. n^2 is even (Def. of even)

Page 98 · EXTRA

1. Post. 5: A committee has at least 2 persons; a club has at least 3 persons not all on
   one committee; the set of all persons has at least 3 persons not all in one club.
   Post. 6: Any 2 persons belong to exactly one committee.   Post. 7: Any 3 persons
   belong to at least one club, and any 3 persons not all on the same committee belong to
   exactly one club.   Post. 8: If 2 persons belong to a club, then the committee containing the persons is in that club.   Post. 9: If 2 clubs have at least one member in
   common, then the member(s) in common form a committee.   Thm. 1-9: If 2
   committees have a person in common, then they have exactly one person in common.
   Thm. 1-10: If there is a committee and a person not in that committee, then exactly
   one club contains the committee and the person.   Thm. 1-11: If 2 committees have a
   person in common, then exactly one club contains them.

2. a. They are satisfied.   b. Bea, Xavera, Carlos; Ann, Bea, Xavera, Carlos and
   Dick, Bea, Xavera, Carlos.

3. Theorems 1-9, 1-10 and 1-11 follow immediately from the post.   Let A, B, C, and
   D be four pts. not all in the same plane.   Then no three of these pts. are collinear.

in the line, then exactly one plane contains them.)

AB), (AC), (AD), (BC), (BD), (CD) and 4 planes

Now let X be a fifth pt.   Case (1). Let X lie on (BC).

es.   (XA) = (AB), for ex., would mean that (BC) and

lso, plane (AXD) is not = any of the 4 planes above.

ex., then (BX) is in plane (ABD); then since C is

contradicts given.   Case (2). Let X lie in plane

B, C, D.   Then (AX), (BX), (CX) and (DX) are

ıy line det. by A, B, C, D.   Planes (AXD),

or ex., if plane (AXD) = plane (ABD), then X

ABC), and therefore X would have to lie on

radicts given.   Case (3). Let X not lie on

X), (BX), (CX), (DX) are new lines, as in

(BCX), (BDX), (CDX) are new because X

C, D.   Thus, the inclusion of X generates

at l   ne, for a total of 8 lines and 5 planes.

<u>4.</u> If th   persons not all in one club, then there are at least eight committees
and five clubs.

<u>5.</u> 15; 10; 20; 6

<u>6.</u> Geometry A satisfies the statement. (In the five-pt. geometry, through pt. D there
are 2 lines ‖ (AB).)

Pages 99-100 · CHAPTER REVIEW

<u>1.</u> 2   <u>2.</u> corr.   <u>3.</u> alt. int.   <u>4.</u> No, they can be skew.   <u>5.</u> 105; 105

<u>6.</u> 6x - 2 = 70; x = 12   <u>7.</u> 8y - 40 + 2y + 20 = 180; 10y = 200; y = 20

<u>8.</u> b ⊥ c; if a trans. is ⊥ to one of 2 ‖ lines, it is ⊥ to the other.

<u>9.</u> $\overleftrightarrow{DE}$; ∠A is supp. to ∠ADE. (If 2 lines are cut by a trans. and s.-s. int. ∠ are supp.,
then the lines are ‖.)

<u>10.</u> $\overleftrightarrow{BH}$ ‖ $\overleftrightarrow{CI}$; both lines are ⊥ to $\overleftrightarrow{DF}$. (In a plane, 2 lines ⊥ to the same line are ‖.)

<u>11.</u> In DFIG, m∠D + m∠F + m∠I + m∠G = (4 - 2)180 = 360; m∠I = 360 -
(115 + 90 + 75) = 80

12. Show that when a trans. cuts the 2 lines, corr. ∠ are ≅, alt. int. ∠ are ≅, or s.-s. int. ∠ are supp. Show that the lines are coplanar and ⊥ to the same line. Show that the 2 lines are both ∥ to a third line.

13. x + 2x - 15 = 90; 3x = 105; x = 35   14. 180   15. 100

16. ∠3 ≅ ∠6 (If 2 ∠ are supp. of ≅ ∠, then the 2 ∠ are ≅.); ∠2 ≅ ∠8 (If 2 ∠ of 1 △ are ≅ to 2 ∠ of another △, then the third ∠ are ≅.)

17. a.    b. 720   c. 360

18. $\dfrac{(18 - 2)180}{18}$ = 16(10) = 160   19. $\dfrac{360}{24}$ = 15

20. $\dfrac{(n - 2)180}{n}$ = 156; 180n - 360 = 156n; 24n = 360; n = 15

21. If a quad. is a square, then it is equilateral.

22. hyp.: a quad. is a square; conc.: it is equilateral.

23. If a quadrilateral is equilateral, then it is a square; false.

24. If 2 seg. are ≅, then their lengths are =. If the lengths of 2 seg. are =, then the segments are ≅.

25. Toddie is an amphibian.   26. No conclusion is possible.

27. A dog isn't a toad.   28. No conclusion is possible.

Page 101 · CHAPTER TEST

1. sometimes   2. sometimes   3. never   4. never   5. never

6. always   7. sometimes   8. 3x - 20 = 180 - x; 4x = 200; x = 50

9. 2x + 12 = 4(x - 7); 2x + 12 = 4x - 28; 2x = 40; x = 20

10. m∠1 = m∠2 = 60; m∠3 = 120

11. m∠1 = 90 - 32 = 58; m∠2 = 90; m∠3 = 32; m∠4 = 180 - (35 + 32) = 113; m∠5 = 35; m∠6 = 90 - 35 = 55

12. m∠4 = $\dfrac{(5 - 2)180}{5}$ = 108; m∠5 = m∠6 = $\dfrac{180 - 108}{2}$ = 36; m∠1 = 180 - 72 - 36 = 72; m∠2 = 180 - m∠DCB = 180 - 108 = 72; m∠3 = 180 - (72 + 72) = 36

13. Answers may vary. For example, ∠EBC ≅ ∠2, so $\overline{EB}$ ∥ $\overline{DF}$. (If 2 lines are cut by a trans. and alt. int. ∠ are ≅, then the lines are ∥.)

14. a. $x = y$ b. $x^2 = y^2$ c. If $x^2 = y^2$, then $x = y$ d. If $x^2 \neq y^2$, then $x \neq y$

15. a. No conclusion is possible   b. $x \neq y$ c. $x^2 = y^2$ d. No conclusion is possible

16. 1. $\overrightarrow{BF}$ bisects $\angle ABE$; $\overrightarrow{DG}$ bisects $\angle CDB$ (Given)   2. $m\angle FBE = \frac{1}{2}m\angle ABE$;
$m\angle GDB = \frac{1}{2}m\angle CDB$ (Angle Bis. Thm.)   3. $\overleftrightarrow{AB} \parallel \overleftrightarrow{CD}$ (Given)   4. $m\angle CDB =$
$m\angle ABE$ (If 2 $\parallel$ lines are cut by a trans., then corr. $\&$ are $\cong$.)   5. $m\angle FBE =$
$m\angle GDB$ (Subst. Prop.)   6. $\overleftrightarrow{BF} \parallel \overleftrightarrow{DG}$ (If 2 lines are cut by a trans. and corr. $\&$
are $\cong$, then the lines are $\parallel$.)

Page 102 · PREPARING FOR COLLEGE ENTRANCE EXAMS

1. C   2. C   3. D   4. C   5. D   6. E   7. B   8. B

Page 103 · CUMULATIVE REVIEW: CHAPTERS 1 AND 2

A   1. congruent   2. 8   3. 45   4. Mult. Prop. of =   5. perpendicular

6. supplementary   7. line   8. 16   9. acute   10. 10

11. exactly one plane   12. contrapositive

13. $m\angle 2 = m\angle 3 = 180 - 140 = 40$; $m\angle 1 = 180 - (m\angle 2 + 65) = 180 - 105 = 75$;
$m\angle 4 = 65$

14. $m\angle 5 = 90$; $m\angle 7 = 36$; $m\angle 6 = m\angle 8 = 90 - 36 = 54$

15. yes; c, d (If 2 lines are cut by a trans. and s.-s. int. $\&$ are supp., then the lines
are $\parallel$.)

16. no

17. yes; a, b (If 2 lines are cut by a trans. and alt. int. $\&$ are $\cong$, then the lines are $\parallel$.)

18. yes; a, b (In a plane, 2 lines $\perp$ to the same line are $\parallel$.)

19. 180; the sum of the meas. of the $\&$ of a $\triangle$ is 180.

20. 180; if $\angle AOC$ is a straight $\angle$ and B is any pt. not on $\overleftrightarrow{AC}$, then $m\angle AOB + m\angle BOC =$
180 (Angle Add. Post.)

21. 360; the sum of the meas. of the ext. $\&$ of a convex polygon, one at each vertex,
is 360.

22. 5; the meas. of an ext. $\angle$ of a $\triangle$ is = to the sum of the meas. of the remote int. $\&$.

23. $\angle 1$; if 2 $\parallel$ lines are cut by a trans., then corr. $\&$ are $\cong$.

Pages 108-109 · WRITTEN EXERCISES

<u>A</u> <u>1.</u> ∠T   <u>2.</u> m∠I   <u>3.</u> CA   <u>4.</u> $\overline{\text{IG}}$ <u>5.</u> △ATC   <u>6.</u> △BGI

<u>7.</u> ∠I, ∠G, ∠A, ∠T   <u>8.</u> definition (≅ △)

<u>9.</u> ∠L ≅ ∠F; ∠X ≅ ∠N; ∠R ≅ ∠E; $\overline{\text{LX}}$ ≅ $\overline{\text{FN}}$; $\overline{\text{XR}}$ ≅ $\overline{\text{NE}}$; $\overline{\text{LR}}$ ≅ $\overline{\text{FE}}$

<u>10.</u> △KRO   <u>11.</u> ∠K; corr. parts of ≅ △ are ≅.

<u>12.</u> $\overline{\text{OK}}$; corr. parts of ≅ △ are ≅. $\overline{\text{SK}}$ <u>13.</u> TO; $\overline{\text{TR}}$

<u>14.</u> <u>a.</u> ∠R; corr. parts of ≅ △ are ≅.   <u>b.</u> If 2 lines are cut by a trans. and alt. int. ∠

(∠S and ∠K or ∠T and ∠R) are ≅, then the lines are ∥.

<u>15.</u> △RLA

<u>16.</u> <u>a.</u> ∠3; corr. parts of ≅ △ are ≅.   <u>b.</u> $\overline{\text{LR}}$; if 2 lines are cut by a trans. and alt.

int. ∠ are ≅, then the lines are ∥.

<u>17.</u> <u>a.</u> ∠4; corr. parts of ≅ △ are ≅.   <u>b.</u> $\overline{\text{PL}}$ ∥ $\overline{\text{AR}}$; if 2 lines are cut by a trans. and

alt. int. ∠ are ≅, then the lines are ∥.

<u>18.</u> <u>a.</u> $\overline{\text{RL}}$ <u>b.</u> $\overline{\text{RA}}$

<u>19.</u>
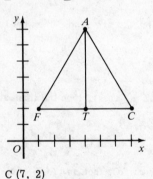

C (7, 2)

<u>20.</u>
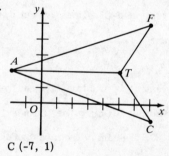

C (-7, 1)

<u>B</u> <u>21.</u>
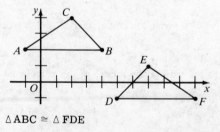

△ABC ≅ △FDE

<u>22.</u>
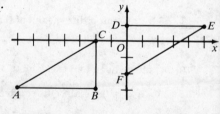

△ABC ≅ △EDF

23.

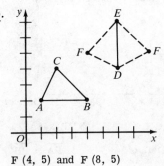

△ ABC ≅ △ FED

24.

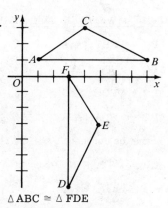

△ ABC ≅ △ FDE

25.

F (4, 5) and F (8, 5)

26.

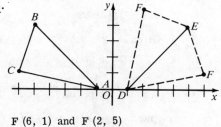

F (6, 1) and F (2, 5)

27. MARO

28. a. Since NERO ≅ MARO, $\overline{NO}$ ≅ $\overline{OM}$. By the def. of midpt., O is the midpt. of $\overline{NM}$.

b. ∠ NOR and ∠ MOR are corr. ∠ of ≅ figures.   c. If 2 lines form ≅ adj. ∠, then

the lines are ⊥.   d. Refl. Prop. of ≅

29. a. Check students' drawings.   b. yes.

30. a. Check students' drawings; yes.   31. Check students' drawings; yes.

C 32. yes; yes; yes   33. a.   b.

Page 109 · CHALLENGE

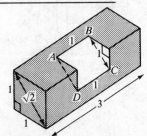

Insert the square end of one block through the other block

at A, B, C and D as shown at the left.

Pages 113-115 · WRITTEN EXERCISES

A   1. △ABC ≅ △NPY; ASA   2. △ABC ≅ △ADC; SAS   3. △ABC ≅ △CKA; SSS

    4. △ABC ≅ △SBC; SAS   5. ≅ cannot be deduced.   6. ≅ cannot be deduced.

    7. △ABC ≅ △PQC; SAS   8. ≅ cannot be deduced.   9. △ABC ≅ △AGC; ASA

    10. △ABC ≅ △CDA; ASA   11. △ABC ≅ △BST; ASA   12. ≅ cannot be deduced.

    13. ≅ cannot be deduced.   14. △ABC ≅ △CGA; SAS   15. △ABC ≅ △MNC; ASA

    16. 1. Given   2. Refl. Prop. of ≅   3. Given   4. If 2 ∥ lines are cut by a trans.,
        then alt. int. ∠ are ≅.   5. SAS

    17. 1. Given   2. T   3. Given   4. $\overline{VT}$; def. of midpt.   5. UVT; vert. ∠ are ≅.
        6. RSV; UTV; ASA

    18. 1. Given   2. ∠RAT; ∠DTS, ∠RTS   3. ∠RTA; ∠RTS   4. DTA; ∠RTA
        5. $\overline{TA}$; $\overline{TA}$ 6. △DAT ≅ △RAT; ASA

B   19. 1. M is the midpt. of $\overline{AB}$ and $\overline{CD}$. (Given)   2. $\overline{AM}$ ≅ $\overline{BM}$; $\overline{DM}$ ≅ $\overline{CM}$ (Def. of
        midpt.)   3. ∠AMD ≅ ∠BMC (Vert. ∠ are ≅.)   4. △MAD ≅ △MBC (SAS)

    20. 1. Plane M bisects $\overline{AB}$. (Given)   2. $\overline{AO}$ ≅ $\overline{BO}$ (Def. of bis.)   3. $\overline{PA}$ ≅ $\overline{PB}$ (Given)
        4. $\overline{PO}$ ≅ $\overline{PO}$ (Refl. Prop. of ≅)   5. △POA ≅ △POB (SSS)

    21. 1. Plane M bisects $\overline{AB}$. (Given)   2. $\overline{AO}$ ≅ $\overline{BO}$ (Def. of bis.)   3. $\overline{PO}$ ⊥ $\overline{AB}$ (Given)
        4. ∠POA ≅ ∠POB (Adj. ∠ formed by ⊥ lines are ≅.)   5. $\overline{PO}$ ≅ $\overline{PO}$ (Refl. Prop.
        of ≅)   6. △POA ≅ △POB (SAS)

    22. a. Check students' drawings.   b. $\overline{AC}$ ≅ $\overline{BC}$; $\overline{CD}$ ≅ $\overline{CD}$; ∠CDA ≅ ∠CDB   c. no

C   23. SAS ($\overline{AB}$ ≅ $\overline{BC}$, ∠ABF ≅ ∠BCG, $\overline{BF}$ ≅ $\overline{CG}$)

    24. SSS ($\overline{AB}$ ≅ $\overline{BC}$, $\overline{VA}$ ≅ $\overline{VB}$, $\overline{VB}$ ≅ $\overline{VC}$)

Page 115 · CHALLENGE

    64 cubes: 6 slicings   Make slice 1; stack section A
    on top of section B, make slice 2, and unstack to
    original formation.   Make slice 3; stack section C
    on top of section D, make slice 4, and unstack to
    original formation.   Make slice 5; position section F
    beside section E and make slice 6.

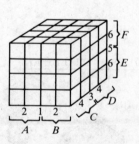

125 cubes: 9 slicings   Make slices 1 and 2;

stack section A on top of section B, make

slice 3 and unstack to original formation.

Make slices 4 and 5; stack section B on top

of section C, make slice 6, and unstack to

original formation.   Make slices 7 and 8;

position section F beside section E and

make slice 9.

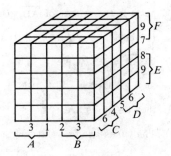

Pages 119-122 · WRITTEN EXERCISES

A 1. 1. Given   2. Given   3. Def. of midpt.   4. Vert. ∠ are ≅.   5. ASA

   6. Corr. parts of ≅ △ are ≅.   7. Def. of midpt.

2. 1. Given   2. Adj. ∠ formed by ⊥ lines are ≅.   3. Given

   4. Def. of midpt.   5. Refl. Prop. of ≅.   6. SAS

   7. Corr. parts of ≅ △ are ≅.

3. 1. $\overline{WO} \cong \overline{ZO}$; $\overline{XO} \cong \overline{YO}$ (Given)   2. ∠WOX ≅ ∠ZOY (Vert. ∠ are ≅.)

   3. △WOX ≅ △ZOY (SAS)   4. ∠W ≅ ∠Z (Corr. parts of ≅ △ are ≅.)

4. 1. ∠X ≅ ∠Y; $\overline{XO} \cong \overline{YO}$ (Given)   2. ∠WOX ≅ ∠ZOY (Vert. ∠ are ≅.)

   3. △WOX ≅ △ZOY (ASA)   4. $\overline{WO} \cong \overline{ZO}$ (Corr. parts of ≅ △ are ≅.)

5. 1. $\overline{SK} \parallel \overline{NR}$; $\overline{SN} \parallel \overline{KR}$ (Given)   2. ∠1 ≅ ∠3; ∠2 ≅ ∠4 (If 2 ∥ lines are cut by a

   trans., then alt. int. ∠ are ≅.)   3. $\overline{SR} \cong \overline{SR}$ (Refl. Prop. of ≅)

   4. △SRK ≅ △RSN (ASA)   5. $\overline{SK} \cong \overline{NR}$; $\overline{SN} \cong \overline{KR}$ (Corr. parts of ≅ △ are ≅.)

6. 1. $\overline{SK} \cong \overline{NR}$; $\overline{SN} \cong \overline{KR}$ (Given)   2. $\overline{SR} \cong \overline{SR}$ (Refl. Prop. of ≅)

   3. △SKR ≅ △RNS (SSS)   4. ∠1 ≅ ∠3; ∠2 ≅ ∠4 (Corr. parts of ≅ △ are ≅.)

   5. $\overline{SK} \parallel \overline{NR}$; $\overline{SN} \parallel \overline{KR}$ (If 2 lines are cut by a trans. and alt. int. ∠ are ≅, then

   the lines are ∥.)

7. a. If the opposite sides of a quad. are ≅, then they are also ∥.   b. yes

B 8. 1. $\overline{AD} \parallel \overline{ME}$; $\overline{MD} \parallel \overline{BE}$. (Given)   2. ∠A ≅ ∠EMB; ∠DMA ≅ ∠B (If 2 ∥ lines are

   cut by a trans., then corr. ∠ are ≅.)   3. M is the midpt. of $\overline{AB}$. (Given)

   4. $\overline{AM} \cong \overline{MB}$ (Def. of midpt.)   5. △ADM ≅ △MEB (ASA)   6. ∠D ≅ ∠E (Corr.

   parts of ≅ △ are ≅.)

9. 1. M is the midpt. of $\overline{AB}$. (Given)   2. $\overline{AM} \cong \overline{MB}$ (Def. of midpt.)   3. $\overline{AD} \parallel \overline{ME}$

(Given)   4. $\angle A \cong \angle EMB$ (If 2 $\parallel$ lines are cut by a trans., then corr. $\angle$ are $\cong$.)

5. $\overline{AD} \cong \overline{ME}$ (Given)   6. $\triangle AMD \cong \triangle MBE$ (SAS)   7. $\angle DMA \cong \angle B$ (Corr. parts

of $\cong$ $\angle$ are $\cong$.)   8. $\overline{DM} \parallel \overline{BE}$ (If 2 lines are cut by a trans. and corr. $\angle$ are $\cong$,

then the lines are $\parallel$.)

10. The wires are of equal length, that is, PA = PB = PC; they are staked at points

equally distant from the base of the tree, that is, TA = TB = TC, and PT = PT = PT

by the Refl. Prop. of $\cong$.   Therefore the $\angle$ PTA, PTB, and PTC are all $\cong$ and the

$\angle$ the 3 wires make with the ground are $\cong$ parts of $\cong$ $\angle$.

11. $\angle Q \cong \angle S$; Proof: 1. $\overline{PQ} \cong \overline{PS}$; $\overline{QR} \cong \overline{SR}$ (Given)   2. $\overline{PR} \cong \overline{PR}$ (Refl. Prop. of $\cong$)

3. $\triangle QPR \cong \triangle SPR$ (SSS)   4. $\angle QPR \cong \angle SPR$ (Corr. parts of $\cong$ $\angle$ are $\cong$.)

12. (1) $\overrightarrow{KO}$ bisects $\angle MKN$.   Proof: 1. $\overline{LM} \cong \overline{LN}$; $\overline{KM} \cong \overline{KN}$ (Given)   2. $\overline{LK} \cong \overline{LK}$

(Refl. Prop. of $\cong$)   3. $\triangle LKM \cong \triangle LKN$ (SSS)   4. $\angle MLK \cong \angle NLK$ (Corr. parts

of $\cong$ $\angle$ are $\cong$.)   5. $\overrightarrow{LO}$ bisects $\angle MLN$. (Def. of $\angle$ bis.)   (2) $\overline{LM} \cong \overline{LN}$;

Proof: 1. $\overline{KM} \cong \overline{KN}$ (Given)   2. $\overrightarrow{KO}$ bisects $\angle MKN$. (Given)   3. $\angle MKO \cong \angle NKO$

(Def. of $\angle$ bis.)   4. $\angle LKM$ and $\angle MKO$ are supp.; $\angle LKN$ and $\angle NKO$ are supp.

(Angle Add. Post. and Def. of supp. $\angle$)   5. $\angle LKM \cong \angle LKN$ (If 2 $\angle$ are supp.

of $\cong$ $\angle$, the 2 $\angle$ are $\cong$.)   6. $\overline{LK} \cong \overline{LK}$ (Refl. Prop. of $\cong$)   7. $\triangle LKM \cong \triangle LKN$

(SAS)   8. $\angle MLK \cong \angle NLK$ (Corr. parts of $\cong$ $\angle$ are $\cong$.)   9. $\overrightarrow{LO}$ bisects $\angle MLN$.

(Def. of $\angle$ bis.)

13. 1. $\overline{WS} \cong \overline{RQ}$; $\overline{ST} \cong \overline{QP}$ (Given)   2. WP = RT (Given)   3. PT = PT (Refl. Prop.

of =)   4. WP + PT = RT + TP (Add. Prop. of =)   5. WP + PT = WT;

RT + TP = RP (Seg. Add. Post.)   6. $\overline{WT} \cong \overline{RP}$ (Subst. Prop.)

7. $\triangle SWT \cong \triangle QRP$ (SSS)   8. $\angle W \cong \angle R$ (Corr. parts of $\cong$ $\angle$ are $\cong$.)   9. $\overline{WS} \parallel \overline{RQ}$

(If 2 lines are cut by a trans. and alt. int. $\angle$ are $\cong$, then the lines are $\parallel$.)

14. 1. $\overline{WS} \parallel \overline{RQ}$; $\overline{ST} \parallel \overline{PQ}$ (Given)   2. $\angle W \cong \angle R$; $\angle STW \cong \angle QPR$ (If 2 $\parallel$ lines are

cut by a trans., then alt. int. $\angle$ are $\cong$.   3. $\angle S \cong \angle Q$ (If 2 $\angle$ of one $\triangle$ are $\cong$ to

2 $\angle$ of another $\triangle$, then the third $\angle$ are $\cong$.)

15. (1) and (2)

16. (1) $\angle 3 \cong \angle 4$ Proof: 1. $\overline{WX} \perp \overline{UV}$ (Given)   2. $\angle 5 \cong \angle 6$ (Adj. $\angle$ formed by $\perp$

lines are $\cong$.)   3. $\overline{WU} \cong \overline{WV}$ (Given)   4. $\overline{WX} \cong \overline{WX}$ (Refl. Prop. of $\cong$)

5. $\triangle XWU \cong \triangle XWV$ (SAS)   6. $\angle 3 \cong \angle 4$ (Corr. parts of $\cong$ $\angle$ are $\cong$.)

(2) $\angle 1 \cong \angle 2$ Proof: 1. $\triangle XWU \cong \triangle XWV$ (Part (1) above)   2. $\angle U \cong \angle V$ (Corr.

parts of $\cong$ ▵ are $\cong$.)   3. $\overline{WX} \perp \overline{UV}$; $\overline{WX} \perp \overline{YZ}$ (Given)   3. $\overline{UV} \parallel \overline{YZ}$ (In a plane,

2 lines $\perp$ to the same line are $\parallel$.)   4. $\angle U \cong \angle 1$; $\angle V \cong \angle 2$ (If 2 $\parallel$ lines are cut by

a trans., then alt. int. ▵ are $\cong$.)   5. $\angle 1 \cong \angle 2$ (Subst. Prop.)

<u>17.</u> 1. $\overline{PA}$ and $\overline{QB}$ are $\perp$ to plane X. (Given)   2. $\overline{PA} \perp \overline{AB}$; $\overline{QB} \perp \overline{AB}$ (Def. of line $\perp$

to plane)   3. $m\angle A = m\angle B = 90$ (Def. of $\perp$ lines, rt. ▵)   4. O is the midpt.

of $\overline{AB}$. (Given)   5. $\overline{AO} \cong \overline{BO}$ (Def. of midpt.)   6. $\angle POA \cong \angle QOB$ (Vert. ▵ are $\cong$.)

7. $\triangle POA \cong \triangle QOB$ (ASA)   8. $\overline{PO} \cong \overline{QO}$ (Corr. parts of $\cong$ ▵ are $\cong$.)   9. O is the

midpt. of $\overline{PQ}$. (Def. of midpt.)

<u>18.</u> Given: $\overline{PQ} \cong \overline{PR}$; $\overrightarrow{PK}$ bisects $\angle QPR$.   Prove: $\overline{PK} \perp \overline{QR}$

Proof: 1. $\overline{PQ} \cong \overline{PR}$ (Given)   2. $\overrightarrow{PK}$ bisects $\angle QPR$. (Given)

3. $\angle QPK \cong \angle RPK$ (Def. of $\angle$ bis.)   4. $\overline{PK} \cong \overline{PK}$ (Refl.

Prop. of $\cong$)   5. $\triangle QPK \cong \triangle RPK$ (SAS)

6. $\angle QKP \cong \angle RKP$ (Corr. parts of $\cong$ ▵ are $\cong$.)   7. $\overline{PK} \perp \overline{QR}$ (If 2 lines form $\cong$

adj. ▵, then the lines are $\perp$.

<u>19.</u> Given: $AB = BC = CD = DE = EA$; $\angle B$ and $\angle E$ are rt. ▵.

Prove: $\overline{AC} \cong \overline{AD}$ Proof: 1. $AB = BC = DE = AE$ (Given)

3. $\angle B$ and $\angle E$ are rt. ▵. (Given)   4. $m\angle B = 90 = m\angle E$

(Def. of rt. $\angle$)   5. $\triangle AED \cong \triangle ABC$ (SAS)   6. $\overline{AC} \cong \overline{AD}$

(Corr. parts of $\cong$ ▵ are $\cong$.)

<u>20.</u> Given: $\overline{AB} \cong \overline{DC}$; $\overline{AB} \parallel \overline{DC}$ Prove: $\overline{AD} \cong \overline{BC}$; $\overline{AD} \parallel \overline{BC}$

Proof: 1. $\overline{AB} \parallel \overline{DC}$ (Given)   2. $\angle BAC \cong \angle ACD$ (If 2 $\parallel$

lines are cut by a trans., then alt. int. ▵ are $\cong$.)

3. $\overline{AB} \cong \overline{DC}$ (Given)   4. $\overline{AC} \cong \overline{AC}$ (Refl. Prop. of $\cong$)   5. $\triangle ADC \cong \triangle CBA$ (SAS)

6. $\angle DAC \cong \angle BCA$ (Corr. parts of $\cong$ ▵ are $\cong$.)   7. $\overline{AD} \parallel \overline{BC}$ (If 2 lines are cut by

a trans. and alt. int. ▵ are $\cong$, then the lines are $\parallel$.)   8. $\overline{AD} \cong \overline{BC}$ (Corr. parts

of $\cong$ ▵ are $\cong$.)

<u>C</u> <u>21.</u> Equilateral. Consider $\triangle EAB$, $\triangle BCG$, and $\triangle EFG$. $\overline{EA}$, $\overline{AB}$, $\overline{BC}$, $\overline{GC}$, $\overline{EF}$, and $\overline{FG}$

are all $\cong$. $\angle EAB$, $\angle BCG$, and $\angle EFG$ are all rt. ▵, so they are $\cong$ ▵. Then

$\triangle EAB \cong \triangle BCG \cong \triangle EFG$ by the SAS Post., and the sides of $\triangle BEG$ are corr.

parts of $\cong$ ▵.

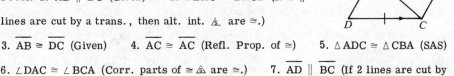

<u>22.</u> ASA.   A is the soldier's eye, C his feet, D the

point on the opposite bank in line with the tip of

his visor, and B is the point on the ground in line

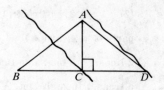

with the tip of his visor. $\overline{AC} \cong \overline{AC}$ and $\angle BCA$

and $\angle ACD$ are both rt. $\angle$s.   By keeping his visor in the same position, the soldier

makes $\angle BAC \cong \angle DAC$.   Then $\triangle BAC \cong \triangle DAC$ and $\overline{CD} \cong \overline{CB}$.

<u>23.</u> $\overline{UR} \cong \overline{WT}$; $\overline{UR} \parallel \overline{WT}$ Proof: 1. X is the midpt. of $\overline{US}$ and $\overline{RV}$. (Given)

2. $\overline{UX} \cong \overline{XS}$; $\overline{RX} \cong \overline{XV}$ (Def. of midpt.)   3. $\angle UXR \cong \angle SXV$ (Vert. $\angle$s are $\cong$.)

4. $\triangle UXR \cong \triangle SXV$ (SAS)   5. $\angle RUX \cong \angle VSX$; $\overline{UR} \cong \overline{VS}$ (Corr. parts of $\cong$ $\triangle$s are $\cong$.)

6. $\overline{UR} \parallel \overline{VS}$ (If 2 lines are cut by a trans. and alt. int. $\angle$s are $\cong$, then the lines are $\parallel$.)

7. Y is the midpt. of $\overline{VT}$ and $\overline{SW}$. (Given)   8. $\overline{VY} \cong \overline{YT}$; $\overline{SY} \cong \overline{YW}$ (Def. of midpt.)

9. $\angle VYS \cong \angle TYW$ (Vert. $\angle$s are $\cong$)   10. $\triangle VYS \cong \triangle TYW$ (SAS)

11. $\angle SVY \cong \angle WTY$; $\overline{VS} \cong \overline{WT}$ (Corr. parts of $\cong$ $\triangle$s are $\cong$.)   12. $\overline{VS} \parallel \overline{WT}$ (If 2

lines are cut by a trans. and alt. int. $\angle$s are $\cong$, then the lines are $\parallel$.)

13. $\overline{UR} \cong \overline{WT}$ (Trans. Prop. of $\cong$)   14. $\overline{UR} \parallel \overline{WT}$ (2 lines $\parallel$ to a third line are $\parallel$

to each other.)

Pages 126-128 · WRITTEN EXERCISES

<u>A</u> <u>1.</u> 5x - 8 = 2x + 7; 3x = 15; x = 5   <u>2.</u> 4x - 6 = 18; 4x = 24; x = 6

<u>3.</u> $x = \frac{1}{2}(180 - 98) = 41$ <u>4.</u> 2x = 90 - x; 3x = 90; x = 30

<u>5.</u> 1. Given   2. $\angle B$; If 2 $\angle$s of a $\triangle$ are $\cong$, the sides opp. those $\angle$s are $\cong$.   3. Given

4. $\angle A$; $\angle 2$; If 2 $\parallel$ lines are cut by a trans., then corr. $\angle$s are $\cong$.   5. $\angle 1 \cong \angle 2$

6. If 2 $\angle$s of a $\triangle$ are $\cong$, the sides opp. those $\angle$s are $\cong$.

<u>6.</u> 1. $\angle R \cong \angle S$; $\angle TUV \cong \angle TVU$ (Given)   2. $\overline{TR} \cong \overline{TS}$; $\overline{TU} \cong \overline{TV}$ (If 2 $\angle$s of a $\triangle$ are $\cong$,

then the sides opp. those $\angle$s are $\cong$.)   3. RU + UT = TR; SV + VT = ST (Seg. Add.

Post.)   4. RU = TR - UT; SV = ST - VT (Subtr. Prop. of =)   5. TR - UT =

ST - VT (Subtr. Prop. of =)   6. RU = SV (Subst. Prop.)

<u>7.</u> 1. $\overline{TU} \cong \overline{TV}$ (Given)   2. $\angle 1 \cong \angle 2$ (If 2 sides of a $\triangle$ are $\cong$, the $\angle$s opp. those sides

are $\cong$.)   3. $\overline{UV} \parallel \overline{RS}$ (Given)   4. $\angle 1 \cong \angle R$; $\angle 2 \cong \angle S$ (If 2 $\parallel$ lines are cut by a

trans., then corr. $\angle$s are $\cong$.)   5. $\angle R \cong \angle S$ (Subst. Prop.)

<u>8.</u> 1. m$\angle 1$ + m$\angle 2$ = m$\angle XYZ$; m$\angle 3$ + m$\angle 4$ = m$\angle XZY$ (Angle Add. Post.)

2. m$\angle 1$ = m$\angle XYZ$ - m$\angle 2$; m$\angle 4$ = m$\angle XZY$ - m$\angle 3$ 3. $\overline{XY} \cong \overline{XZ}$; $\overline{OY} \cong \overline{OZ}$

(Given)   4. m∠XYZ = m∠XZY; m∠2 = m∠3 (If 2 sides of a △ are ≅, then the ∠

opp. those sides are ≅.)   5. m∠XYZ - m∠2 = m∠XZY - m∠3 (Subtr. Prop. of =)

6. m∠1 = m∠4 (Subst. Prop.)

9. 1. $\overline{XY} \cong \overline{XZ}$ (Given)   2. m∠XYZ = m∠XZY (If 2 sides of a △ are ≅, then the ∠ opp.

those sides are ≅.)   3. $\overrightarrow{YO}$ bisects ∠XYZ; $\overrightarrow{ZO}$ bisects ∠XZY. (Given)

4. m∠XYZ = 2m∠2; m∠XZY = 2m∠3 (Angle Bisector Thm.)   5. 2m∠2 = 2m∠3

(Subst. Prop.)   6. m∠2 = m∠3 (Div. Prop. of =)   7. $\overline{YO} \cong \overline{ZO}$ (If 2 ∠ of a △

are ≅, then the sides opp. those ∠ are ≅.)

10. (1) and (3)   11. (1) and (2)

12. 1. $\overline{AB} \cong \overline{AC}$ (Given)   2. ∠B ≅ ∠C (If 2 sides of a △ are ≅, then the ∠ opp. those

sides are ≅.)   3. $\overline{AX}$ and $\overline{AY}$ trisect ∠BAC. (Given)   4. ∠1 ≅ ∠2 ≅ ∠3

(Def. of trisectors)   5. △ABX ≅ △ACY (ASA)   6. $\overline{AX} \cong \overline{AY}$ (Corr. parts of ≅

∠ are ≅.)

B 13. 1. ∠4 ≅ ∠7, ∠1 ≅ ∠3 (Given)   2. ∠B ≅ ∠C (If 2 ∠ of one △ are ≅ to 2 ∠ of

another △, then the 3rd ∠ are ≅.)   3. $\overline{AB} \cong \overline{AC}$ (If 2 ∠ of a △ are ≅, then the

sides opp. those ∠ are ≅.)   4. △ABC is isos. (Def. of isos. △)

14. 1. ∠1 ≅ ∠2 (Given)   2. $\overline{OP} \cong \overline{OQ}$ (If 2 ∠ of a △ are ≅, then the sides opp. those

∠ are ≅.)   3. ∠POS ≅ ∠QOR (Vert. ∠ are ≅.)   4. △POS ≅ △QOR (ASA)

5. $\overline{OS} \cong \overline{OR}$ (Corr. parts of ≅ ∠ are ≅.)   6. ∠5 ≅ ∠6 (If 2 sides of a △ are ≅,

then the ∠ opp. those sides are ≅.)

15. a. m∠2 = m∠1 = 40; m∠7 = 180 - (m∠1 + m∠2) = 180 - 80 = 100; m∠5 =

m∠6 = $\frac{1}{2}$(180 - m∠SOR) = $\frac{1}{2}$(180 - m∠7) = $\frac{1}{2}$(180 - 100) = 40; yes

b. m∠2 = m∠1 = x; m∠7 = 180 - (m∠1 + m∠2) = 180 - 2x; m∠5 = m∠6 =

$\frac{1}{2}$(180 - m∠SOR) = $\frac{1}{2}$(180 - m∠7) = $\frac{1}{2}$[180 - (180 - 2x)] = x; yes

16. a. yes; m∠XAC = $\frac{1}{2}$(180 - m∠A) = $\frac{1}{2}$(180 - 80) = 50; m∠C = $\frac{1}{2}$(180 - m∠A) =

$\frac{1}{2}$(180 - 80) = 50; since ∠XAC and ∠C are ≅ alt. int. ∠ $\overrightarrow{AX} \parallel \overline{BC}$.   b. no

17. a. 40; 40; 60   b. 2x; 2x; 180 - [(180 - 4x) + x] = 3x

18. a. m∠2 = m∠1 = 35; m∠3 = m∠1 + m∠2 = 70; m∠5 = $\frac{1}{2}$(180 - m∠3) =

$\frac{1}{2}$(180 - 70) = 55; m∠ABC = m∠2 + m∠5 = 35 + 55 = 90

b. m∠2 = m∠1 = x; m∠3 = m∠1 + m∠2 = 2x; m∠5 = $\frac{1}{2}$(180 - m∠3) =

$\frac{1}{2}$(180 - 2x) = 90 - x; m∠ABC = m∠2 + m∠5 = 90 - x + x = 90

19. <u>a.</u> m∠2 = m∠1 = 23; m∠4 = meas. of supp. of ∠3 = m∠1 + m∠2 = 46; m∠5 =

$\frac{1}{2}$(180 - m∠4) = $\frac{1}{2}$(180 - 46) = 67; m∠7 = 180 - (m∠5 + m∠2) =

180 - (67 + 23) = 90

<u>b.</u> m∠2 = m∠1 = x; m∠4 = meas. of supp. of ∠3 = m∠1 + m∠2 = 2x; m∠5 =

$\frac{1}{2}$(180 - m∠4) = $\frac{1}{2}$(180 - 2x) = 90 - x; m∠7 = 180 - (m∠5 + m∠2) =

180 - (90 - x + x) = 90

20. 4x - y = 7 and 2x + 3y = 7; y = 4x - 7; substituting, 2x + 3(4x - 7) = 7;

2x + 12x - 21 = 7; 14x = 28; x = 2; y = 4x - 7 = 1

21. x + y + 2x - y = 120; 3x = 120; x = 40; x + y = 60; y = 20

22. 2x - y = x + 2y so x = 3y. The sum of the meas. of the ∠ of a △ is 180 so

(2x + 2y) + (2x - y) + (x + 2y) = 180; 5x + 3y = 180; 5x + x = 180; x = 30;

3y = 30; y = 10

23. △DAC ≅ △DAB; Proof: 1. ∠ACB ≅ ∠ABC; ∠DCB ≅ ∠DBC (Given)   2. $\overline{AB}$ ≅ $\overline{AC}$;

$\overline{DB}$ ≅ $\overline{DC}$ (If 2 ∠ of a △ are ≅, then the sides opp. those ∠ are ≅.)   3. $\overline{DA}$ ≅ $\overline{DA}$

(Refl. Prop. of ≅)   4. △DAC ≅ △DAB (SSS)

24. m∠AED = 108; m∠DEF = 90; m∠AEF = 360 - (108 + 90) = 162; $\overline{EA}$ ≅ $\overline{EF}$ so

m∠EAF = m∠EFA = $\frac{1}{2}$(180 - m∠AEF) = $\frac{1}{2}$(180 - 162) = 9; $\overline{ED}$ ≅ $\overline{EF}$ so

m∠EFD = m∠EDF = $\frac{1}{2}$(180 - m∠DEF) = $\frac{1}{2}$(180 - 90) = 45; m∠AFD =

m∠AFE + m∠EFD = 9 + 45 = 54

25. △DEF is isos. $\overline{AB}$ ≅ $\overline{AC}$; D, E, and F are the midpts. of

$\overline{AB}$, $\overline{BC}$, and $\overline{AC}$, resp. ∠B ≅ ∠C; DB = $\frac{1}{2}$AB and

FC = $\frac{1}{2}$AC; $\overline{DB}$ ≅ $\overline{FC}$; $\overline{BE}$ ≅ $\overline{EC}$; so △DBE ≅ △FCE and

$\overline{ED}$ ≅ $\overline{EF}$. Thus △DEF is also an isos. △.

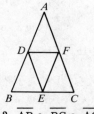

26. △DEF is equilateral.   Proof: 1. △ABC is equilateral. (Given)   2. $\overline{AB}$ ≅ $\overline{BC}$ ≅ $\overline{AC}$

(Def. of equilateral)   3. m∠A = m∠B = m∠C (An equilateral △ is also equiangular.)

4. m∠CAD = m∠ABE = m∠BCF (Given)   5. m∠A - m∠CAD = m∠B - m∠ABE

= m∠C - m∠BCF (Subtr. Prop. of =)   6. m∠BAE + m∠CAD = m∠A;

m∠FBC + m∠ABE = m∠B; m∠ACD + m∠BCF = m∠C (Angle Add. Post.)

7. m∠A - m∠CAD = m∠BAE; m∠B - m∠ABE = m∠FBC; m∠C - m∠BCF =

m∠ACD (Subtr. Prop. of =)   8. m∠BAE = m∠FBC = m∠ACD (Subst. Prop.)

9. △BAE ≅ △FBC ≅ △ACD (ASA)   10. ∠AEB ≅ ∠CDA ≅ ∠BFC (Corr. parts of

≅ ⧌ are ≅.)   11. ∠FED ≅ ∠EDF ≅ ∠EFD (If 2 ⧌ are supp. of ≅ ⧌, then the 2

⧌ are ≅.)   12. △DEF is equilateral. (An equiangular △ is also equilateral.)

<u>27</u>. 1. $\overline{SX}$ ≅ $\overline{SY}$ (Given)   2. ∠SXY ≅ ∠SYX (If 2 sides of a △ are ≅, then the ⧌ opp.

those sides are ≅.)   3. ∠SYX and ∠SYT are supp.; ∠RXY and ∠SXY are supp.

(Angle Add. Post. and def. of supp. ⧌)   4. ∠RXY ≅ ∠SYT (If 2 ⧌ are supp. of

≅ ⧌, then the 2 ⧌ are ≅.)   5. $\overline{XY}$ ≅ $\overline{YT}$; $\overline{RX}$ ≅ $\overline{SY}$ (Given)   6. △RXY ≅ △SYT

(SAS)   7. $\overline{ST}$ ≅ $\overline{RY}$ (Corr. parts of ≅ ⧌ are ≅.)

<u>28</u>. a. m∠1 = m∠3 = $\frac{1}{2}$(180 − 108) = 36; m∠2 = 108 − (m∠1 + m∠3) = 108 − 72 = 36

<u>b</u>. m∠1 = m∠4 = $\frac{1}{2}$(180 − 120) = 30; m∠2 = m∠3; m∠2 + m∠3 + 60 = 120;

2m∠2 = 60; m∠2 = m∠3 = 30

Pages 132-135 · WRITTEN EXERCISES

<u>A</u>   <u>1</u>. 1. Given   2. Def. of rt. △   3. Given   4. $\overline{XZ}$ ≅ $\overline{XZ}$ 5. △YXZ; HL

6. $\overline{WZ}$ ≅ $\overline{YZ}$ (Corr. parts of ≅ ⧌ are ≅.)

<u>2</u>. 1. Given   2. J   3. Given   4. ∠1; ∠2   5. $\overline{KA}$; Refl. Prop. of ≅

6. △JKA; AAS   7. $\overline{LK}$ ≅ $\overline{JK}$ (Corr. parts of ≅ ⧌ are ≅.)

<u>3</u>. 1. $\overline{EF}$ ⊥ $\overline{EG}$; $\overline{HG}$ ⊥ $\overline{EG}$ (Given)   2. △EGH and △GEF are rt. ⧌. (Def. of ⊥ lines,

rt. △)   3. $\overline{EH}$ ≅ $\overline{GF}$ (Given)   4. $\overline{EG}$ ≅ $\overline{EG}$ (Refl. Prop. of ≅)

5. △EGH ≅ △GEF (HL)   6. ∠H ≅ ∠F (Corr. parts of ≅ ⧌ are ≅.)

<u>4</u>. 1. $\overline{EF}$ ∥ $\overline{HG}$ (Given)   2. ∠FEG ≅ ∠HGE (If 2 ∥ lines are cut by a trans., then alt.

int. ⧌ are ≅.)   3. ∠H ≅ ∠F (Given)   4. $\overline{EG}$ ≅ $\overline{EG}$ (Refl. Prop. of ≅)

5. △FEG ≅ △HGE (AAS)   6. $\overline{HE}$ ≅ $\overline{FG}$ (Corr. parts of ≅ ⧌ are ≅.)

<u>5</u>. 1. Given   2. ∠PRQ; the ⧌ opp. those sides are ≅.   3. Given   4. Refl. Prop.

of ≅.   5. △QRT; SAS   6. Corr. parts of ≅ ⧌ are ≅.

<u>6</u>. 1. Given   2. Add. Prop. of =   3. m∠4; m∠JNM; Angle Add. Post.

4. Subst. Prop.   5. $\overline{MN}$ ≅ $\overline{MN}$ 6. △NLM; ASA   7. $\overline{MJ}$ ≅ $\overline{NL}$; Corr.

parts of ≅ ⧌ are ≅.

<u>7</u>. 1. $\overline{RT}$ ≅ $\overline{AS}$; $\overline{RS}$ ≅ $\overline{AT}$ (Given)   2. $\overline{ST}$ ≅ $\overline{ST}$ (Refl. Prop. of ≅)   3. △TSA ≅ △STR

(SSS)   4. ∠TSA ≅ ∠STR (Corr. parts of ≅ ⧌ are ≅.)

<u>8</u>. 1. $\overline{DH}$ ⊥ $\overline{DJ}$; $\overline{JK}$ ⊥ $\overline{DJ}$ (Given)   2. △HDJ and △KJD are rt. ⧌. (Def. of ⊥ lines,

rt. △)   3. $\overline{JH}$ ≅ $\overline{DK}$ (Given)   4. $\overline{DJ}$ ≅ $\overline{DJ}$ (Refl. Prop. of ≅)   5. △HDJ ≅ △KJD

(HL)   6. ∠H ≅ ∠K (Corr. parts of ≅ ⧌ are ≅.)

9. A line is ⊥ to a plane if it is ⊥ to all lines in the plane that pass through the pt. where the line intersects the plane.

10. SAS   11. AAS   12. HL

B 13. a. yes; △AOB ≅ △AOC (SSS) so ∠AOB ≅ ∠AOC.   b. no

14. a. true   b. true   15. ∠1 ≅ ∠2; ∠3 ≅ ∠4 so $\overline{PQ}$ ≅ $\overline{PT}$; ASA

16. ∠7 ≅ ∠8 so $\overline{PR}$ ≅ $\overline{PS}$; ∠3 ≅ ∠4 so $\overline{PQ}$ ≅ $\overline{PT}$; $\overline{QR}$ ≅ $\overline{ST}$; SSS

17. a. Check students' drawings.   b. △RMS, △RNT; △MNS, △NMT; △ONS, △OMT; △NST, △MTS

18. 1. ∠1 ≅ ∠2 ≅ ∠3 (Given)   2. $\overline{HE}$ ≅ $\overline{HD}$ (If 2 ∠ of a △ are ≅, the sides opp. those ∠ are ≅.)   3. $\overline{ES}$ ≅ $\overline{DT}$ (Given)   4. △HES ≅ △HDT (SAS)   5. ∠4 ≅ ∠5 (Corr. parts of ≅ △ are ≅.)

19. Check students' drawings.   1. AB = AC (Given)   2. m∠ABC = m∠ACB (If 2 sides of a △ are ≅, the ∠ opp. those sides are ≅.)   3. $\frac{1}{2}$m∠ABC = $\frac{1}{2}$m∠ACB (Mult. Prop. of =)   4. $\overrightarrow{BX}$ bis. ∠ABC; $\overrightarrow{CY}$ bis. ∠ACB. (Given)   5. m∠XBC = $\frac{1}{2}$m∠ABC; m∠YCB = $\frac{1}{2}$m∠ACB (Angle Bis. Thm.)   6. m∠XBC = m∠YCB (Subst. Prop.)   7. $\overline{BC}$ ≅ $\overline{BC}$ (Refl. Prop. of ≅)   8. △XCB ≅ △YBC (ASA)   9. BX = CY (Corr. parts of ≅ △ are ≅.)

20. Given: $\overline{AB}$ ≅ $\overline{AC}$; M and N midpts. of $\overline{AB}$ and $\overline{AC}$, resp., $\overline{MX}$ ⊥ $\overline{BC}$ and $\overline{NY}$ ⊥ $\overline{BC}$.   Prove: $\overline{MX}$ ≅ $\overline{NY}$
Plan: Since AB = AC, then ∠B ≅ ∠C.   Also, MB = $\frac{1}{2}$AB and NC = $\frac{1}{2}$AC, by Midpt. Thm.   By Subst. Prop., MB = NC. ∠MXB and ∠NYC both have meas. 90, so ∠MXB ≅ ∠NYC, and △MXB ≅ △NYC (AAS). $\overline{MX}$ ≅ $\overline{NY}$ (Corr. parts of ≅ △ are ≅.)

21. Given: $\overline{FL}$ ≅ $\overline{AK}$; $\overline{SF}$ ≅ $\overline{SK}$; M is the midpt. of $\overline{SF}$; N is the midpt. of $\overline{SK}$. Prove: $\overline{AM}$ ≅ $\overline{LN}$ Plan: △FSK is isos., so ∠F ≅ ∠K.   Add seg. $\overline{LA}$ to $\overline{FL}$ and $\overline{KA}$, resp., so that FA = KL.   Use Midpt. Thm. and Subst. Prop. to show $\overline{FM}$ ≅ $\overline{KN}$.   Then △FAM ≅ △KLN (SAS), and $\overline{AM}$ ≅ $\overline{LN}$, as corr. parts of ≅ △.

C 22. 1. ∠ADC ≅ ∠NCE ≅ ∠FED; ∠CDE ≅ ∠ECD ≅ ∠DEC (Def. of square; an equilateral △ is also equiangular.)   2. m∠ADC + m∠CDE = m∠NCE + m∠ECD = m∠FED + m∠DEC (Add. Prop. of =)   3. m∠ADE = m∠ADC + m∠CDE; m∠NCD = m∠NCE + m∠ECD; m∠FEC = m∠FED + m∠DEC (Angle Add. Post.)

4. ∠ADE ≅ ∠NCD ≅ ∠FEC (Subst. Prop.)   5. $\overline{AD}$ ≅ $\overline{DE}$ ≅ $\overline{NC}$ ≅ $\overline{CD}$ ≅ $\overline{FE}$ ≅ $\overline{EC}$

(Def. of square and of equilateral △)   6. △ADE ≅ △NCD ≅ △FEC (SAS)

7. AE = ND = FC (Corr. parts of ≅ △ are ≅.)

23. 1. AE = FC = ND; m∠AED = m∠FCE = m∠NDC (Ex. 22, above; corr. parts of

≅ △ are ≅.)   2. m∠FED + m∠AED = m∠NCE + m∠FCE = m∠ADC + m∠NDC

(Ex. 22, above; Add. Prop. of =)   3. m∠AEF = m∠FED + m∠AED; m∠FCN =

m∠NCE + m∠FCE; m∠NDA = m∠ADC + m∠NDC (Angle Add. Post.)

4. ∠AEF ≅ ∠FCN ≅ ∠NDA (Subst. Prop.)   5. $\overline{FE}$ ≅ $\overline{AD}$ ≅ $\overline{NC}$ (Def. of square)

6. △AEF ≅ △NDA ≅ △FCN (SAS)   7. $\overline{FA}$ ≅ $\overline{AN}$ ≅ $\overline{NF}$ (Corr. parts of ≅ △ are ≅.)

8. △FAN is equilateral. (Def. of equilateral △)

Pages 140-142 · WRITTEN EXERCISES

A 1. a, b. Check students' drawings.   b. no (alt. ≅ bis. ≅ med.)

  2-5. Check students' drawings.   5. yes; the midpt. of the hypotenuse

  6. $\overline{KS}$; $\overline{KN}$ 7. $\overline{NS}$; $\overline{NK}$ 8. bis. of ∠S   9. L; A   10. A; F

  11. ⊥ bis. of $\overline{LF}$.

  12. 1. P is on the ⊥ bis. of $\overline{AB}$ and $\overline{BC}$. (Given)   2. PA = PB; PB = BC (If a pt.

  lies on the ⊥ bis. of a seg., then it is equidistant from the endpts. of the seg.)

  3. PA = PC (Subst. Prop.)

B 13. 1. $\overleftrightarrow{AX}$ is the ⊥ bis. of $\overline{BC}$. (Given)   2. m∠AXB = m∠AXC = 90; $\overline{XB}$ ≅ $\overline{XC}$ (Def.

  of ⊥ bis.)   3. $\overline{AX}$ ≅ $\overline{AX}$ (Refl. Prop. of ≅)   4. △AXB ≅ △AXC (SAS)

  5. AB = AC (Corr. parts of ≅ △ are ≅.)

  14. 1. S and V are equidistant from E and D. (Given)   2. S and V are on the ⊥ bis. of

  $\overline{ED}$. (If a pt. is equidistant from the endpts. of a seg., then it is on the ⊥ bis. of the

  seg.)   3. $\overleftrightarrow{SV}$ is the ⊥ bis. of $\overline{ED}$. (Through any 2 pts. there is exactly one line.)

  15. a.   b.   c.

  16. 1. Draw the median, $\overline{AX}$, from A to $\overline{BC}$. (Ruler Post.; through any 2 pts., there is

  exactly one line.)   2. XB = XC (Def. of median)   3. AX = AX (Refl. Prop. of =)

4. AB = AC (Given)   5. △ AXB ≅ △ AXC (SSS)   6. ∠ AXB ≅ ∠ AXC (Corr. parts

of ≅ ⩩ are ≅.)   7. $\overleftrightarrow{AX}$ ⊥ $\overline{BC}$ (If 2 lines form ≅ adj. ⩩ , then the lines are ⊥.)

8. $\overleftrightarrow{AX}$ is the ⊥ bis. of $\overline{BC}$. (Def. of ⊥ bis.)   9. A is on the ⊥ bis. of $\overline{BC}$.

(A is on $\overleftrightarrow{AX}$.)

17. a. 1. $\overrightarrow{BZ}$ bisects ∠ ABC. (Given)   2. ∠ PBX ≅ ∠ PBY (Def. of ∠ bis.)

3. $\overline{PX}$ ⊥ $\overrightarrow{BA}$; $\overline{PY}$ ⊥ $\overrightarrow{BC}$ (Given)   4. m∠ PXB = 90 = m∠ PYB (Def. of ⊥ lines,

rt. ⩩)   5. $\overline{PB}$ ≅ $\overline{PB}$ (Refl. Prop. of ≅)   6. △ PXB ≅ △ PYB (AAS)

7. PX = PY (Corr. parts of ≅ ⩩ are ≅.)

b. 1. $\overline{PX}$ ⊥ $\overrightarrow{BA}$; $\overline{PY}$ ⊥ $\overrightarrow{BC}$ (Given)   2. △ PXB and △ PYB are rt. ⩩ . (Def. of ⊥

lines, rt. ⩩)   3. PB = PB (Refl. Prop. of =)   4. PX = PY (Given)

5. △ PXB ≅ △ PYB (HL)   6. ∠ PBX ≅ ∠ PBY (Corr. parts of ≅ ⩩ are ≅.)

7. $\overrightarrow{BP}$ bisects ∠ ABC. (Def. of ∠ bis.)

18. 1. $\overline{BE}$ ≅ $\overline{CD}$; $\overline{BD}$ ≅ $\overline{CE}$ (Given)   2. $\overline{BC}$ ≅ $\overline{BC}$ (Refl. Prop. of ≅)   3. △ EBC ≅

△ DCB (SSS)   4. ∠ EBC ≅ ∠ DCB (Corr. parts of ≅ ⩩ are ≅.)   5. $\overline{AB}$ ≅ $\overline{AC}$ (If

2 ⩩ of a △ are ≅, then the sides opp. those ⩩ are ≅.)   6. △ ABC is isos. (Def.

of isos. △)

19. a. 1. $\overline{AB}$ ≅ $\overline{AC}$ (Given)   2. $\overline{BD}$ ⊥ $\overline{AC}$; $\overline{CE}$ ⊥ $\overline{AB}$ (Given)   3. m∠ ADB = 90 =

m∠ AEC (Def. of ⊥ lines, rt. ∠)   4. ∠ A ≅ ∠ A (Refl. Prop. of ≅)   5. △ ADB ≅

△ AEC (AAS)   6. $\overline{BD}$ ≅ $\overline{CE}$ (Corr. parts of ≅ ⩩ are ≅.)

b. The altitudes drawn to the legs of an isos. △ are ≅.

20. Given: AB = AC; $\overline{CM}$ and $\overline{BN}$ are medians.

Prove: $\overline{CM}$ ≅ $\overline{BN}$ Proof: 1. AB = AC (Given)

2. $\frac{1}{2}$AB = $\frac{1}{2}$AC (Mult. Prop. of =)   3. $\overline{CM}$ and $\overline{BN}$ are

medians. (Given)   4. M is the midpt. of $\overline{AB}$; N is the

midpt. of $\overline{AC}$. (Def. of median)   5. MB = $\frac{1}{2}$AB;

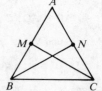

NC = $\frac{1}{2}$AC (Midpt. Thm.)   6. MB = NC (Subst. Prop.)   7. ∠ ABC ≅ ∠ ACB (If

2 sides of a △ are ≅, then the ⩩ opp. those sides are ≅.)   8. $\overline{BC}$ ≅ $\overline{BC}$ (Refl.

Prop. of ≅)   9. △ MBC ≅ △ NCB (SAS)   10. $\overline{CM}$ ≅ $\overline{BN}$ (Corr. parts of ≅ ⩩ are ≅.)

21. 1. $\overleftrightarrow{SR}$ is the ⊥ bis. of $\overline{QT}$; $\overleftrightarrow{QR}$ is the ⊥ bis. of $\overline{SP}$. (Given)   2. S is on the ⊥ bis.

of $\overline{QT}$; Q is on the ⊥ bis. of $\overline{SP}$. (S is on $\overleftrightarrow{SR}$; Q is on $\overleftrightarrow{QR}$.)   3. QS = ST; PQ = QS

(If a pt. is on the ⊥ bis. of a seg., then it is equidistant from the endpts. of the seg.)

4. PQ = ST (Trans. Prop. of =)

C 22. 1. $\overrightarrow{DP}$ bisects ∠ADE: $\overrightarrow{EP}$ bisects ∠DEC. (Given)   2. P is on the bis. of ∠ADE and the bis. of ∠DEC. (P is on $\overrightarrow{DP}$ and $\overrightarrow{EP}$.)   3. Draw $\overline{PX}$, $\overline{PY}$, and $\overline{PZ}$, ⊥s from P to $\overrightarrow{BA}$, $\overline{DE}$, and $\overrightarrow{BC}$, resp. (Through a pt. outside a line there is exactly one line ⊥ to the given line.)   4. PX = PY; PY = PZ (If a pt. is on the bis. of an ∠, then it is equidistant from the sides of the ∠.)   5. PX = PZ (Trans. Prop. of =)   6. P is on the ⊥ bis. of ∠ABC. (If a pt. is equidistant from the sides of an ∠, it lies on the bis. of the ∠.)   7. $\overrightarrow{BP}$ is the bis. of ∠ABC. (Through any 2 pts. there is exactly one line.)

23. 1. $\overleftrightarrow{MN}$ is the ⊥ bis. of $\overline{TS}$. (Given)   2. m∠MNS = m∠MNT = 90 (Def. of ⊥ lines, rt. ∠)   3. MT = MS, NT = NS (If a pt. is on the ⊥ bis. of a seg., then it is equidistant from the endpts. of the seg.)   4. △MNT ≅ △MNS (HL)   5. ∠NMT ≅ ∠NMS (Corr. parts of ≅ ▵ are ≅.)   6. m∠RTS = 90 (Given)   7. $\overline{RT}$ ⊥ $\overline{TS}$ (Def. of rt. ∠, ⊥ lines)   8. $\overline{RT}$ ∥ $\overline{MN}$ (In a plane, 2 lines ⊥ to the same line are ∥.) 9. ∠RTM ≅ ∠NMT (If 2 ∥ lines are cut by a trans., then alt. int. ▵ are ≅.) 10. ∠TRM ≅ ∠NMS (If 2 ∥ lines are cut by a trans., then corr. ▵ are ≅.) 11. ∠TRM ≅ ∠RTM (Trans. Prop. of ≅)   12. $\overline{RM}$ ≅ $\overline{TM}$ (If 2 ▵ of a △ are ≅, then the sides opp. those ▵ are ≅.)   13. $\overline{RM}$ ≅ $\overline{MS}$ (Trans. Prop. of ≅) 14. M is the midpt. of $\overline{RS}$. (Def. of midpt.)   15. $\overline{TM}$ is a median. (Def. of median)

24. a. 1. $\overline{AB}$ ⊥ plane M. (Given)   2. $\overline{AB}$ ⊥ $\overline{OD}$ (Def. of line ⊥ plane)   3. O is the midpt. of $\overline{AB}$. (Given)   3. $\overleftrightarrow{OD}$ is the ⊥ bis. of $\overline{AB}$ in the plane det. by $\overleftrightarrow{AB}$ and D. (Def. of ⊥ bis.)   4. $\overline{AD}$ ≅ $\overline{BD}$ (If a pt. is on the ⊥ bis. of a seg., then it is equidistant from the endpts. of the seg.)   b. 1. $\overline{AB}$ ⊥ plane M (Given)   2. $\overline{AB}$ ⊥ $\overline{OC}$ (Def. of line ⊥ plane)   3. O is the midpt. of $\overline{AB}$. (Given)   4. $\overleftrightarrow{OC}$ is the ⊥ bis. of $\overline{AB}$ in the plane det. by $\overleftrightarrow{AB}$ and C. (Def. of ⊥ bis.)   5. $\overline{AC}$ ≅ $\overline{BC}$ (If a pt. is on the ⊥ bis. of a seg., then it is equidistant from the endpts. of the seg.) c. 1. $\overline{AD}$ ≅ $\overline{BD}$; $\overline{AC}$ ≅ $\overline{BC}$ (Parts a and b, above)   2. $\overline{CD}$ ≅ $\overline{CD}$ (Refl. Prop. of ≅) 3. △ACD ≅ △BCD (SSS)   4. ∠CAD ≅ ∠CBD (Corr. parts of ≅ ▵ are ≅.)

25. Using ≅ ▵ of △PRQ, rt. ▵ at M and N, and side $\overline{RQ}$, prove △RMQ ≅ △QNR (AAS). As corr. parts of ≅ ▵ $\overline{RM}$ ≅ $\overline{NQ}$. Then use vert. ▵ MOR and NOQ to show △RMO ≅ △QNO (AAS). As corr. parts of ≅ ▵ $\overline{OM}$ ≅ $\overline{ON}$ and △MNO is isos.

26. Draw $\overline{AP}$ and $\overline{BP}$ ⊥s from A and B to $\overrightarrow{OX}$ and $\overrightarrow{OY}$, respectively. Since $\overleftrightarrow{OZ}$ is the ⊥ bis. of $\overline{AB}$, OA = OB and AM = BM. ∠1 = ∠3, and ∠OPA and ∠OMB are rt. ▵,

so $\triangle$ OPA $\cong$ $\triangle$ OMB (AAS) and AP = BM, by corr. parts.   Similarly, $\triangle$ OAM $\cong$ $\triangle$ OBQ,

and AM = BQ.   From the Trans. Prop., AP = BQ.

Pages 144-148 · WRITTEN EXERCISES

A   1. a. SSS   b. Corr. parts of $\cong$ $\triangle$ are $\cong$.   c. SAS   d. Corr. parts of $\cong$ $\triangle$ are $\cong$.

2. a. SSS   b. Corr. parts of $\cong$ $\triangle$ are $\cong$.   c. AAS   d. Corr. parts of $\cong$ $\triangle$ are $\cong$.

3. a. AAS   b. Corr. parts of $\cong$ $\triangle$ are $\cong$.   c. SAS   d. Corr. parts of $\cong$ $\triangle$ are $\cong$.

4. a. SAS   b. Corr. parts of $\cong$ $\triangle$ are $\cong$.   c. ASA   d. Corr. parts of $\cong$ $\triangle$ are $\cong$.

5. a. SAS   b. Corr. parts of $\cong$ $\triangle$ are $\cong$.   c. HL   d. Corr. parts of $\cong$ $\triangle$ are $\cong$.

6. Answers may vary. $\triangle$ AOD $\cong$ $\triangle$ BOD (SAS or SSS or HL); $\triangle$ AOC $\cong$ $\triangle$ BOC (SAS or

SSS or HL); $\triangle$ ACB $\cong$ $\triangle$ ADB (SSS); $\triangle$ ACD $\cong$ $\triangle$ BCD (SSS)

B   7. 1. $\overline{FL}$ $\cong$ $\overline{FK}$; $\overline{LA}$ $\cong$ $\overline{KA}$ (Given)   2. $\overline{FA}$ $\cong$ $\overline{FA}$ (Refl. Prop. of $\cong$)   3. $\triangle$ FLA $\cong$

$\triangle$ FKA (SSS)   4. $\angle 1$ $\cong$ $\angle 2$ (or $\angle 5$ $\cong$ $\angle 6$) (Corr. parts of $\cong$ $\triangle$ are $\cong$.)   5. $\overline{FJ}$ $\cong$ $\overline{FJ}$

(or $\overline{JA}$ $\cong$ $\overline{JA}$) (Refl. Prop. of $\cong$)   6. $\triangle$ FLJ $\cong$ $\triangle$ FKJ (or $\triangle$ LAJ $\cong$ $\triangle$ KAJ) (SAS)

7. $\overline{LJ}$ $\cong$ $\overline{KJ}$ (Corr. parts of $\cong$ $\triangle$ are $\cong$.)

8. 1. $\overleftrightarrow{FA}$ bis. $\angle$ LFK and $\angle$ LAK. (Given)   2. $\angle 1$ $\cong$ $\angle 2$; $\angle 5$ $\cong$ $\angle 6$ (Def. of $\angle$ bis.)

3. $\overline{FA}$ $\cong$ $\overline{FA}$ (Refl. Prop. of $\cong$)   4. $\triangle$ FLA $\cong$ $\triangle$ FKA (ASA)   5. $\overline{LA}$ $\cong$ $\overline{KA}$ (Corr.

parts of $\cong$ $\triangle$ are $\cong$.)   6. $\overline{JA}$ $\cong$ $\overline{JA}$ (Refl. Prop. of $\cong$)   7. $\triangle$ LJA $\cong$ $\triangle$ KJA (SAS)

8. $\angle 3$ $\cong$ $\angle 4$ (Corr. parts of $\cong$ $\triangle$ are $\cong$.)   9. $\overleftrightarrow{FA}$ bisects $\angle$ LJK (Def. of $\angle$ bis.)

9. 1. $\triangle$ RST $\cong$ $\triangle$ XYZ (Given)   2. $\angle$ RST $\cong$ $\angle$ XYZ; $\overline{ST}$ $\cong$ $\overline{YZ}$; $\angle$ T $\cong$ $\angle$ Z (Corr. parts

of $\cong$ $\triangle$ are $\cong$.)   3. $\frac{1}{2}$ m$\angle$ RST = $\frac{1}{2}$ m$\angle$ XYZ (Mult. Prop. of =)   4. $\overrightarrow{SK}$ bis. $\angle$ RST;

$\overrightarrow{YL}$ bis. $\angle$ XYZ. (Given)   5. m$\angle$ KST = $\frac{1}{2}$ m$\angle$ RST; m$\angle$ LYZ = $\frac{1}{2}$ m$\angle$ XYZ (Angle Bis.

Thm.)   6. m$\angle$ KST = m$\angle$ LYZ (Subst. Prop.)   7. $\triangle$ KST $\cong$ $\triangle$ LYZ (ASA)

8. $\overline{SK}$ $\cong$ $\overline{YL}$ (Corr. parts of $\cong$ $\triangle$ are $\cong$.)

10. 1. Draw $\overline{AC}$ and $\overline{AE}$. (Through any 2 pts. there is exactly one line.)   2. $\overline{CD}$ $\cong$ $\overline{ED}$;

$\angle$ CDA $\cong$ $\angle$ EDA (Given)   3. $\overline{AD}$ $\cong$ $\overline{AD}$ (Refl. Prop. of $\cong$)   4. $\triangle$ CDA $\cong$ $\triangle$ EDA (SAS)

5. $\overline{AC}$ $\cong$ $\overline{AE}$ (Corr. parts of $\cong$ $\triangle$ are $\cong$.)   6. $\overline{AB}$ $\cong$ $\overline{AF}$; $\overline{BC}$ $\cong$ $\overline{FE}$ (Given)

7. $\triangle$ ABC $\cong$ $\triangle$ AFE (SSS)   8. $\angle$ B $\cong$ $\angle$ F (Corr. parts of $\cong$ $\triangle$ are $\cong$.)

<u>11</u>. Given: △ PAY ≃ △ NOW; $\overline{PE}$ and $\overline{NF}$

are altitudes.   Prove: $\overline{PE}$ ≃ $\overline{NF}$

Proof: 1. △ PAY ≃ △ NOW (Given)

2. $\overline{PY}$ ≃ $\overline{NW}$; ∠ Y ≃ ∠ W (Corr. parts

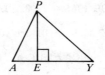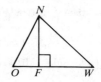

of ≃ ▲ are ≃.)   3. $\overline{PE}$ and $\overline{NF}$ are alt. (Given)   4. m∠ PEY = 90 = m∠ NFW

(Def. of alt., ⊥ lines)   5. △ PEY ≃ △ NFW (AAS)   6. $\overline{PE}$ ≃ $\overline{NF}$ (Corr. parts

of ≃ ▲ are ≃.)

<u>12</u>. 1. △ LMN ≃ △ RST (Given)   2. $\overline{LM}$ ≃ $\overline{RS}$; ∠ LMN ≃ ∠ RST (Corr. parts of ≃ ▲ are ≃.)

3. ∠ LMN, ∠ LMX are supp; ∠ RST, ∠ RSY are supp. (Angle Add. Post.; def. of supp.)

4. ∠ LMX ≃ ∠ RSY (If 2 ▲ are supp. of ≃ ▲, then the 2 ▲ are ≃.)   5. $\overline{LX}$ and $\overline{RY}$

are alt. (Given)   6. m∠ X = 90 = m∠ Y (Def. of alt., ⊥ lines)   7. △ LXM ≃

△ RYS (AAS)   8. $\overline{LX}$ ≃ $\overline{RY}$ (Corr. parts of ≃ ▲ are ≃.)

<u>13</u>. 1. $\overline{DE}$ ≃ $\overline{FG}$; $\overline{GD}$ ≃ $\overline{EF}$ (Given)   2. $\overline{GE}$ ≃ $\overline{GE}$ (Refl. Prop. of ≃)   3. △ GDE ≃

△ EFG (SSS)   4. ∠ DEH ≃ ∠ FGK (Corr. parts of ≃ ▲ are ≃.)   5. ∠ HDE and

∠ KFG are rt. ▲. (Given)   6. m∠ HDE = 90 = m∠ KFG (Def. of rt. ∠)

7. △ DEH ≃ △ FGK (ASA)   8. $\overline{DH}$ ≃ $\overline{FK}$ (Corr. parts of ≃ ▲ are ≃.)

<u>14</u>. 1. $\overline{GD}$ ∥ $\overline{EF}$ (Given)   2. ∠ DGE ≃ ∠ FEG (If 2 ∥ lines are cut by a trans., then alt.

int. ▲ are ≃.)   3. ∠ GDE ≃ ∠ EFG (Given)   4. $\overline{GE}$ ≃ $\overline{GE}$ (Refl. Prop. of ≃)

5. △ DGE ≃ △ FEG (AAS)   6. $\overline{DG}$ ≃ $\overline{FE}$ (Corr. parts of ≃ ▲ are ≃.)   7. $\overline{GH}$ ≃ $\overline{EK}$

(Given)   8. △ DGH ≃ △ FEK (SAS)   9. ∠ DHG ≃ ∠ FKE (Corr. parts of ≃ ▲ are ≃.)

10. ∠ DHE and ∠ DHG are supp. ▲; ∠ FKG and ∠ FKE are supp. ▲ (∠ Add. Post.,

Def. of supp. ▲)   11. ∠ DHE ≃ ∠ FKG (If 2 ▲ are supp. of ≃ ▲, the 2 ▲ are ≃.)

12. $\overline{DH}$ ∥ $\overline{FK}$ (If 2 lines are cut by a trans. and alt. int. ▲ are ≃, then the lines are ∥.)

<u>15</u>. Given: $\overline{SO}$ ≃ $\overline{OX}$; $\overline{TO}$ ≃ $\overline{OY}$ Prove: $\overline{PO}$ ≃ $\overline{OQ}$

Proof: 1. $\overline{TO}$ ≃ $\overline{OY}$; $\overline{SO}$ ≃ $\overline{OX}$ (Given)   2. ∠ TOS ≃

∠ YOX (Vert. ▲ are ≃.)   3. △ TOS ≃ △ YOX (SAS)

4. ∠ STO ≃ ∠ XYO (Corr. parts of ≃ ▲ are ≃.)

5. ∠ TOP ≃ ∠ YOQ (Vert. ▲ are ≃.)   6. △ TOP ≃ △ YOQ (ASA)   7. $\overline{PO}$ ≃ $\overline{OQ}$

(Corr. parts of ≃ ▲ are ≃.)

<u>16</u>. 1. Since DB = EC and BA = CA, then DA = EA.   Using ∠ A in both ▲, △ DCA ≃

△ EBA (SAS).   2. From △ DCA ≃ △ EBA, ∠ D ≃ ∠ E and DC = BE, as corr. parts;

48

then △ DBC ≅ △ ECB (SAS).   3. ∠ DBC and ∠ ECB are corr. parts of ≅ ▲ and are

therefore ≅; ∠ ABC and ∠ ACB are supp. of these ∡, so ∠ ABC ≅ ∠ ACB.

<u>C</u> <u>17.</u> 1. $\overline{AM}$ ≅ $\overline{MB}$; $\overline{AD}$ ≅ $\overline{BC}$; ∠ MDC ≅ ∠ MCD (Given)   2. $\overline{DM}$ ≅ $\overline{CM}$ (If 2 ∡ of a △

are ≅, then the sides opp. those ∡ are ≅.)   3. △ ADM ≅ △ BCM (SSS)

4. ∠ ADM ≅ ∠ BCM (Corr. parts of ≅ ▲ are ≅.)   5. m∠ ADM + m∠ MDC =

m∠ BCM + m∠ MCD (Add. Prop. of =)   6. m∠ ADC = m∠ BCD (Angle Add. Post.,

Subst. Prop.)   7. $\overline{DC}$ ≅ $\overline{DC}$ (Refl. Prop. of ≅)   8. △ ADC ≅ △ BCD (SAS)

9. $\overline{AC}$ ≅ $\overline{BD}$ (Corr. parts of ≅ ▲ are ≅.)

<u>18.</u> 1. ∠ 3 ≅ ∠ 4 (Given)   2. ∠ 3 and ∠ 7 are supp. ∡; ∠ 4 and ∠ 8 are supp. ∡ (∠ Add.

Post., Def. of supp. ∡)   3. ∠ 7 ≅ ∠ 8 (If 2 ∡ are supp. of ≅ ∡, then the 2 ∡

are ≅.)   4. $\overline{AG}$ ≅ $\overline{AF}$ (If 2 ∡ of a △ are ≅, then the sides opp. those ∡ are ≅.)

5. ∠ 1 ≅ ∠ 2 (Given)   6. △ BAG ≅ △ EAF (ASA)   7. $\overline{AB}$ ≅ $\overline{AE}$ (Corr. parts of

≅ ▲ are ≅.)   8. ∠ 5 ≅ ∠ 6 (Given)   9. $\overline{AC}$ ≅ $\overline{AD}$ (If 2 ∡ of a △ are ≅, then the

sides opp. those ∡ are ≅.)   10. △ BAC ≅ △ EAD (SAS)   11. $\overline{BC}$ ≅ $\overline{ED}$ (Corr.

parts of ≅ ▲ are ≅.)

<u>19.</u> isos.; $\overline{AX}$ ≅ $\overline{AY}$; $\overline{AZ}$ ≅ $\overline{AZ}$; ∠ XAZ ≅ ∠ YAZ; △ XAZ ≅ △ YAZ (SAS); $\overline{XZ}$ ≅ $\overline{YZ}$ (Corr.

parts of ≅ ▲ are ≅.)

<u>20.</u> <u>a.</u> 1. $\overline{SN}$ and $\overline{TM}$ are medians. (Given)   2. $\overline{RN}$ ≅ $\overline{NT}$; $\overline{RM}$ ≅ $\overline{MS}$ (Def. of median,

midpt.)   3. $\overline{SN}$ ≅ $\overline{NP}$; $\overline{TM}$ ≅ $\overline{MQ}$ (Given)   4. ∠ RNP ≅ ∠ TNS; ∠ RMQ ≅ ∠ SMT

(Vert. ∡ are ≅.)   5. △ RNP ≅ △ TNS; △ RMQ ≅ △ SMT (SAS)   6. $\overline{RP}$ ≅ $\overline{TS}$;

$\overline{RQ}$ ≅ $\overline{TS}$ (Corr. parts of ≅ ▲ are ≅.)   7. $\overline{RQ}$ ≅ $\overline{RP}$ (Trans. Prop. of ≅)

<u>b.</u> 1. △ RNP ≅ △ TNS; △ RMQ ≅ △ SMT (Part <u>a</u> above)   2. ∠ RPS ≅ ∠ TSP;

∠ RQT ≅ ∠ STQ (Corr. parts of ≅ ▲ are ≅.)   3. $\overline{RP}$ ∥ $\overline{ST}$; $\overline{RQ}$ ∥ $\overline{ST}$ (If 2 lines are

cut by a trans. and alt. int. ∡ are ≅, then the lines are ∥.)

<u>c.</u> 1. $\overleftrightarrow{RP}$ ∥ $\overline{ST}$ and $\overleftrightarrow{RQ}$ ∥ $\overline{ST}$ (Part <u>b</u> above)   2. $\overleftrightarrow{RP}$ = $\overleftrightarrow{RQ}$ (Through a pt. outside

a line, there is exactly one line ∥ to the given line.)   3. P, R, and Q are collinear.

(Def. of collinear pts.)

<u>21.</u> <u>a.</u> $\overline{AE}$ ∥ $\overline{BD}$ and $\overline{BC}$ ∥ $\overline{AD}$, so ∠ EAD ≅ ∠ BDA and ∠ BDA ≅ ∠ DBC; then ∠ EAD ≅

∠ DBC; since $\overline{AD}$ ≅ $\overline{BD}$, ∠ DAB ≅ ∠ DBA; then by Add. Prop. of =, ∠ EAB ≅ ∠ CBA;

$\overline{AE}$ ≅ $\overline{BC}$; △ EAB ≅ △ CBA (SAS); then $\overline{AC}$ ≅ $\overline{BE}$. (Corr. parts of ≅ ▲ are ≅.)

<u>b.</u> From Part <u>a</u> above, $\overline{AE}$ ≅ $\overline{BC}$ and $\overline{AC}$ ≅ $\overline{BE}$; $\overline{EC}$ ≅ $\overline{EC}$, so △ CEB ≅ △ ECA (SSS)

and ∠ CEB ≅ ∠ ECA (Corr. parts of ≅ ▲ are ≅.)   Then △ EOC is isos. and

$\overline{OE} \cong \overline{OC}$; OA = AC - OC and OB = BE - OE; OA = OB; since $\triangle$ OAB is isos.,

$\angle$ OAB $\cong$ $\angle$ OBA; from Part a above, $\angle$ DAB $\cong$ $\angle$ DBA and by subtr., $\angle$ DAC $\cong$ $\angle$ DBE.

Then $\triangle$ DAC $\cong$ $\triangle$ DBE (SAS) and DE = DC.   Pts. O and D are equidistant from A

and B and from E and C, so O and D are on the $\perp$ bis. of $\overline{EC}$ and $\overline{AB}$.   Then $\overleftrightarrow{OD}$ is

the $\perp$ bis. of $\overline{EC}$ and $\overline{AB}$.   Since $\overleftrightarrow{OD}$ is $\perp$ to both $\overline{EC}$ and $\overline{AB}$, $\overline{EC} \parallel \overline{AB}$ (In a

plane, 2 lines $\perp$ to the same line are $\parallel$.)

22. Since $\overleftrightarrow{AM}$ is the $\perp$ bis. of $\overline{BC}$, AB = AC. (If a pt. lies on the $\perp$ bis. of a seg., then

it is equidistant from the endpts. of the seg.) $\angle$1 $\cong$ $\angle$2, so $\overrightarrow{DA}$ bisects $\angle$ BDF.

$\overline{AE} \perp \overline{BD}$ and $\overline{AF} \perp \overline{DF}$, so AE = AF. (If a pt. lies on the bis. of an $\angle$, then the pt.

is equidistant from the sides of the $\angle$.)   Then rt. $\triangle$ ABE $\cong$ rt. $\triangle$ ACF (HL), so

BE = CF.

23. $\overleftrightarrow{RX}$ and $\overleftrightarrow{TX}$ are $\perp$ bis. of $\overline{AB}$, so RA = RB and TA = TB.   RT = RT and

$\triangle$ ART $\cong$ $\triangle$ BRT (SSS).   If P is the pt. where $\overline{XS}$ int. $\overline{RT}$, then $\angle$ ARP $\cong$ $\angle$ BRP;

RP = RP and $\triangle$ ARP $\cong$ $\triangle$ BRP (SAS) and AP = BP.   XP = XP and XA = XB, so

$\triangle$ AXP $\cong$ $\triangle$ BXP (SSS).   Then $\angle$ AXS $\cong$ $\angle$ BXS and $\overleftrightarrow{AB} \perp \overleftrightarrow{SX}$. (If 2 lines form $\cong$

adj. $\angle$, then the lines are $\perp$.)

Pages 149-150 · WRITTEN EXERCISES

A 1. 256; 1024   2. 6; 3   3. $\frac{1}{81}$; $\frac{1}{243}$

   4. 25; 36   5. 17; 23   6. 40; 52

   7. 15; 4   8. $-\frac{1}{4}$; $\frac{1}{8}$

   9. Chan is older than Sarah   10. none   11. Polygon G has 7 sides.

   12. none   13. none   14. Prince likes oats.

   15. no; deductively   16. 1234 $\times$ 9 + 5 = 11111

   17. 9876 $\times$ 9 + 4 = 88888   18. 9999^2 = 99980001

B 19. a. 16   b. expected number = 32; actual number = 31

   20. Opp. $\angle$ are $\cong$; opp. sides are $\cong$.

C 21. a. 1^2 + 1 + 11 = 13; 2^2 + 2 + 11 = 17; 3^2 + 3 + 11 = 23; 4^2 + 4 + 11 = 31;

       5^2 + 5 + 11 = 41; 6^2 + 6 + 11 = 53; 7^2 + 7 + 11 = 67; 8^2 + 8 + 11 = 83;

       9^2 + 9 + 11 = 101   b. prime   c. 10^2 + 10 + 11 = 121, which is not prime.

       11^2 + 11 + 11 = 143, which is not prime.

22.

Number of sides	3	4	5	6	7	8	n
Number of diagonals	0	2	5	9	14	20	$\frac{n(n-3)}{2}$

23. 5-pointed star: 180; 6-pointed star: 360; n-pointed star: 180(n - 4) (The diag. form a reg. n-gon and n isos. $\triangle$. Each $\angle$ of the n-gon has meas. $\frac{(n-2)180}{n}$. Then each base $\angle$ of the isos. $\triangle$ has meas. $180 - \frac{(n-2)180}{n} = \frac{180n - 180n + 360}{n} = \frac{360}{n}$ and the vertex $\angle$ have meas. $180 - 2(\frac{360}{n}) = \frac{180n - 720}{n}$. The sum of the $\angle$ at the tips of the stars is $n(\frac{180n - 720}{n}) = 180n - 720 = 180(n - 4)$.

Page 151 · EXTRA

1. Check students' work.   2. none of it   3. one

4. a non-Möbius (2-sided) band twice as long

5. The band separates into 2 non-Möbius (2-sided) bands linked together.   6. two

7. Two non-Möbius (2-sided) bands linked together

8. A short Möbius band and a long non-Möbius (2-sided) band, both 1 cm wide, linked together.

Page 152 · CALCULATOR KEY-IN

1. $6 \times 7 = 42$

         $66 \times 67 = 4422$

         $666 \times 667 = 444222$

         $6666 \times 6667 = 44442222$

2. $8 \times 8 = 64$

         $98 \times 98 = 9604$

         $998 \times 998 = 996004$

         $9998 \times 9998 = 99960004$

3. $7 \times 9 = 63$

         $77 \times 99 = 7623$

         $777 \times 999 = 776223$

         $7777 \times 9999 = 77762223$

Pages 153-154 · CHAPTER REVIEW

1. $\triangle$ RSQ   2. $\angle$ QRS   3. QS; midpt. of $\overline{PQ}$

4. 48   5. $\triangle$ ABC $\cong$ $\triangle$ DEC; SAS   6. no

7. $\triangle$ ABC $\cong$ $\triangle$ DEC; ASA   8. no

9. 1. $\overline{JM} \cong \overline{LM}$; $\overline{JK} \cong \overline{LK}$ (Given)   2. $\overline{MK} \cong \overline{MK}$ (Refl. Prop. of $\cong$)   3. $\triangle MJK \cong$ $\triangle MLK$ (SSS)   4. $\angle MJK \cong \angle MLK$ (Corr. parts of $\cong$ $\triangle$ are $\cong$.)

10. 1. $\angle JMK \cong \angle LMK$; $\overline{MK} \perp$ plane P (Given)   2. $\overline{MK} \perp \overline{JK}$; $\overline{MK} \perp \overline{LK}$ (Def. of line $\perp$ plane)   3. m$\angle$MKJ = 90 = m$\angle$MKL (Def. of $\perp$ lines, rt. $\angle$)   4. $\overline{MK} \cong$ $\overline{MK}$ (Refl. Prop. of $\cong$)   5. $\triangle MKJ \cong \triangle MKL$ (ASA)   6. $\overline{JK} \cong \overline{LK}$ (Corr. parts of $\cong$ $\triangle$ are $\cong$.)

11. $\angle E \cong \angle F$; if 2 sides of a $\triangle$ are $\cong$, then the $\angle$ opp. those sides are $\cong$.

12. 7t - 12 = 12 - t; 8t = 24; t = 3; DF = 7(3) - 12 = 9

13. 5x - y = 12; y = 5x - 12; x + y = 12; x + (5x - 12) = 12; 6x = 24; x = 4; y = 5(4) - 12 = 8

14. 1. $\overline{GH} \perp \overline{HJ}$; $\overline{KJ} \perp \overline{HJ}$ (Given)   2. m$\angle$GHJ = 90 = m$\angle$KJH (Def. of $\perp$ lines)   3. $\angle G \cong \angle K$ (Given)   4. $\overline{HJ} \cong \overline{HJ}$ (Refl. Prop. of $\cong$)   5. $\triangle GHJ \cong \triangle KJH$ (AAS)

15. 1. $\overline{GH} \perp \overline{HJ}$; $\overline{KJ} \perp \overline{HJ}$ (Given)   2. $\triangle GHJ$ and $\triangle KJH$ are rt. $\triangle$. (Def. of $\perp$ lines, rt. $\triangle$)   3. $\overline{GJ} \cong \overline{KH}$ (Given)   4. $\overline{HJ} \cong \overline{HJ}$ (Refl. Prop. of $\cong$)   5. $\triangle GHJ \cong \triangle KJH$ (HL)   6. $\overline{GH} \cong \overline{KJ}$ (Corr. parts of $\cong$ $\triangle$ are $\cong$.)

16. Check students' drawings.

17. Answers may vary. Possible answers include: $\overline{QP} \perp \overline{AB}$; $\overline{AP} \cong \overline{PB}$ (P is the midpt. of $\overline{AB}$); $\triangle QAP \cong \triangle QBP$; $\overline{QA} \cong \overline{QB}$ ($\triangle QAB$ is isos.)

18. the bis. of $\angle AQB$ 19. altitude

20. 1. ASA   2. Corr. parts of $\cong$ $\triangle$ are $\cong$.   3. Refl. Prop. of $\cong$ 4. HL 5. Corr. parts of $\cong$ $\triangle$ are $\cong$.

21. a. Answers may vary. She will get tails; she will get heads.

b. Yes; her conclusion is based on inductive reasoning.

22. 125; 216   23. $\dfrac{1}{100}$; $-\dfrac{1}{1000}$

Pages 154-155 · CHAPTER TEST

1. $\overline{MA}$; $\triangle EGL$ 2. $\overline{AB}$; $\overline{AC}$; 25   3. $\overline{RT}$; $\overline{XZ}$

4. HL   5. 60   6. altitude

7. the endpts. of the seg.   8. 79; 72   9. yes; SSS

10. yes; HL   11. no   12. yes; AAS

13. no   14. yes ($\triangle RST \cong \triangle RWZ$); SAS

15. a. D; B   b. D, B   16. $\triangle ABD$; $\triangle CBD$

<u>17.</u> △AMB ≅ △AMD; △CMB ≅ △CMD; △ADC ≅ △ABC

<u>18.</u> x + y = 2x + 10; y = x + 10; (x + y) + (2x + 10) + (x + 2y) = 180; 4x + 3y = 170;

4x + 3(x + 10) = 170; 7x + 30 = 170; 7x = 140; x = 20; y = 20 + 10 = 30

<u>19.</u> 1. ∠1 ≅ ∠2; ∠PQR ≅ ∠SRQ (Given)   2. $\overline{QR}$ ≅ $\overline{QR}$ (Refl. Prop. of ≅)

3. △PQR ≅ △SRQ (ASA)   4. $\overline{PR}$ ≅ $\overline{SQ}$ (Corr. parts of ≅ ⧍ are ≅.)

<u>20.</u> 1. $\overline{WZ}$ ⊥ plane M (Given)   2. $\overline{WZ}$ ⊥ $\overline{XZ}$; $\overline{WZ}$ ⊥ $\overline{YZ}$ (Def. of line ⊥ plane)

3. m∠WZX = 90 = m∠WZY (Def. of ⊥ lines, rt. ∠)   4. ∠ZXY ≅ ∠ZYX (Given)

5. $\overline{ZX}$ ≅ $\overline{ZY}$ (If 2 ⧌ of a △ are ≅, then the sides opp. those ⧌ are ≅.)

6. $\overline{WZ}$ ≅ $\overline{WZ}$ (Refl. Prop. of ≅)   7. △WZX ≅ △WZY (SAS)

8. $\overline{WX}$ ≅ $\overline{WY}$ (Corr. parts of ≅ ⧍ are ≅.)

Page 156 · MIXED REVIEW

<u>1.</u> $\dfrac{(40 - 2)180}{40} = \dfrac{6840}{40} = 171$

<u>2.</u> <u>a.</u> If a triangle is equiangular, then it is isos.

<u>b.</u> If a triangle is isos., then it is equiangular. (Check students' drawings.)

<u>3.</u> 92; 141

<u>4.</u> M is equidistant from N and P (Given); ∠NMO ≅ ∠PMO (Given); $\overline{MO}$ ≅ $\overline{MO}$ (Refl.

Prop. of ≅); △NMO ≅ △PMO (SAS); ON = OP; M and O are on the ⊥ bis. of $\overline{NP}$

(If a pt. is equidist. from the endpts. of a seg., then the pt. is on the ⊥ bis. of the

seg.); $\overleftrightarrow{QO}$ is the ⊥ bis. of $\overline{NP}$ (Through any 2 pts. there is exactly one line.)

<u>5.</u> SSS

<u>6.</u> Show that given a trans. of the 2 lines, corr. ⧌ are ≅, alt. int. ⧌ are ≅, or s.-s.

int. ⧌ are supp.; show that both lines are ∥ to a third line; show that both lines

are ⊥ to a third line, with all three lines coplanar.

<u>7.</u> x² = 6x; x² - 6x = 0; x (x - 6) = 0; x = 0 (reject) or x = 6; x² = 6x = 36

<u>8.</u> Given: △ABC, $\overline{AB}$ ≅ $\overline{AC}$.

Prove: ∠1 ≅ ∠4.

Proof: 1. $\overline{AB}$ ≅ $\overline{AC}$ (Given)   2. ∠2 ≅ ∠3 (If 2 sides of a

△ are ≅, then the ⧌ opp. those sides are ≅.)   3. ∠1 and

∠2 are supp.; ∠3 and ∠4 are supp. (Angle Add. Post., Def. of supp. ⧌)

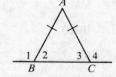

4. ∠1 ≅ ∠4 (If 2 ⧌ are supp. of ≅ ⧌, the 2 ⧌ are ≅.)

9. 1. $\angle R \cong \angle T$ (Given)   2. $\overline{RU} \parallel \overline{ST}$ (Given)   3. $\angle RUS \cong \angle UST$ (If 2 $\parallel$ lines are

cut by a trans., then alt. int. $\angle$s are $\cong$.)   4. $\angle RSU \cong \angle SUT$ (If 2 $\angle$s of one $\triangle$ are $\cong$

to 2 $\angle$s of another $\triangle$, then the third $\angle$s are $\cong$.)   5. $\overline{RS} \parallel \overline{UT}$ (If 2 lines are cut by a

trans. and alt. int. $\angle$s are $\cong$, then the lines are $\parallel$.)

10. one

11. $2(\frac{3}{2}x + 21) = 5x - 4$; $3x + 42 = 5x - 4$; $2x = 46$; $x = 23$; $m\angle ABC = 5(23) - 4 =$

111; obtuse

12. $(y + 10) + (2y - 31) = 180$; $3y - 21 = 180$; $3y = 201$; $y = 67$; $m\angle G =$

$180 - (2y - 40) = 180 - 94 = 86$

13. postulate   14. corollary   15. parallel

16. contrapositive   17. Seg. Add. Post.

18. Given: $\overline{AX}$ is a median and an altitude of $\triangle ABC$

Prove: $\triangle ABC$ is isosceles.

Proof: $\overline{AX}$ is a median and an alt. of $\triangle ABC$ (Given);

$\overleftrightarrow{AX}$ is the $\perp$ bis. of $\overline{BC}$ (Def. of $\perp$ bis.), so $AB = AC$

(If a pt. lies on the $\perp$ bis. of a seg., then the pt. is

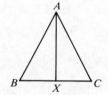

equidistant from the endpts. of the seg.) and $\triangle ABC$ is isos. (Def. of isos. $\triangle$)

Page 157 · ALGEBRA REVIEW

1. $(x + 6)(x - 1) = 0$; $x + 6 = 0$ or $x - 1 = 0$; $x = -6$ or $x = 1$

2. $(a - 4)(a - 2) = 0$; $a - 4 = 0$ or $a - 2 = 0$; $a = 4$ or $a = 2$

3. $(c - 9)(c + 2) = 0$; $c - 9 = 0$ or $c + 2 = 0$; $c = 9$ or $c = -2$

4. $x(x + 8) = 0$; $x = 0$ or $x + 8 = 0$; $x = 0$ or $x = -8$

5. $3y^2 - 15y = 0$; $3y(y - 5) = 0$; $3y = 0$ or $y - 5 = 0$; $y = 0$ or $y = 5$

6. $2z(z + \frac{7}{2}) = 0$; $2z = 0$ or $z + \frac{7}{2} = 0$; $z = 0$ or $z = -\frac{7}{2}$

7. $n^2 = 164$; $n = \pm\sqrt{164} = \pm 2\sqrt{41}$

8. $y^2 = \frac{2}{50}$; $y = \pm\sqrt{\frac{2}{50}} = \pm\sqrt{\frac{1}{25}} = \pm\frac{1}{5}$

9. $\frac{1}{2}q^2 = 18$; $q^2 = 36$; $q = \pm\sqrt{36} = \pm 6$ 10. $(x - 2)^2 = 0$; $x - 2 = 0$; $x = 2$

11. $(b + 5)(b - 2) = 0$; $b + 5 = 0$ or $b - 2 = 0$; $b = -5$ or $b = 2$

12. $(3x - 1)(x + 1) = 0$; $3x - 1 = 0$ or $x + 1 = 0$; $x = \frac{1}{3}$ or $x = -1$

13. $(9j + 4)(j - 1) = 0$; $9j + 4 = 0$ or $j - 1 = 0$; $j = -\frac{4}{9}$ or $j = 1$

14. $2x^2 - x - 10 = 0$; $(2x - 5)(x + 2) = 0$; $2x - 5 = 0$ or $x + 2 = 0$; $x = \frac{5}{2}$ or $x = -2$

15. $x = \dfrac{-7 \pm \sqrt{49-12}}{2} = \dfrac{-7 \pm \sqrt{37}}{2}$

16. $(d+6)(d+2) = 0$; $d + 6 = 0$ or $d + 2 = 0$; $d = -6$ or $d = -2$

17. $e^2 + 5e - 24 = 0$; $(e+8)(e-3) = 0$; $e + 8 = 0$ or $e - 3 = 0$; $e = -8$ or $e = 3$

18. $v^2 - 10v + 25 = 0$; $(v-5)^2 = 0$; $v - 5 = 0$; $v = 5$

19. $x^2 - 3x - 4 = 0$; $(x-4)(x+1) = 0$; $x - 4 = 0$ or $x + 1 = 0$; $x = 4$ or $x = -1$

20. $t^2 - t - 20 = 0$; $(t-5)(t+4) = 0$; $t - 5 = 0$ or $t + 4 = 0$; $t = 5$ or $t = -4$

21. $x^2 - 20x + 36 = 0$; $(x-18)(x-2) = 0$; $x - 18 = 0$ or $x - 2 = 0$; $x = 18$ or $x = 2$

22. $x = \dfrac{5 \pm \sqrt{25-12}}{2} = \dfrac{5 \pm \sqrt{13}}{2}$

23. $5p^2 - 2p - 7 = 0$; $(5p-7)(p+1)$; $5p - 7 = 0$ or $p + 1 = 0$; $p = \dfrac{7}{5}$ or $p = -1$

24. $4m^2 - 7m = 0$; $m(4m-7) = 0$; $m = 0$ or $4m - 7 = 0$; $m = 0$ or $m = \dfrac{7}{4}$

25. $x^2 - x = 2$; $x^2 - x - 2 = 0$; $(x-2)(x+1) = 0$; $x - 2 = 0$ or $x + 1 = 0$;
    $x = 2$ or $x = -1$

26. $a^2 = 4a - 4$; $a^2 - 4a + 4 = 0$; $(a-2)^2 = 0$; $a - 2 = 0$; $a = 2$

27. $c^2 + 3c = 10$; $c^2 + 3c - 10 = 0$; $(c+5)(c-2) = 0$; $c + 5 = 0$ or $c - 2 = 0$;
    $c = -5$ or $c = 2$

28. $y^2 - 10y + 25 = 16$; $y^2 - 10y + 9 = 0$; $(y-9)(y-1) = 0$; $y - 9 = 0$ or
    $y - 1 = 0$; $y = 9$ or $y = 1$

29. $z^2 = 8z - 12$; $z^2 - 8z + 12 = 0$; $(z-6)(z-2) = 0$; $z - 6 = 0$ or $z - 2 = 0$;
    $z = 6$ or $z = 2$

30. $x^2 + 5x = 14$; $x^2 + 5x - 14 = 0$; $(x+7)(x-2) = 0$; $x + 7 = 0$ or $x - 2 = 0$;
    $x = -7$ or $x = 2$

31. $10b - b^2 = 24$; $b^2 - 10b + 24 = 0$; $(b-6)(b-4) = 0$; $b - 6 = 0$ or $b - 4 = 0$;
    $b = 6$ or $b = 4$

32. $10r + r^2 = 24$; $r^2 + 10r - 24 = 0$; $(r+12)(r-2) = 0$; $r + 12 = 0$ or
    $r - 2 = 0$; $r = -12$ or $r = 2$

33. $s^2 - 6s + 9 = s - 1$; $s^2 - 7s + 10 = 0$; $(s-2)(s-5) = 0$; $s - 2 = 0$ or
    $s - 5 = 0$; $s = 2$ or $s = 5$

34. $3x^2 + 3x - 4 = 0$; $x = \dfrac{-3 \pm \sqrt{9+48}}{6} = \dfrac{-3 \pm \sqrt{57}}{6}$

35. $4y^2 - 17y + 15 = 0$; $y = \dfrac{17 \pm \sqrt{289-240}}{8} = \dfrac{17 \pm \sqrt{49}}{8} = \dfrac{17 \pm 7}{8}$; $y = 3$ or $y = \dfrac{5}{4}$

36. $x = \dfrac{-11 \pm \sqrt{121-48}}{12} = \dfrac{-11 \pm \sqrt{73}}{12}$

$\underline{37}$. $x^2 - 28 = 9x + 8$; $x^2 - 9x - 36 = 0$; $(x + 3)(x - 12) = 0$; $x + 3 = 0$ or

   $x - 12 = 0$; $x = -3$ (reject, if $x = -3$, $9x + 8 = -19$) or $x = 12$; $x = 12$

$\underline{38}$. $x^2 + 1 = 4x - 2$; $x^2 - 4x + 3 = 0$; $(x - 3)(x - 1) = 0$; $x - 3 = 0$ or $x - 1 = 0$;

   $x = 3$ or $x = 1$; if $x = 3$, $RS = 3(3) + 2 = 11$; $ST = RT = 3^2 + 1 = 10$; if $x = 1$,

   $RS = 3(1) + 2 = 5$; $ST = RT = 1^2 + 1 = 2$

Pages 161-163 · WRITTEN EXERCISES

A 1. 10   2. 9   3. 100   4. 105   5. 110   6. 30   7. 100   8. 14

9. $5x = 3x + 12$; $2x = 12$; $x = 6$ 10. $2x + 5 = 47 - 4x$; $6x = 42$; $x = 7$

11. $x + 3 = \frac{1}{2}(22)$; $x + 3 = 11$; $x = 8$ 12. $\frac{1}{2}x = 10$; $x = 20$

13. $6y - 20 = 2y + 80$; $4y = 100$; $y = 25$ 14. $80 - y = y + 40$; $2y = 40$; $y = 20$

15. $y + 10 = \frac{1}{2}y + 15$; $\frac{1}{2}y = 5$; $y = 10$

16. $\frac{y}{4} + \frac{y + 60}{2} = 180$; $y + 2y + 120 = 720$; $3y = 600$; $y = 200$

17. 1. Draw diagonal $\overline{EG}$. (Through any 2 pts. there is exactly one line.)   2. EFGH is
a $\square$ (Given)   3. $\overline{HG} \parallel \overline{EF}$; $\overline{HE} \parallel \overline{GF}$ (Def. of $\square$)   4. $\angle 1 \cong \angle 2$, $\angle 3 \cong \angle 4$ (If 2 $\parallel$
lines are cut by a trans., then alt. int. $\angle$ are $\cong$.)   5. $\overline{EG} \cong \overline{EG}$ (Refl. Prop.)
6. $\triangle GHE \cong \triangle EFG$ (ASA)   7. $\overline{EF} \cong \overline{HG}$; $\overline{FG} \cong \overline{EH}$ (Corr. parts of $\cong$ $\triangle$ are $\cong$.)

18. (Use $\square EFGH$ from text page 159, as in Ex. 17 above.)   Given: $\square EFGH$
Prove: $\angle H \cong \angle F$; $\angle E \cong \angle G$ Proof: 1. EFGH is a $\square$ (Given)   2. $\overline{EF} \cong \overline{GH}$;
$\overline{EH} \cong \overline{GF}$ (Opp. sides of a $\square$ are $\cong$.)   3. Draw $\overline{EG}$ and $\overline{FH}$ (Through any 2 pts.
there is exactly one line.)   4. $\overline{EG} \cong \overline{EG}$; $\overline{FH} \cong \overline{FH}$ (Refl. Prop.)   5. $\triangle GHE \cong$
$\triangle EFG$; $\triangle GHF \cong \triangle EFH$ (SSS)   6. $\angle H \cong \angle F$; $\angle E \cong \angle G$ (Corr. parts of $\cong$ $\triangle$ are $\cong$.)

19. 1. QRST is a $\square$ (Given)   2. $\overline{QR} \parallel \overline{TS}$ (Def. of $\square$)   3. $\angle 1 \cong \angle 2$; $\angle 3 \cong \angle 4$ (If 2
$\parallel$ lines are cut by a trans., then alt. int. $\angle$ are $\cong$.)   4. $\overline{QR} \cong \overline{TS}$ (Opp. sides of a
$\square$ are $\cong$.)   5. $\triangle QMR \cong \triangle SMT$ (ASA)   6. $\overline{QM} \cong \overline{MS}$; $\overline{TM} \cong \overline{MR}$ (Corr. parts of
$\cong$ $\triangle$ are $\cong$.)   7. $\overline{QS}$ and $\overline{TR}$ bisect each other (Def. of seg. bis.)

20. 1. ABCX is a $\square$; DXFE is a $\square$ (Given)   2. $\angle E \cong \angle FXD$; $\angle B \cong \angle CXA$ (Opp. $\angle$
of a $\square$ are $\cong$.)   3. $\angle FXD \cong \angle CXA$ (Vert. $\angle$ are $\cong$.)   4. $\angle B \cong \angle E$ (Trans. Prop.)

B 21. $2x + y = 12$; $y = 12 - 2x$; $x + 2y = 9$; $x + 2(12 - 2x) = 9$; $-3x = -15$;
$x = 5$; $y = 12 - 2(5) = 2$

22. $x + y = 2x - y$; $x = 2y$; $3x - 2y = 12$; $3(2y) - 2y = 12$; $4y = 12$; $y = 3$;
$x = 2(3) = 6$; $CK = DE = 9$; $KD = EC = 12$; perimeter of $\square DECK = 2(9 + 12) = 42$

23. $4x = x^2 - 60$; $x^2 - 4x - 60 = 0$; $(x + 6)(x - 10) = 0$; $x = -6$ (reject) or $x = 10$;
$m\angle CED = m\angle CKD = m\angle 1 + m\angle 2 = 4(10) + 3(10) = 70$

24. $x^2 + 20 = 9x$; $x^2 - 9x + 20 = 0$; $(x - 5)(x - 4) = 0$; $x = 5$ or $x = 4$;

m∠2 = 25 or 16

25. 1. PQRS is a ▱; $\overline{PJ} \cong \overline{RK}$ (Given) 2. ∠P ≅ ∠R (Opp. ∠ of a ▱ are ≅.)

3. $\overline{SP} \cong \overline{QR}$ (Opp. sides of a ▱ are ≅.) 4. △SPJ ≅ △QRK (SAS)

5. $\overline{SJ} \cong \overline{QK}$ (Corr. parts of ≅ ▲ are ≅.)

26. 1. JQKS is a ▱. (Given) 2. ∠SJQ ≅ ∠SKQ (Opp. ∠ of a ▱ are ≅.) 3. ∠1 ≅

∠2 (If 2 ∠ are supp. of ≅ ∠, the 2 ∠ are ≅.) 4. $\overline{PJ} \cong \overline{RK}$ (Given) 5. $\overline{SJ} \cong \overline{QK}$

(Opp. sides of a ▱ are ≅.) 6. △SPJ ≅ △QRK (SAS) 7. ∠P ≅ ∠R (Corr. parts

of ≅ ▲ are ≅.)

27. 1. ABCD is a ▱; $\overline{CD} \cong \overline{CE}$ (Given) 2. $\overline{AB} \parallel \overline{CD}$ (Def. of ▱) 3. ∠CDE ≅ ∠A

(If 2 ∥ lines are cut by a trans., then corr. ∠ are ≅.) 4. ∠CDE ≅ ∠E (If 2 sides

of a △ are ≅, then the ∠ opp. those sides are ≅.) 5. ∠A ≅ ∠E (Subst. Prop.)

28. 1. RSTQ is a ▱ (Given) 2. $\overline{QT} \parallel \overline{RS}$ (Def. of ▱) 3. ∠OYQ ≅ ∠OXS (If 2 ∥

lines are cut by a trans., then alt. int. ∠ are ≅.) 4. $\overline{QO} \cong \overline{OS}$ (The diag. of a ▱

bisect each other.) 5. ∠YOQ ≅ ∠XOS (Vert. ∠ are ≅.) 6. △OYQ ≅ △OXS (AAS)

7. $\overline{OX} \cong \overline{OY}$ (Corr. parts of ≅ ▲ are ≅.)

29. Answers may vary. Example: $\overline{DX} \parallel \overline{BY}$ Proof: 1. ABCD is a ▱. (Given)

2. $\overline{DA} \parallel \overline{CB}$ (Def. of ▱) 3. ∠3 ≅ ∠4 (If 2 ∥ lines are cut by a trans., then alt.

int. ∠ are ≅.) 4. $\overline{DA} \cong \overline{CB}$ (Opp. sides of a ▱ are ≅.) 5. ∠1 ≅ ∠2 (Given)

6. △DXA ≅ △BYC (ASA) 7. ∠DXA ≅ ∠BYC (Corr. parts of ≅ ▲ are ≅.)

8. ∠DXY ≅ ∠XYB (If 2 ∠ are supp. of ≅ ∠, then the 2 ∠ are ≅.) 9. $\overline{DX} \parallel \overline{BY}$ (If

2 lines are cut by a trans. and alt. int. ∠ are ≅, then the lines are ∥.)

30. Answers may vary. Example: $\overline{JI} \cong \overline{GF}$ Proof: 1. EFIH and EGHJ are ▱. (Given)

2. $\overline{HJ} \cong \overline{EG}$; $\overline{HI} \cong \overline{EF}$ (Opp. sides of a ▱ are ≅) 3. ∠1 ≅ ∠2 (Given)

4. △HJI ≅ △EGF (SAS) 5. $\overline{JI} \cong \overline{GF}$ (Corr. parts of ≅ ▲ are ≅.)

31. a. No; opp. sides of a ▱ are ≅. b. Any diagram with EFIH a ▱ and EGJH and

GFIJ not ▱ will suffice.

C 32. a. 1. j ∥ k (Given) 2. $\overleftrightarrow{AB}$ is in P; $\overleftrightarrow{XY}$ is in Q (If 2 pts. are in a plane, then the

line joining the pts. is in the plane.) 3. A, B, X, and Y are coplanar, say they are

in plane M. (By def., ∥ lines are coplanar.) 4. M int. P in $\overleftrightarrow{AB}$; M int. Q in $\overleftrightarrow{XY}$.

(If 2 planes int., then their int. is a line.) 5. Plane P ∥ plane Q. (Given)

6. $\overleftrightarrow{AB} \parallel \overleftrightarrow{XY}$ (If 2 $\parallel$ planes are cut by a third plane, then the lines of int. are $\parallel$.)

7. ABYX is a $\square$. (Def. of $\square$)   8. AX = BY (Opp. sides of a $\square$ are $\cong$.)

b. If $\parallel$ planes int. $\parallel$ lines, then they cut off $\cong$ seg.

33. See Ex. 28 above.

34. Given: $\overline{AB} \cong \overline{AC}$; X a pt. on $\overline{BC}$; $\overline{XY} \perp \overline{AB}$; $\overline{XZ} \perp \overline{AC}$;

$\overline{BD} \perp \overline{AC}$.   Prove: BD = XY + XZ   Proof: Since

$\overline{BD} \perp \overline{AC}$ and $\overline{XZ} \perp \overline{AC}$, $\overline{BD} \parallel \overline{XZ}$. Then $\angle DBC \cong$

$\angle ZXC$. Also, since $\angle ABC \cong \angle ACB$, $\angle YXB \cong \angle ZXC$.

(If 2 $\angle$ of one $\triangle$ are $\cong$ to 2 $\angle$ of another $\triangle$, then the

third $\angle$ are $\cong$.)   Then $\overline{BE} \cong \overline{XE}$. (If 2 $\angle$ of a $\triangle$ are $\cong$,

then the sides opp. those $\angle$ are $\cong$.) Now draw $\overline{XW} \perp \overline{BD}$. XWDZ is a $\square$, so

$\overline{XZ} \cong \overline{WD}$. Also, $\triangle BEY \cong \triangle XEW$ (AAS), so $\overline{EY} \cong \overline{EW}$. Then BD =

BE + EW + WD = XE + EY + XZ = XY + XZ.

Pages 166-168 · WRITTEN EXERCISES

A 1. Def. of $\square$

2. If both pairs of opp. sides of a quad. are $\cong$, then the quad. is a $\square$.

3. If one pair of opp. sides of a quad. are both $\cong$ and $\parallel$, then the quad. is a $\square$.

4. If the diag. of a quad. bis. each other, then the quad. is a $\square$.

5. If both pairs of opp. $\angle$ of a quad. are $\cong$, then the quad. is a $\square$.

6. If $\triangle$ SOK $\cong \triangle$ COA, then the diag. of SACK bis. each other and SACK is a $\square$. (Or $\overline{SK}$

and $\overline{CA}$ are both $\parallel$ and $\cong$, making SACK a $\square$.)

7. 15   8. 6   9. 5x = 2x + 12; 3x = 12; x = 4

10. 22 - x = 3x - 22; 4x = 44; x = 11

B 11. 2x - y = x + y; x = 2y; x + y = 15; 2y + y = 15; 3y = 15; y = 5; x = 2(5) = 10

12. $\frac{1}{2}$(8x) = 12; 4x = 12; x = 3; 2x + 3y = 12; 6 + 3y = 12; 3y = 6; y = 2

13. $\overline{NC} \parallel \overline{AM}$ and NC = $\frac{1}{2}$DC = $\frac{1}{2}$AB = AM. If one pair of opp. sides of a quad. are

both $\cong$ and $\parallel$, then the quad. is a $\square$. So AMCN is a $\square$.

14. m$\angle$A = m$\angle$C, so m$\angle$NAM = $\frac{1}{2}$m$\angle$A = $\frac{1}{2}$m$\angle$C = m$\angle$NCM. m$\angle$DNA = m$\angle$NAM =

m$\angle$NCM, so $\overline{AN}$ and $\overline{CM}$ are $\parallel$.   Then AMCN is a $\square$, by def. of $\square$.

15. OD = OB, OA = OC (diag. of a $\square$ bis. each other); OZ = $\frac{1}{2}$OD = $\frac{1}{2}$OB = OX and

OW = $\frac{1}{2}$OA = $\frac{1}{2}$OC = OY. If the diag. of a quad. bis. each other, then the quad. is a

$\square$. So WXYZ is a $\square$.

16. Draw $\overline{AC}$ int. $\overline{DB}$ at Z.   Since DZ = ZB and DE = FB, EZ = DZ - DE =

ZB - FB = ZF.   Also, AZ = ZC.   If the diag. of a quad. bis. each other, then the

quad. is a ▱.   So AFCE is a ▱.

17. $\overline{AB}$ ∥ $\overline{CD}$ ∥ $\overline{EF}$ so $\overline{AB}$ ∥ $\overline{EF}$. (2 lines ∥ to a third line are ∥ to each other.)

$\overline{AB}$ ≅ $\overline{CD}$ ≅ $\overline{EF}$.   If one pair of opp. sides of a quad. are both ≅ and ∥, then the quad.

is a ▱.   So ABEF is a ▱.

18. a. If a quad. is a ▱, then both pairs of opp. sides are ≅.

b. Thm. 4-4: If both pairs of opp. sides of a quad. are ≅, then the quad. is a ▱.

19. 1. $\overline{TQ}$ ≅ $\overline{SR}$; $\overline{TS}$ ≅ $\overline{QR}$ (Given)   2. $\overline{QS}$ ≅ $\overline{QS}$ (Refl. Prop.)   3. △TQS ≅ △RSQ

(SSS)   4. ∠3 ≅ ∠4; ∠1 ≅ ∠2 (Corr. parts of ≅ ▲ are ≅.)   5. $\overline{TS}$ ∥ $\overline{QR}$;

$\overline{TQ}$ ∥ $\overline{SR}$ (If 2 lines are cut by a trans. and alt. int. ▲ are ≅, then the lines are ∥.)

6. QRST is a ▱. (Def. of ▱)

20. 1. $\overline{AB}$ ≅ $\overline{CD}$; $\overline{AB}$ ∥ $\overline{CD}$ (Given)   2. ∠1 ≅ ∠2 (If 2 ∥ lines are cut by a trans., then

alt. int. ▲ are ≅.)   3. $\overline{AC}$ ≅ $\overline{AC}$ (Refl. Prop.)   4. △ABC ≅ △CDA (SAS)

5. $\overline{BC}$ ≅ $\overline{AD}$ (Corr. parts of ≅ ▲ are ≅.)   5. ABCD is a ▱. (If both pairs of opp.

sides of a quad. are ≅, then the quad. is a ▱.)

21. a. Given: $\overline{AC}$ and $\overline{BD}$ bis. each other.

Prove: ABCD is a ▱

Proof: 1. $\overline{AC}$ and $\overline{BD}$ bis. each other (Given)

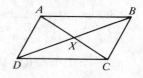

2. $\overline{AX}$ ≅ $\overline{XC}$; $\overline{DX}$ ≅ $\overline{XB}$ (Def. of bis.)   3. ∠AXD ≅

∠CXB; ∠AXB ≅ ∠CXD (Vert. ▲ are ≅.)   4. △AXD ≅ △CXB; △AXB ≅ △CXD (SAS)

5. $\overline{AD}$ ≅ $\overline{BC}$; $\overline{AB}$ ≅ $\overline{DC}$ (Corr. parts of ≅ ▲ are ≅.)   6. ABCD is a ▱ (If both

pairs of opp. sides of a quad. are ≅, then the quad. is a ▱.)

b. Answers may vary.   Example: Prove △AXD ≅ △CXB, as in part a, above.   Then

$\overline{AD}$ ≅ $\overline{CB}$ and ∠DAX ≅ ∠BCX (Corr. parts of ≅ ▲ are ≅.)   Then $\overline{AD}$ ∥ $\overline{CB}$ (∠DAX

and ∠BCX are ≅ alt. int. ▲) and ABCD is a ▱. (If one pair of opp. sides of a quad.

are both ≅ and ∥, then the quad. is a ▱.)

22. $4x + y = 42$; $y = 42 - 4x$; $3x - 2y = 26$; $3x - 2(42 - 4x) = 26$; $11x - 84 = 26$;

$11x = 110$; $x = 10$; $y = 42 - 4(10) = 2$

23. $x + y = 33$; $y = 33 - x$; $5x - 3y = 3x + y$; $4y = 2x$; $y = \frac{1}{2}x$; $\frac{1}{2}x = 33 - x$;

$\frac{3}{2}x = 33$; $x = 22$; $y = \frac{1}{2}(22) = 11$

24. $x - \frac{y}{2} = 5$; $\frac{y}{2} = x - 5$; $y = 2x - 10$; $2y - x = 2x - y$; $3y = 3x$; $y = x$;

$x = 2x - 10$; $x = 10$; $y = 10$

25. 1. $\angle DBC \cong \angle C$(Given)   2. $\overline{BD} \cong \overline{CD}$ (If 2 $\angle$ of a $\triangle$ are $\cong$, then the sides opp.

those $\angle$ are $\cong$.)   3. $\overline{AE} \cong \overline{CD}$ (Given)   4. $\overline{AE} \cong \overline{BD}$ (Subst. Prop.)   5. $\angle A \cong$

$\angle DBC$ (Given)   6. $\overline{AE} \parallel \overline{BD}$ (If 2 lines are cut by a trans. and corr. $\angle$ are $\cong$, then

the lines are $\parallel$.)   7. ABDE is a $\square$. (If one pair of opp. sides of a quad. are both $\cong$

and $\parallel$, then the quad. is a $\square$.)

26. 1. KGLJ is a $\square$. (Given)   2. JO = OG; KO = OL (The diag. of a $\square$ bis. each

other.)   3. FK = LH (Given)   4. FK + KO = OL + LH (Add. Prop. of =)

5. FO = OH (Seg. Add. Post., Subst. Prop.)   5. FGHJ is a $\square$. (If the diag. of a

quad. bis. each other, then the quad. is a $\square$.)

27. 1. Plane X $\parallel$ plane Y. (Given)   2. $\overline{LM} \parallel \overline{ON}$ (If 2 $\parallel$ planes are cut by a third plane,

then the lines of int. are $\parallel$.)   3. $\overline{LM} \cong \overline{ON}$ (Given)   4. LMNO is a $\square$. (If one

pair of opp. sides of a quad. are both $\cong$ and $\parallel$, then the quad. is a $\square$.)

C 28. 1. Draw $\overline{AF}$, int. plane Q at X. (Through any 2 pts. there is exactly one line.)

2. Let M be the plane cont. $\overleftrightarrow{AC}$ and $\overleftrightarrow{AF}$; let N be the plane cont. $\overleftrightarrow{AF}$ and $\overleftrightarrow{DF}$. (If 2

lines int., then exactly one plane cont. them.)   3. $\overleftrightarrow{BX}$ is the int. of M and Q; $\overleftrightarrow{CF}$ is

is the int. of M and R; $\overleftrightarrow{XE}$ is the int. of N and Q; $\overleftrightarrow{AD}$ is the int. of N and P. (If 2

planes int., then they int. in a line.)   4. P, Q, and R are $\parallel$ planes. (Given)

5. $\overleftrightarrow{BX} \parallel \overleftrightarrow{CF}$; $\overleftrightarrow{XE} \parallel \overleftrightarrow{AD}$ (If 2 $\parallel$ planes are cut by a third plane, then the lines of int.

are $\parallel$.)   6. AB = BC (Given)   7. AX = XF (A line that cont. the midpt. of one

side of a $\triangle$ and is $\parallel$ to another side bisects the third side.)   8. DE = EF (A line

that cont. the midpt. of one side of a $\triangle$ and is $\parallel$ to another side bisects the third side.)

29. ABCD and BEDF are $\boxed{s}$. IN $\square$ABCD, draw

diag. $\overline{BD}$ and $\overline{AC}$, bisecting each other at O.

(The diag. of a $\square$ bisect each other.)   In $\square$BEDF,

draw diag. $\overline{EF}$.   Since $\overline{BD}$ is also a diag. of $\square$BEDF,

$\overline{EF}$ must also be bisected at O. $\overline{EF}$ and $\overline{AC}$ are then

bisected at O, and AECF is a $\square$. (If the diag. of a quad. bis. each other, the

quad. is a $\square$.)

Pages 171-173 · WRITTEN EXERCISES

		Property	▱	Rect.	Rhombus	Square
A	1.	Opp. sides are ‖.	✓	✓	✓	✓
	2.	Opp. sides are ≅.	✓	✓	✓	✓
	3.	Opp. ∠ are ≅.	✓	✓	✓	✓
	4.	A diag. forms 2 ≅ △.	✓	✓	✓	✓
	5.	Diag. bis. each other.	✓	✓	✓	✓
	6.	Diags. are ≅.		✓		✓
	7.	Diags. are ⊥.			✓	✓
	8.	A diag. bis. 2 ∠.			✓	✓
	9.	All ∠ are rt. ∠.		✓		✓
	10.	All sides are ≅.			✓	✓

11. Sum of measures of ∠ = 360; each ∠ has meas. $\frac{360}{4}$ = 90; each ∠ is a rt. ∠; by def. the quad. is a rect.

12. By Ex. 11 above, the quad. is a rect. Then since all 4 sides are ≅, it is a square.

13. 13   **14.** 13   **15.** 20   **16.** 40

17. 1. WXYZ is ▱; m∠1 = 90 (Given)   2. m∠2 = m∠1 = 90 (Vert. ∠ are ≅.) 3. ∠2 is a rt. ∠. (Def. of rt. ∠)   4. WXYZ is a rect. (If an ∠ of a ▱ is a rt. ∠, then the ▱ is a rect.)

18. 1. ∠3 ≅ ∠4 (Given)   2. BN = BC (If 2 ∠ of a △ are ≅, then the sides opp. those ∠ are ≅.)   3. DC = BN (Given)   4. BC = DC (Subst. Prop.)   5. ABCD is a ▱. (Given)   6. ABCD is a rhombus. (If 2 consecutive sides of a ▱ are ≅, then the ▱ is a rhombus.)

19. 1. ABCD is a rhombus. (Given)   2. ∠DAC ≅ ∠CAB (Each diag. of a rhombus bisects 2 ∠ of the rhombus; def. of ∠ bis.)   3. ∠1 ≅ ∠CAB; ∠2 ≅ ∠DAC (Vert. ∠ are ≅.)   4. ∠1 ≅ ∠2 (Subst. Prop.)

20. 1. ABCD is a rhombus. (Given)   2. $\overline{AC}$ ⊥ $\overline{DB}$ (The diag. of a rhombus are ⊥.) 3. $\overline{EF}$ ‖ $\overline{AC}$ (Given)   4. $\overline{EF}$ ⊥ $\overline{DB}$ (If a trans. is ⊥ to one of 2 ‖ lines, then it is ⊥ to the other one also.)

21. 1. QRST is rect; RKST is ▱. (Given)   2. $\overline{SK}$ ≅ $\overline{TR}$ (Opp. sides of a ▱ are ≅.) 3. $\overline{RT}$ ≅ $\overline{QS}$ (The diag. of a rect. are ≅.)   4. $\overline{SK}$ ≅ $\overline{SQ}$ (Trans. Prop.)   5. △QSK is isos. (Def. of isos. △)

<u>22.</u> 1. QRST is rect; RKST and JQST are ▱ (Given)   2. KS = RT; JT = QS (Opp.

sides of a ▱ are ≅.)   3. RT = QS (The diag. of a rect. are ≅.)   4. JT = KS

(Subst. Prop.)

<u>23.</u> Given: Rect. QRST   Prove: RT = QS   Proof: 1. QRST is rect. (Given)

2. m∠Q = 90 = m∠R (Def. of rect., rt. ∠)   3. $\overline{TQ}$ ≅ $\overline{SR}$ (Opp. sides of a ▱

are ≅.)   4. $\overline{QR}$ ≅ $\overline{QR}$ (Refl. Prop.)   5. △TQR ≅ △SRQ (SAS)

6. $\overline{TR}$ ≅ $\overline{QS}$ (Corr. parts of ≅ △ are ≅.)

<u>24.</u> Given: Rhombus EFGH   Prove: $\overline{EG}$ bisects ∠E and ∠G   Proof: 1. EFGH is a

rhombus (Given)   2. $\overline{FE}$ ≅ $\overline{FG}$; $\overline{HE}$ ≅ $\overline{HG}$; $\overline{HE}$ ∥ $\overline{GF}$ (Def. of rhombus)

3. ∠2 ≅ ∠4; ∠1 ≅ ∠3 (If 2 sides of a △ are ≅, then the △ opp. those sides are ≅.)

4. ∠1 ≅ ∠4; ∠2 ≅ ∠3 (If 2 ∥ lines are cut by a trans., then alt. int. △ are ≅.)

5. ∠1 ≅ ∠2; ∠3 ≅ ∠4 (Trans. Prop.)   6. $\overline{EG}$ bisects ∠E and ∠G (Def. of ∠ bis.)

<u>25.</u> Given: ▱ABCD; $\overline{AC}$ ⊥ $\overline{DB}$ Prove: ABCD is a rhombus.   Proof: 1. ABCD is

a ▱ (Given)   2. DX = XB (The diag. of a ▱ bis. each other.)   3. $\overline{AC}$ ⊥ $\overline{DB}$

(Given)   4. ∠AXD ≅ ∠AXB (Adj. △ formed by ⊥ lines are ≅.)   4. $\overline{AX}$ ≅ $\overline{AX}$

(Refl. Prop.)   5. △AXD ≅ △AXB (SAS)   6. $\overline{AD}$ ≅ $\overline{AB}$ (Corr. parts of ≅△ are ≅.)

7. ABCD is a rhombus. (If 2 consecutive sides of a ▱ are ≅, the ▱ is a rhombus.)

<u>26.</u> Given: ▱ABCD; $\overline{AC}$ ≅ $\overline{BD}$ Prove: ABCD is a rect.   Proof: 1. ABCD is a ▱

(Given)   2. $\overline{AB}$ ≅ $\overline{DC}$ (Opp. sides of a ▱ are ≅.)   3. $\overline{AD}$ ≅ $\overline{AD}$ (Refl. Prop.)

4. $\overline{AC}$ ≅ $\overline{BD}$ (Given)   5. △BAD ≅ △CDA (SSS)   6. ∠BAD ≅ ∠CDA (Corr. parts

of ≅ △ are ≅.)   7. $\overline{AB}$ ∥ $\overline{DC}$ (Def. of ▱)   8. m∠BAD + m∠CDA = 180 (If 2 ∥

lines are cut by a trans., then s.-s. int. △ are supp.)   9. 2m∠BAD = 180;

m∠BAD = 90 (Subst. Prop.; Div. Prop. of =)   10. ∠BAD is a rt. ∠ (Def. of rt. ∠)

11. ABCD is a rect. (If an ∠ of a ▱ is a rt. ∠, the ▱ is a rect.)

<u>27.</u> m∠V = 90 - m∠Z = 60; m∠1 = 90 - 60 = 30; m∠2 = $\frac{1}{2}$(90) - 30 = 15;

m∠3 = 180 - 2(60) - (30 + 15) = 15; m∠4 = 30

<u>28.</u> m∠V = 90 - m∠Z = 90 - k; m∠1 = 90 - (90 - k) = k; m∠2 = $\frac{1}{2}$(90) - k =

45 - k; m∠3 = (90 - k) - (k + 45 - k) = 45 - k; m∠4 = k

<u>29.</u> a. Yes.   It has 2 ≅ consecutive sides.

Given: $\overline{AB}$ ∥ $\overline{DC}$; ∠ADB ≅ ∠CDB.

Prove: $\overline{AB}$ ≅ $\overline{AD}$

Proof: 1. $\overline{AB}$ ∥ $\overline{DC}$ (Given)   2. ∠ABD ≅ ∠CDB (If 2 ∥

lines are cut by a trans., then alt. int. $\angle$ are $\cong$.)   3. $\angle$ ADB $\cong$ $\angle$ CDB (Given)

4. $\angle$ ABD $\cong$ $\angle$ ADB (Trans. Prop.)   5. $\overline{AB}$ $\cong$ $\overline{AD}$ (If 2 $\angle$ of a $\triangle$ are $\cong$, then the

sides opp. those $\angle$ are $\cong$.)

b. The quad. is a rhombus.   Given: $\overline{AB}$ ∥ $\overline{DC}$; $\angle$ ADB $\cong$ $\angle$ CDB; $\angle$ ABD $\cong$ $\angle$ CBD

Prove: ABCD is a rhombus.   Proof: 1. $\angle$ ADB $\cong$ $\angle$ CDB; $\angle$ ABD $\cong$ $\angle$ CBD (Given)

2. $\overline{DB}$ $\cong$ $\overline{DB}$ (Refl. Prop.)   3. $\triangle$ ADB $\cong$ $\triangle$ CBD (ASA)   4. $\overline{AB}$ $\cong$ $\overline{CB}$; $\overline{AD}$ $\cong$ $\overline{CD}$

(Corr. parts of $\cong$ $\triangle$ are $\cong$.)   5. $\overline{AB}$ ∥ $\overline{DC}$ (Given)   6. $\angle$ ABD $\cong$ $\angle$ CDB (If 2 ∥

lines are cut by a trans., then alt. int. $\angle$ are $\cong$.)   7. $\angle$ ABD $\cong$ $\angle$ ADB;

$\angle$ CDB $\cong$ $\angle$ CBD (Trans. Prop.)   8. $\overline{AB}$ $\cong$ $\overline{AD}$ $\cong$ $\overline{CD}$ $\cong$ $\overline{CB}$ (If 2 $\angle$ of a $\triangle$ are $\cong$,

then the sides opp. those $\angle$ are $\cong$; Subst. Prop.)   9. ABCD is a rhombus.

(Def. of rhombus)

30. AXDE is a rhombus.   Consider isos. $\triangle$ ABC and BCD.

$\angle$ BAC $\cong$ $\angle$ BCA and $\angle$ CBD $\cong$ $\angle$ CDB.   Each of these 4

$\angle$ has meas. $\frac{1}{2}(180 - 108) = 36$.   Then m$\angle$ AXD =

m$\angle$ BXC = 180 - (m$\angle$ DBC + m$\angle$ BCA) = 180 - 72 =

108 = m$\angle$ E.   Also, m$\angle$ EAX = 108 - m$\angle$ BAC = 72 and m$\angle$ EDX = 108 - m$\angle$ CDB =

72.   Since both pairs of opp. $\angle$ of AXDE are $\cong$, AXDE is a $\square$. $\overline{AE}$ $\cong$ $\overline{DE}$

(ABCDE is reg.), so AXDE is a rhombus.   (If 2 consecutive sides of a $\square$ are $\cong$,

then the $\square$ is a rhombus.)

31. $\triangle$ RYZ is equilateral.   Proof: Since RSTW is a $\square$ and $\triangle$ YWT and STZ are

equilateral, $\overline{WR}$ $\cong$ $\overline{SZ}$ $\cong$ $\overline{TZ}$ and $\overline{WY}$ $\cong$ $\overline{SR}$ $\cong$ $\overline{TY}$.   m$\angle$ YWR = 60 + 90 = 150,

m$\angle$ RSZ = 90 + 60 = 150, and m$\angle$ YTZ = 360 - (90 + 60 + 60) = 150.   Then

$\triangle$ YWR $\cong$ $\triangle$ RSZ $\cong$ $\triangle$ YTZ and $\overline{YR}$ $\cong$ $\overline{RZ}$ $\cong$ $\overline{YZ}$.

Pages 175-177 · WRITTEN EXERCISES

A   1. 12; 12   2. 2k; k   3. 5x - 8 = 3x; 2x = 8, x = 4

4. 8x = 2(3x + 2); 8x = 6x + 4; 2x = 4; x = 2   5. MN = 11   6. RQ = 16

7. 4.3   8. $3\frac{1}{4}$ 9. x + 3 = $\frac{1}{2}(10 + 18)$ = 14; x = 11

10. 2x + 4 = $\frac{1}{2}(3x + 2 + 2x + 1)$; 4x + 8 = 5x + 3; x = 5

11. 5x = $\frac{1}{2}(5x + 10 + 2x)$; 10x = 7x + 10; 3x = 10; x = $3\frac{1}{3}$ 12. AD = $\frac{1}{2}$BE

13. AD = $\frac{1}{2}$BE; BE = $\frac{1}{2}$(AD + CF) = $\frac{1}{2}(\frac{1}{2}$BE + CF) = $\frac{1}{4}$BE + $\frac{1}{2}$CF; $\frac{3}{4}$BE = $\frac{1}{2}$CF;

BE = $\frac{2}{3}$CF; AD = $\frac{1}{2}(\frac{2}{3}$CF) = $\frac{1}{3}$CF

14. 14; 21   15. 13; 39   16. x + 6 = 2x; x = 6; CF = 3x = 18

B 17. 2(x + 3) = x + y; 2x + 6 = x + y; y = x + 6; 3(x + 3) = 36; 3x + 9 = 36;

3x = 27; x = 9; y = 9 + 6 = 15

18. 2(x + y) = 20; x + y = 10; y = 10 - x; 3(x + y) = 4x - y; x = 4y = 4(10 - x);

x = 40 - 4x; 5x = 40; x = 8; y = 10 - 8 = 2; CF = 4(8) - 2 = 30

19. AD must be $\frac{1}{3}$CF.

20. Since BE = 2 · AD and CF = 3 · AD, any positive value of x is a solution.

21. rectangle   22. rhombus   23. parallelogram   24. rhombus

25. 1. M is the midpt. of $\overline{QR}$. (Given)   2. PQRS is a $\square$. (Given)   3. X is the midpt. of $\overline{RP}$. (The diag. of a $\square$ bis. each other.)   4. MX = $\frac{1}{2}$PQ (The seg. that joins the midpts. of 2 sides of a △ has a length = to half the length of the third side.)

26. 1. ∠1 ≅ ∠2 (Given)   2. $\overline{XE}$ ≅ $\overline{XY}$ (If 2 ∠ of a △ are ≅, then the sides opp. those ∠ are ≅.)   3. WXYZ is a $\square$. (Given) 4. $\overline{XY}$ ≅ $\overline{WZ}$ (Opp. sides of a $\square$ are ≅.) 5. $\overline{XE}$ ≅ $\overline{WZ}$ (Trans. Prop.)   6. $\overline{ZE}$ ∥ $\overline{WX}$ (Def. of $\square$)   7. $\overline{WZ}$ ∥ $\overline{XY}$; $\overline{XE}$ ∦ $\overline{XY}$ (Def. of $\square$, ∥ lines)   8. $\overline{WZ}$ ∦ $\overline{XE}$ (Two lines ∥ to a third line are ∥ to each other.) 9. WXEZ is an isos. trap. (Def. of isos. trap.)

27. 1. ABCD is a trap. with $\overline{AB}$ ∥ $\overline{DC}$. (Given and def. of trap.)   2. Draw $\overline{DP}$ ⊥ $\overline{AB}$ and $\overline{CQ}$ ⊥ $\overline{AB}$. (Through a pt. outside a line there is exactly one line ⊥ to the given line.)   3. $\overline{DP}$ ≅ $\overline{CQ}$ (If 2 lines are ∥, then all pts. on one line are equidistant from the other line.)   4. $\overline{AD}$ ≅ $\overline{BC}$ (Given)   5. △APD and △BQC are rt. △. (Def. of ⊥ lines, rt. △)   6. △APD ≅ △BQC (HL)   7. ∠A ≅ ∠B (Corr. parts of ≅ △ are ≅.) 8. ∠ADC is supp. to ∠A; ∠BCD is supp. to ∠B. (If 2 ∥ lines are cut by a trans., then s.-s. int. ∠ are supp.)   9. ∠ADC ≅ ∠BCD (If 2 ∠ are supp. of ≅ ∠, then the 2 ∠ are ≅.)

28. 1. ABCD is a trap. with $\overline{DC}$ ∥ $\overline{AB}$. (Given and def. of trap.)   2. Draw $\overline{CE}$ ∥ $\overline{AD}$ (Through a pt. outside a line, there is exactly one ∥ to the given line.)   3. AECD is a $\square$. (Def. of $\square$)   4. $\overline{EC}$ ≅ $\overline{AD}$ (Opp. sides of a $\square$ are ≅.)   5. $\overline{AD}$ ≅ $\overline{BC}$ (Given) 6. $\overline{BC}$ ≅ $\overline{EC}$ (Trans. Prop.)   7. ∠CEB ≅ ∠B (If 2 sides of a △ are ≅, then the ∠ opp. those sides are ≅.)   8. ∠CEB ≅ ∠A (If 2 ∥ lines are cut by a trans., then corr. ∠ are ≅.)   9. ∠A ≅ ∠B (Trans. Prop.)   10. ∠ADC is supp. to ∠A; ∠BCD is supp. to ∠B. (If 2 ∥ lines are cut by a trans., then s.-s. int. ∠ are supp.) 11. ∠ADC ≅ ∠BCD (If 2 ∠ are supp. of ≅ ∠, then the 2 ∠ are ≅.)

29. Since P, M, O, and N are midpts. of $\overline{SW}$, $\overline{SK}$, $\overline{WE}$ and $\overline{KE}$, resp., $\overline{PM} \parallel \overline{WK}$ and

$\overline{ON} \parallel \overline{WK}$ (The seg. that joins the midpts. of 2 sides of a △ is ∥ to the third side.).

So $\overline{PM} \parallel \overline{ON}$ (2 lines ∥ to a third line are ∥ to each other.)   Also, since $\overline{PM}$ and $\overline{ON}$

join midpts. of 2 sides of △ SWK and △ EWK, respectively, PM = $\frac{1}{2}$WK = ON.   Then

PMNO is a ▱. (If one pair of opp. sides of a ▱ are both ≅ and ∥, then the quad. is a ▱.)

30. The diag. of an isos. trap. are ≅.

Given: Trap. ABCD, $\overline{AD} \cong \overline{BC}$ Prove: $\overline{AC} \cong \overline{BD}$

Proof: 1. $\overline{AD} \cong \overline{BC}$ (Given)   2. ∠ADC ≅ ∠BCD

(Base ∡ of an isos. trap. are ≅.)   3. $\overline{DC} \cong \overline{DC}$ (Refl. Prop.)   4. △ADC ≅ △BCD

(SAS)   5. $\overline{AC} \cong \overline{BD}$ (Corr. parts of ≅ △ are ≅.)

31. This follows directly from Thm. 4-8. (If 3 ∥ lines cut off ≅ seg. on one trans., then

they cut off ≅ seg. on every trans.)

32. ME = $\frac{1}{2}$DC = 3; FN = $\frac{1}{2}$DC = 3; MN = $\frac{1}{2}$(DC + AB) = 11; EF = MN − (ME + FN) =

11 − (3 + 3) = 5

C 33. ME = FN = $\frac{1}{2}$DC = $\frac{3}{2}$x; EF = MN − (ME + FN) = MN − 3x; MN = $\frac{1}{2}$(2x² + 3x);

7 = $\frac{1}{2}$(2x² + 3x) − 3x; 2x² + 3x − 6x = 14; 2x² − 3x − 14 = 0; (x + 2)(2x − 7) = 0;

x = −2 (reject) or 2x = 7; x = 3$\frac{1}{2}$

34. Given: Trap. ABCD; $\overline{AD} \cong \overline{BC}$; $\overline{EF}$ the ⊥ bis. of $\overline{DC}$

Prove: $\overline{EF}$ is the ⊥ bis. of $\overline{AB}$.   Proof: 1. ABCD

is a trap.; $\overline{AB} \parallel \overline{DC}$ (Given; Def. of trap.)

2. $\overline{EF} \perp \overline{DC}$ (Given)   3. $\overline{EF} \perp \overline{AB}$ (If a trans. is

⊥ to one of 2 ∥ lines, then it is ⊥ to the other one also.)   4. △AEF and △BEF are

rt. ∡. (Def. of ⊥ lines, rt. △)   5. $\overline{DF} \cong \overline{FC}$ (Given; def. of ⊥ bis.)

6. $\overline{AD} \cong \overline{BC}$ (Given)   7. ∠D ≅ ∠C (Base ∡ of an isos. △ are ≅.)   8. △ADF ≅

△BCF (SAS)   9. $\overline{FA} \cong \overline{FB}$ (Corr. parts of ≅ △ are ≅.)   10. $\overline{FE} \cong \overline{FE}$ (Refl.

Prop.)   11. △AEF ≅ △BEF (HL)   12. $\overline{AE} \cong \overline{BE}$ (Corr. parts of ≅ △ are ≅.)

13. $\overline{EF}$ is the ⊥ bis. of $\overline{AB}$ (Def. of ⊥ bis.)

35. If the diag. of a trap. are ≅, then the trap. is isos.

Given: Trap. ABCD; $\overline{AC} \cong \overline{BD}$

Prove: $\overline{AD} \cong \overline{BC}$ Proof: 1. Draw $\overleftrightarrow{DP} \perp \overleftrightarrow{AB}$ and

$\overleftrightarrow{CQ} \perp \overleftrightarrow{AB}$. (Through a pt. outside a line, there is

exactly one line ⊥ to the given line.)   2. ABCD is a trap.; $\overline{AB} \parallel \overline{DC}$ (Given;

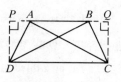

Def. of trap.)   3. $\overleftrightarrow{DP} \perp \overleftrightarrow{DC}$ and $\overleftrightarrow{CQ} \perp \overleftrightarrow{DC}$ (If a trans. is $\perp$ to one of 2 $\parallel$ lines, it

is $\perp$ to the other one also.)   4. $\overline{DP} \cong \overline{CQ}$ (If 2 lines are $\parallel$, all pts. on one line are

equidistant from the other line.)   5. $\overline{AC} \cong \overline{BD}$ (Given)   6. $\triangle DPB$ and $\triangle CQA$ are

rt. $\triangle$. (Def. of $\perp$ lines, rt. $\triangle$)   7. $\triangle DPB \cong \triangle CQA$ (HL)   8. $\angle ABD \cong \angle BAC$

(Corr. parts of $\cong \triangle$ are $\cong$.)   9. $\overline{AB} \cong \overline{AB}$ (Refl. Prop.)   10. $\triangle ABD \cong \triangle BAC$ (SAS)

11. $\overline{DA} \cong \overline{CB}$ (Corr. parts of $\cong \triangle$ are $\cong$.)   12. ABCD is an isos. trap. (Def. of

isos. trap.)

36. Rhombus.   By Thm. 4-17 on page 174, KJ = $\frac{1}{2}$VE = LM and $\overline{KJ} \parallel \overline{VE}$ and $\overline{LM} \parallel \overline{VE}$

so $\overline{KJ} \parallel \overline{LM}$.   Since $\overline{KJ}$ and $\overline{LM}$ are both $\cong$ and $\parallel$, JKLM is a $\square$.   Also, KJ =

$\frac{1}{2}$VE = $\frac{1}{2}$FG = KL so JKLM is a rhombus. (If 2 consecutive sides of a $\square$ are $\cong$,

then the $\square$ is a rhombus.)

Pages 181-182 · WRITTEN EXERCISES

A   1. Assume temp. that $\angle Y$ is not an acute $\angle$.   Then m$\angle Y \geq$ 90 and m$\angle X$ + m$\angle Y$ +

m$\angle Z \geq$ 190 + m$\angle Z$.   Since m$\angle Z >$ 0, the sum of the meas. of the $\triangle$ of $\triangle XYZ$ is

$\geq$ 190.   This contradicts the fact that the sum of the meas. of the $\triangle$ of a $\triangle$ is 180.

Our temp. assumption that $\angle Y$ is not an acute $\angle$ must be false.   It follows that

$\angle Y$ is an acute $\angle$.

2. Assume temp. that a $\parallel$ b.   Then $\angle 1 \cong \angle 3$ and since vert. $\triangle$ 2 and 3 are $\cong$, $\angle 1 \cong \angle 2$.

But this contradicts the given fact that m$\angle 1 \neq$ m$\angle 2$.   Our temp. assumption that

a $\parallel$ b must be false.   It follows that a $\nparallel$ b.

3. Assume temp. that $\overrightarrow{OE}$ bis. $\angle JOK$.   Then $\angle 1 \cong \angle 2$, $\overline{OJ} \cong \overline{OK}$, and $\overline{OE} \cong \overline{OE}$ so

$\triangle OJE \cong \triangle OKE$ (SAS) and $\overline{JE} \cong \overline{KE}$. (Corr. parts of $\cong \triangle$ are $\cong$.)   This contradicts

the given fact that $\overline{JE} \neq \overline{KE}$.   Our temp. assumption that $\overrightarrow{OE}$ bis. $\angle JOK$ must be

false.   It follows that $\overrightarrow{OE}$ doesn't bisect $\angle JOK$.

4. Assume temp. that $\angle J$ and $\angle K$ are both rt. $\triangle$.   Then $\angle J \cong \angle K$, $\angle 1 \cong \angle 2$, and

$\overline{OE} \cong \overline{OE}$ so $\triangle OJE \cong \triangle OKE$ (AAS) and $\overline{OJ} \cong \overline{OK}$ (Corr. parts of $\cong \triangle$ are $\cong$.)

This contradicts the given fact that $\overline{OJ} \neq \overline{OK}$.   Our temp. assumption that $\angle J$ and $\angle K$

are both rt. $\triangle$ must be false.   It follows that $\angle J$ and $\angle K$ are not both rt. $\triangle$.

B   5. Assume temp. that planes P and Q do not intersect, that is, they are $\parallel$.   If 2 $\parallel$ planes

are cut by a third plane, then the lines of int. are $\parallel$.   This contradicts the given fact

that $\overline{AB} \nparallel \overline{CD}$.   Our temp. assumption that P and Q do not int. must be false.   It

follows that P and Q intersect.

6. Assume temp. that △RST is equilateral.   Then RS = TS = VS = VR = RT.   This

contradicts the given fact that △RVS is not equilateral.   Our temp. assumption that

△RST is equilateral must be false.   It follows that △RST is not equilateral.

7. Assume temp. that E, F, G, and H are coplanar.   Then EFGH is a polygon.   The

sum of the meas. of the ∡ of EFGH is 350.   This contradicts the fact that the sum of

the meas. of the int. ∡ of a quad. is (4 - 2)180 = 360.   Our temp. assumption that

E, F, G, and H are coplanar must be false.   It follows that E, F, G, and H are

not coplanar.

8. Assume temp. that ∠ACB is a rt. ∠.   Then △ACB is a rt. △ and T is the midpt. of

the hyp.   The midpt. of the hyp. of a rt. △ is equidistant from its vert.   This

contradicts the given fact that CT = 4 ≠ AT.   Our temp. assumption that ∠ACB is

a rt. ∠ must be false.   It follows that ∠ACB is not a rt. ∠.

9. Assume temp. that n ∥ m.   Since m ∥ ℓ, then n ∥ ℓ.   (Two lines ∥ to a third line are

∥ to each other.)   This contradicts the given fact that n intersects ℓ.   Our temp.

assumption that n ∥ m must be false.   It follows that n ∦ m and since n and m are

coplanar, n must intersect m.

10. Assume temp. that there is a smallest pos. number, say n.   Since $\frac{1}{2} > 0$ and $n > 0$,

$\frac{1}{2}n > 0$.   Since n is the smallest pos. number, $\frac{1}{2}n \geq n$, and $\frac{1}{2} \geq 1$, which is false.

Our temp. assumption that there is a smallest pos. number must then be false.   It

follows that there is no smallest positive number.

11. Assume temp. that there is an even number, n, of quarters.   Since the total value of

the coins is 95¢, n must be 2.   The value of the remaining coins must be 45¢.   This

contradicts the given fact that the remaining coins are dimes.   Our temp. assumption

that there is an even number of quarters must be false.   It follows that there is an

odd number of quarters.

12. Assume temp. that there is a regular n-gon with a 155° ∠.   The meas. of each ext. ∠

is 25 and the total meas. of the ext. ∡, one at each vertex, is 25n.   Then 25n = 360

and n = 14.4.   This contradicts the fact that n must be an integer.   Our temp.

assumption that there is such a polygon must be false.   It follows that there is no

regular polygon with a 155° ∠.

13. Given: Trap. ABCD   Prove: $\overline{AC}$ and $\overline{BD}$ do not bisect each other.   Proof: Assume

temp. that $\overline{AC}$ and $\overline{BD}$ bisect each other.   Then ABCD is a ▱. (If the diag. of a quad. bisect each other, then the quad. is a $\square$.)   This contradicts the fact that ABCD

is a trap.   Our temp. assumption that the diag. bisect each other must be false.   The

diag. of a trap. do not bisect each other.

<u>C</u> 14. Given: $r > 0$, $s > 0$ Prove: $r + s \geq \sqrt{r^2 + s^2}$ Assume temp. that $r + s <$

$\sqrt{r^2 + s^2}$.   Then $(r + s)^2 < (\sqrt{r^2 + s^2})^2$; $r^2 + 2rs + s^2 < r^2 + s^2$; $2rs < 0$.   If

$2rs < 0$, then either $r < 0$ or $s < 0$.   This contradicts the given fact that r and s are

both pos.   Our temp. assumption that $r + s < \sqrt{r^2 + s^2}$ must be false.   It follows

that $r + s \geq \sqrt{r^2 + s^2}$.

   <u>15.</u> Given: $j \perp P$; $k \perp P$ Prove: $j \parallel k$ Assume temp. that j int. k, say at X.

Since $j \perp P$, $j \perp \overleftrightarrow{AB}$ and since $k \perp P$, $k \perp \overleftrightarrow{AB}$.   This contradicts the fact that

through a pt. (such as X) outside a line there is exactly one line $\perp$ to the given line.

Our temp. assumption that j int. k must be false.   It follows that j and k do not

intersect.

   <u>16.</u> Temp. assume that $\overleftrightarrow{RT}$ and $\overleftrightarrow{SW}$ are not skew.   Case 1: $\overleftrightarrow{RT}$ int. $\overleftrightarrow{SW}$.   If $\overleftrightarrow{RT}$ and

$\overleftrightarrow{SW}$ intersect, exactly one plane contains them.

Then R, S, T, and W are coplanar so $\overleftrightarrow{RS}$ and $\overleftrightarrow{TW}$

are coplanar.   This contradicts the given fact that

$\overleftrightarrow{RS}$ and $\overleftrightarrow{TW}$ are skew.   Case 2: $\overleftrightarrow{RT} \parallel \overleftrightarrow{SW}$.

$\overleftrightarrow{RT}$ and $\overleftrightarrow{SW}$ are coplanar so R, S, T, and W are coplanar and so are $\overleftrightarrow{RS}$ and $\overleftrightarrow{TW}$.

This contradicts the given fact that $\overleftrightarrow{RS}$ and $\overleftrightarrow{TW}$ are skew.   In either case, our temp.

assumption that $\overleftrightarrow{RT}$ and $\overleftrightarrow{SW}$ are not skew must be false.   It follows that $\overleftrightarrow{RT}$ and $\overleftrightarrow{SW}$

are skew.

Pages 185-187 · WRITTEN EXERCISES

<u>A</u> 1. 3; 15   <u>2.</u> 2; 28   <u>3.</u> 0; 200   <u>4.</u> 0; 4.6   <u>5.</u> 5; 2k + 5

   <u>6.</u> a - b; a + b   <u>7.</u> 2   <u>8.</u> 1   <u>9.</u> 3   <u>10.</u> $\overline{DF}$ <u>11.</u> $\overline{WT}$ <u>12.</u> $\overline{OA}$

<u>B</u> <u>13.</u> $\overline{WY}$ <u>14.</u> $\overline{VB}$ <u>15.</u> c; d; e; b; a   <u>16.</u> m∠3; m∠1; m∠2

   <u>17.</u> m∠2; m∠X; m∠XZY; m∠Y; m∠1

   <u>18.</u> 1. AB + BC > AC; CD + DA > AC (△ Ineq. Thm.)   2. AB + BC + CD + DA >

       2 · AC (Add. Prop. of Ineq.)

   <u>19.</u> 1. EFGH is $\square$. (Given)   2. EF = HG; FG = EH (Opp. sides of a $\square$ are $\cong$.)

       3. EF > FG (Given)   4. HG > EH (Subst. Prop.)   5. m∠1 > m∠2 (If one side

of a △ is longer than a second side, then the ∠ opp. the first side is larger than the ∠

opp. the second side.)

<u>C</u> <u>20.</u> The perimeter of a quad. is greater than the sum of lengths

of the diag.   Given: Quad. ABCD   Prove: Perimeter

of ABCD > AC + BD   Proof: By the △ Ineq. Thm.,

AB + BC > AC, AD + DC > AC, AB + AD > BD, and BC + CD > BD.   Let P =

perimeter of ABCD = AB + BC + DC + AD.   Then P > 2 · AC and P > 2 · BD

So 2P > 2 · AC + 2 · BD and P > AC + BD.

<u>21.</u> Given: $\overline{AN}$, $\overline{BP}$, and $\overline{CM}$ are medians of △ ABC.

Prove: AN + BP + CM > $\frac{1}{2}$(AB + BC + AC)

Proof: 1. BP + AP > AB; CM + MB > BC;

AN + NC > AC (△ Ineq. Thm.)   2. $\overline{AN}$, $\overline{BP}$,

and $\overline{CM}$ are medians. (Given)   3. N, M, and P are midpts. (Def. of median)

4. AP = $\frac{1}{2}$AC; MB = $\frac{1}{2}$AB; NC = $\frac{1}{2}$BC (Midpt. Thm.)   5. BP + $\frac{1}{2}$AC > AB;

CM + $\frac{1}{2}$AB > BC; AN + $\frac{1}{2}$BC > AC (Subst. Prop.)   6. BP + $\frac{1}{2}$AC + CM + $\frac{1}{2}$AB +

AN + $\frac{1}{2}$BC > AB + BC + AC (Add. Prop. of Ineq.)   7. BP + CM + AN >

AB + BC + AC - $\frac{1}{2}$(AB + BC + AC); BP + CM + AN > $\frac{1}{2}$(AB + BC + AC) (Subtr.

Prop. of Ineq.)

<u>22.</u> Yes (In fact, since the proof below doesn't depend

on ⊥ lines, the seg. can be any 3 seg., one from

each vertex to the opp. side.)   Given: $\overline{AY}$, $\overline{BZ}$,

and $\overline{CX}$ are alt. of △ABC.

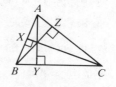

Prove: AY + BZ + CX > $\frac{1}{2}$(AB + BC + AC)   Proof: 1. AY + YC > AC and

AY + BY > AB; BZ + ZC > BC and BZ + AZ > AB; CX + AX > AC and

CX + XB > BC. (△ Ineq. Thm.)   2. 2 · AY + BC > AC + AB; 2 · BZ + AC >

AB + BC; 2 · CX + AB > AC + BC (Seg. Add. Post., Subst. Prop., Add. Prop.

of Ineq.)   3. 2 · AY + BC + 2 · BZ + AC + 2 · CX + AB > AC + AB + AB +

BC + AC + BC (Add. Prop. of Ineq.)   4. 2 · AY + 2 · BZ + 2 · CX >

AB + BC + AC or AY + BZ + CX > $\frac{1}{2}$(AB + BC + AC) (By algebra)

<u>23.</u> If $\overline{AD}$ is the longest side of quad. ABCD, then

AB + BC + CD > AD.   Given: Quad. ABCD;

$\overline{AD}$ the longest side   Prove: AB + BC + CD >

AD   Proof: 1. Draw $\overline{BD}$ (Through any 2 pts.

there is exactly one line.)   2. BC + CD > BD; AB + BD > AD ($\triangle$ Ineq. Thm.)

3. AB + BD + BC + CD > AD + BD (Add. Prop. of Ineq.)   4. AB + BC + CD >

AD (Subtr. Prop. of Ineq.)

<u>24.</u> Given: P inside $\triangle$XYZ   Prove: ZX + ZY >

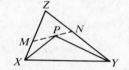

PX + PY   Proof: 1. Let M be any pt. between

Z and X.   Draw $\overleftrightarrow{MP}$ intersecting $\overline{ZY}$ at N.

(Through any 2 pts. there is exactly one line.)

2. ZM + ZN > MN; MX + MP > PX; PN + NY > PY ($\triangle$ Ineq. Thm.)

3. ZM + ZN + MX + MP + PN + NY > MN + PX + PY (Add. Prop. of Ineq.)

4. ZX + ZY + MN > MN + PX + PY (Seg. Add. Post., Subst. Prop.)

5. ZX + ZY > PX + PY (Subtr. Prop. of Ineq.)

Page 188 · APPLICATION

<u>1.</u> Def. of $\perp$ bis.

<u>2.</u> If a pt. is on the $\perp$ bis. of a seg., then it is equidistant from the endpts. of the seg.

<u>3.</u> Seg. Add. Post.   <u>4.</u> Subst. Prop.

<u>5.</u> If a pt. is on the $\perp$ bis. of a seg., then it is equidistant from the endpts. of the seg.

<u>6.</u> $\triangle$ Ineq. Thm.   <u>7.</u> Subst. Prop.   <u>8.</u> Check student's drawings; yes.

<u>9.</u> 1. ℓ is the $\perp$ bis. of $\overline{BC}$. (Given)   2. $\overline{PC} \cong \overline{PB}$; $\overline{SC} \cong \overline{SB}$ (If a pt. is on the $\perp$ bis.

of a seg., then it is equidistant from the endpts. of the seg.)   3. $\overline{SP} \cong \overline{SP}$ (Refl.

Prop.)   4. $\triangle$SPC $\cong \triangle$SPB (SSS)   5. $\angle$PSC $\cong \angle$PSB (Corr. parts of $\cong$ $\triangle$ are $\cong$.)

6. $\angle$PSC $\cong \angle$QSA (Vert. $\angle$ are $\cong$.)   7. $\angle$QSA $\cong \angle$PSB (Trans. Prop.)

Pages 191-193 · WRITTEN EXERCISES

<u>A</u> <u>1.</u> always   <u>2.</u> sometimes   <u>3.</u> never   <u>4.</u> sometimes   <u>5.</u> always

<u>6.</u> always   <u>7.</u> sometimes   <u>8.</u> never   <u>9.</u> always   <u>10.</u> never

<u>11.</u> $\overline{XY}$ <u>12.</u> $\angle 1$

<u>B</u> <u>13.</u> $\angle$VRT ($\overline{VR} \cong \overline{VR}$; $\overline{RS} \cong \overline{RT}$; VT > VS)

14. $\angle$ T (VR = VS = VT and m$\angle$RVS > m$\angle$RVT > m$\angle$SVT.   Consider $\triangle$RVS, RVT, and

SVT; RS > RT > ST, and $\angle$T is the largest $\angle$ of $\triangle$RST.)

15. $\angle$VRS ($\overline{VT} \simeq \overline{VT}$; $\overline{TS} \simeq \overline{TR}$; m$\angle$VTS > m$\angle$VTR; VS > VR, so m$\angle$VRS > m$\angle$VSR.)

16. 1. TU = US = SV (Given)   2. m$\angle$SUV = m$\angle$V; m$\angle$T = m$\angle$TSU (If 2 sides of a $\triangle$

are $\simeq$, then the $\angle$ opp. those sides are $\simeq$.)   3. m$\angle$V = m$\angle$SUV = 2m$\angle$T > m$\angle$T.

(The meas. of an ext. $\angle$ of a $\triangle$ = the sum of the meas. of the 2 remote int. $\angle$;

algebra)   4. ST > SV (If one $\angle$ of a $\triangle$ is larger than a second $\angle$, then the side opp.

the first $\angle$ is longer than the side opp. the second $\angle$.)

17. 1. AB > AC (Given)   2. m$\angle$ACB > m$\angle$ABC (If one side of a $\triangle$ is longer than a

second side, then the $\angle$ opp. the first side is larger than the $\angle$ opp. the second side.)

3. BD = EC (Given)   4. BC = BC (Refl. Prop.)   5. BE > CD (SAS Ineq. Thm.)

18. Given: $\square$ABCD; m$\angle$A > m$\angle$B.

Prove: BD > AC   Proof: 1. ABCD is a $\square$. (Given)

2. $\overline{AD} \simeq \overline{BC}$ (Opp. sides of a $\square$ are $\simeq$.)

3. $\overline{AB} \simeq \overline{AB}$ (Refl. Prop.)   4. m$\angle$A > m$\angle$B (Given)   5. Consider $\triangle$BAD and

$\triangle$ABC. BD > AC (SAS Ineq. Thm.)

19. CA > BA   Proof: m$\angle$BAC = 90, so BAC is a rt. $\triangle$.   Since M is the midpt. of $\overline{BC}$,

AM = BM = CM. (The midpt. of the hyp. of a rt. $\triangle$ is equidistant from the 3 vertices.)

Then $\triangle$BMA and CMA are isosceles, so m$\angle$B = 46, m$\angle$C = 44, and CA > BA. (If

one $\angle$ of a $\triangle$ is larger than a second $\angle$, then the side opp. the first $\angle$ is longer than

the side opp. the second $\angle$.)

20. $\overleftrightarrow{XZ}$ is not $\perp$ to plane P.   Proof: Assume temp. that $\overleftrightarrow{XZ}$ is $\perp$ to plane P.   Then

$\overline{XZ} \perp \overline{WY}$ and $\angle$XYW $\simeq$ $\angle$ZYW. $\overline{WY} \simeq \overline{WY}$ and since P bisects $\overline{XZ}$ at Y, $\overline{XY} \simeq \overline{YZ}$.

Then $\triangle$XYW $\simeq$ $\triangle$ZYW (SAS) and WZ = WX.   This contradicts the given fact that

WZ > WX.   Our temp. assumption that $\overleftrightarrow{XZ} \perp$ P must be false.   It follows that $\overleftrightarrow{XZ}$

is not $\perp$ to P.

C 21. $\triangle$PCA and $\triangle$QBC are isos., so $\angle$PCA $\simeq$ $\angle$PAC and $\angle$QBC $\simeq$ $\angle$QCB.   From the

diagram, AC > BC; PA = PC = QC = QB (Given); so m$\angle$P > m$\angle$Q (SSS Ineq. Thm.)

Then m$\angle$PCA = $\frac{1}{2}$(180 - m$\angle$P) < $\frac{1}{2}$(180 - m$\angle$Q) = m$\angle$QCB.

22. On $\overline{EK}$ take Z so that EZ = EJ. (Ruler Post.) $\overline{DE} \perp \overline{EZ}$ and $\overline{DE} \perp \overline{EJ}$, so

m$\angle$DEZ = m$\angle$DEJ = 90. $\overline{DE} \simeq \overline{DE}$ and $\triangle$DEZ $\simeq$ $\triangle$DEJ (SAS).   Then $\overline{DZ} \simeq \overline{DJ}$.

m$\angle$DZK = m$\angle$DEZ + m$\angle$EDZ > 90 > m$\angle$K, so m$\angle$DZK > m$\angle$K.   Then in $\triangle$DZK,

DK > DZ. (If one ∠ of a △ is larger than a second ∠, then the side opp. the first ∠ is longer than the side opp. the second ∠.) By the Subst. Prop., DK > DJ.

23. <u>a</u>. ∠VBC and ∠VAC are the largest ∠, with meas. > 60.

<u>b</u>. ∠BVC, ∠BCV, ∠AVC, and ∠ACV are the largest ∠, with meas. > 60.

Pages 194-195 · COMPUTER KEY-IN

<u>1</u>. Answers will vary. Check students' answers.

<u>3</u>. Computer results will vary. Sample values for P include 0.15, 0.25, 0.32, 0.2, 0.17, 0.125.

<u>4</u>. Computer results will vary. Possible results include, for D = 100, P = 0.22; for D = 400, P = 0.255; for D = 800, P = 0.234. The prob. appears to be $< \frac{1}{2}$.

Pages 198-199 · CHAPTER REVIEW

<u>1</u>. 110   <u>2</u>. 28   <u>3</u>. 70 - 32 = 38   <u>4</u>. 8x - 7 = 5x + 11; 3x = 18; x = 6

<u>5-8</u>. Answers may vary.   <u>5</u>. GS = 5   <u>6</u>. ∠SGN ≅ ∠NAS   <u>7</u>. $\overline{GZ} \cong \overline{AZ}$

<u>8</u>. GN = 17   <u>9</u>. ▱   <u>10</u>. square   <u>11</u>. rhombus   <u>12</u>. rect.

<u>13</u>. $\overline{ZO}$; $\overline{DI}$ <u>14</u>. 14   <u>15</u>. 4   <u>16</u>. 100   <u>17</u>. c; d; a; b   <u>18</u>. X

<u>19</u>. BN; BA   <u>20</u>. 3; 21   <u>21</u>. >   <u>22</u>. <   <u>23</u>. =   <u>24</u>. >

Page 200 · CHAPTER TEST

<u>1</u>. always   <u>2</u>. sometimes   <u>3</u>. sometimes   <u>4</u>. always   <u>5</u>. sometimes

<u>6</u>. never   <u>7</u>. never   <u>8</u>. always   <u>9</u>. 7   <u>10</u>. $4\frac{1}{2}$

<u>11</u>. MN = $\frac{1}{2}$(5j + 7k + 9j - 3k) = $\frac{1}{2}$(14j + 4k) = 7j + 2k

<u>12</u>. 4; 20   <u>13</u>. RSTU is not a ▱.

<u>14</u>. If both pairs of opp. ∠ of a quad. are ≅, then the quad. is a ▱.

<u>15</u>. If one pair of opp. sides of a quad. are both ≅ and ∥, then the quad. is a ▱.

<u>16</u>. If the diag. of a quad. bis. each other, then the quad. is a ▱.

<u>17</u>. If both pairs of opp. sides of a quad. are ≅, then the quad. is a ▱.

<u>18</u>. VUE; VEU   <u>19</u>. EU; EO   <u>20</u>. UE; UO   <u>21</u>. VUE

<u>22</u>. 1. ABCD is a ▱; $\overline{AB} \parallel \overline{DC}$ (Given; def. of ▱)   2. ∠D ≅ ∠1 (Given)

3. $\overline{AD} \parallel \overline{ST}$ (If 2 lines are cut by a trans. and corr. ∠ are ≅, then the lines are ∥.)

4. ASTD is a ▱. (Def. of ▱)

<u>23</u>. 1. $\overline{EM}$ is a median of $\triangle$ EFG. (Given)   2. M is the midpt. of $\overline{FG}$. (Def. of median)

3. $\overline{FM} \cong \overline{MG}$ (Def. of midpt.)   4. $\overline{EM} \cong \overline{EM}$ (Refl. Prop.)   5. m$\angle$2 > m$\angle$3

(Given)   6. EF > EG (SAS Ineq. Thm.)   7. m$\angle$G > m$\angle$F (If one side of a $\triangle$ is

longer than a second side, then the $\angle$ opp. the first side is larger than the $\angle$ opp.

the second side.)

Page 201 · PREPARING FOR COLLEGE ENTRANCE EXAMS

<u>1</u>. B   <u>2</u>. C   <u>3</u>. A   <u>4</u>. D   <u>5</u>. A   <u>6</u>. B   <u>7</u>. C   <u>8</u>. E

<u>9</u>. D   <u>10</u>. B

Pages 202-203 · CUMULATIVE REVIEW: CHAPTERS 1-4

<u>A</u>   <u>1</u>. coord. of midpt. $= \dfrac{-5 + 3}{2} = \dfrac{-2}{2} = -1$

<u>2</u>. <u>a</u>. Trans. Prop. of $\cong$ <u>b</u>. Subst. Prop. of =   <u>3</u>. bisects; $\perp$

<u>4</u>. one   <u>5</u>. <u>a</u>. yes; skew   <u>b</u>. no   <u>6</u>. 180 - 50 = 130

<u>7</u>. j $\parallel$ k (In a plane, 2 lines $\perp$ to the same line are $\parallel$.)

<u>8</u>. no; an equiangular $\triangle$ is also equilateral   <u>9</u>. (5 - 2)180 = 3 · 180 = 540

<u>10</u>. $\dfrac{360}{12} = 30$ <u>11</u>. false

<u>12</u>. If you enjoy winter weather, then you are a member of the skiing club.

<u>13</u>. <u>a</u>. $\triangle$RTA   <u>b</u>. m$\angle$E   <u>c</u>. $\overline{AR}$

<u>14</u>. <u>a</u>. yes; SAS Post.   <u>b</u>. yes; ASA Post.   <u>c</u>. no   <u>d</u>. yes; AAS Thm.

<u>15</u>. <u>a</u>. A and B   <u>b</u>. $\overrightarrow{SR}$ and $\overrightarrow{ST}$

<u>16</u>. <u>a</u>. HL Thm.   <u>b</u>. Corr. parts of $\cong$ $\triangle$ are $\cong$.   <u>c</u>. Def. of $\perp$ bis.   <u>d</u>. If a pt.

lies on the $\perp$ bis. of a seg., then it is equidistant from the endpts. of the seg.

<u>17</u>. <u>a</u>. sometimes   <u>b</u>. sometimes   <u>c</u>. never   <u>d</u>. always   <u>e</u>. always   <u>f</u>. always

<u>18</u>. <u>a</u>. $\overline{ST}$ <u>b</u>. $\overline{RT}$ <u>19</u>. <u>a</u>. $\overline{RS}$ <u>b</u>. SAS Ineq. Thm.

<u>B</u>   <u>20</u>. <u>a</u>. $\square$ <u>b</u>. rhombus   <u>c</u>. rectangle   <u>d</u>. isos. trapezoid   <u>e</u>. square

<u>21</u>. 2x + 7 = 4x - 1; 2x = 8; x = 4

<u>22</u>. x - (180 - x) = 38; 2x - 180 = 38; 2x = 218; x = 109; 180 - 109 = 71; 109 and 71

<u>23</u>. By the $\triangle$ Ineq. Thm., z + 6 < z + z + 3 or z > 3.

<u>24</u>. MN $= \dfrac{1}{2}(2r + s + 4r - 3s) = \dfrac{1}{2}(6r - 2s) = 3r - s$

<u>25</u>. no; AB + BC = AC; so 3.2y + 2y + 1 = 6y - 1; 0.8y = 2; y = 2.5; but AB =

3.2(2.5) = 8 and BC = 2(2.5) + 1 = 6

<u>26.</u> 1. WP = ZP; PY = PX (Given)   2. ∠WPX ≅ ∠ZPY (Vert. ∠ are ≅.)

3. △WPX ≅ △ZPY (SAS)   4. m∠WXP = m∠ZYP (Corr. parts of ≅ △ are ≅.)

5. m∠PXY = m∠PYX (If 2 sides of a △ are ≅, then the ∠ opp. those sides are ≅.)

6. m∠WXP + m∠PXY = m∠ZYP + m∠PYX (Add. Prop. of =)   7. m∠WXY =

m∠WXP + m∠PXY; m∠ZYX = m∠ZYP + m∠PYX (Angle Add. Post.)

8. m∠WXY = m∠ZYX or ∠WXY ≅ ∠ZYX (Subst. Prop.)

<u>27.</u> 1. $\overline{AD}$ ≅ $\overline{BC}$; $\overline{AD}$ ∥ $\overline{BC}$ (Given)   2. ABCD is a ▱. (If one pair of opp. sides of a

quad. are both ≅ and ∥, then the quad. is a ▱.)   3. ∠CGF ≅ ∠AEF (If 2 ∥ lines are

cut by a trans., then alt. int. ∠ are ≅.)   4. AF = FC (The diag. of a ▱ bis. each

other.)   5. ∠AFE ≅ ∠CFG (Vert. ∠ are ≅.)   6. △GFC ≅ △EFA (AAS)

7. $\overline{EF}$ ≅ $\overline{FG}$ (Corr. parts of ≅ △ are ≅.) (Alternate proof: Draw a line ∥ to $\overline{DC}$ and

$\overline{AB}$ through F.   Since the 3 ∥ lines cut off ≅ seg. on $\overline{DB}$, they cut off ≅ seg. on $\overline{GE}$.)

CHAPTER 5 · Similar Polygons

A   1. $15:9 = 5:3$ 2. $15:15 = 1:1$ 3. $30:150 = 1:5$ 4. $150:30 = 5:1$

      5. $9:48 = 3:16$ 6. $12:8 = 3:2$ 7. $24:12 = 2:1$ 8. $20:24 = 5:6$

      9. $\frac{8}{36} = \frac{2}{9}$ 10. $\frac{36}{12} = \frac{3}{1}$ 11. $\frac{4}{20} = \frac{1}{5}$ 12. $12:8:24 = 3:2:6$

      13. $24:12:8 = 6:3:2$ 14. $12:20:32 = 3:5:8$ 15. $\frac{1}{0.8} = \frac{5}{4}$ 16. $\frac{0.4}{0.3} = \frac{4}{3}$

      17. $\frac{40}{200} = \frac{1}{5}$ 18. $\frac{20}{5} = \frac{4}{1}$ 19. $\frac{3000}{150} = \frac{20}{1}$ 20. $\frac{80}{500} = \frac{4}{25}$ 21. $\frac{3}{4b}$

      22. $\frac{2d}{5c}$ 23. $\frac{3}{a}$ 24. $\frac{2}{1}$ 25. $\frac{3}{x + y}$ 26. $\frac{1}{4}$

B   27. Let 4x and 5x be the measures; $4x + 5x = 90$; $9x = 90$; $x = 10$; $4x = 40$; $5x = 50$;

      40 and 50   28. Let 11x and 4x be the measures; $11x + 4x = 180$; $15x = 180$; $x = 12$;

      $11x = 132$; $4x = 48$; 132 and 48   29. Let 3x, 4x, and 5x be the measures;

      $3x + 4x + 5x = 180$; $12x = 180$; $x = 15$; $3x = 45$; $4x = 60$; $5x = 75$; 45, 60, and 75

      30. Let 5x and 7x be the measures; $5x + 7x = 90$; $12x = 90$; $x = 7.5$; $5x = 37.5$;

      $7x = 52.5$; 37.5 and 52.5   31. Let 3x, 3x, and 4x be the measures; $3x + 3x + 4x =$

      180; $10x = 180$; $x = 18$; $3x = 54$; $4x = 72$; 54, 54, and 72

      32. Let 4x, 6x, 6x, 7x, 8x, and 9x be the measures; $4x + 6x + 6x + 7x + 8x + 9x = 720$;

        $40x = 720$; $x = 18$; $4x = 72$; $6x = 108$; $7x = 126$; $8x = 144$; $9x = 162$; 72, 108,

        108, 126, 144, and 162

      33. Let 9x, 11x, and 12x be the lengths; $9x + 11x + 12x = 96$; $32x = 96$; $x = 3$; $9x = 27$;

        $11x = 33$; $12x = 36$; 27 cm, 33 cm, and 36 cm

      34. Let 6x, 7x, 11x, and 12x be the measures; $6x + 7x + 11x + 12x = 360$; $36x = 360$;

        $x = 10$; $6x = 60$; $7x = 70$; $11x = 110$; $12x = 120$; 2 of the cons. ∠ are supp. If 2

        lines are cut by a trans. and s.-s. int. ∠ are supp., then the lines are ∥.

      35. $\frac{(10 - 2)180}{10} : \frac{360}{10} = 144:36 = 4:1$; $\frac{(n - 2)180}{n} : \frac{360}{n} = (n - 2):2$

      36. a. Let h = number of hits; $\frac{h}{325} = \frac{320}{1000}$; $1000h = 104000$; $h = 104$

        b. $\frac{104}{335} \approx 0.310$

C   37. Let x = number of throws she must make; $\frac{24 + x}{30 + x} \geq 0.85$; $24 + x \geq 0.85(30 + x)$;

        $24 + x \geq 25.5 + 0.85x$; $0.15x \geq 1.5$; $x \geq 10$

38. $\dfrac{AB}{BD} = \dfrac{3}{4}$ and $\dfrac{AC}{CD} = \dfrac{5}{6}$; $AB = \dfrac{3}{4}BD$ and $CD = \dfrac{6}{5}AC$; $AB + BD = AD$ and $AC + CD =$

   AD; $AB + BD = AC + CD$; $\dfrac{7}{4}BD = \dfrac{11}{5}AC$; $AC = \dfrac{5}{11} \cdot \dfrac{7}{4} \cdot BD = \dfrac{5}{11} \cdot \dfrac{7}{4} \cdot 66 = 52.5$

39. $\dfrac{4}{y} + \dfrac{3}{x} = \dfrac{12}{y} - \dfrac{2}{x}$; $xy\left(\dfrac{4}{y} + \dfrac{3}{x}\right) = xy\left(\dfrac{12}{y} - \dfrac{2}{x}\right)$; $4x + 3y = 12x - 2y$; $5y = 8x$;

   $\dfrac{x}{y} = \dfrac{5}{8}$ or $5:8$

Pages 210-212 · WRITTEN EXERCISES

A 1. 15   2. 56   3. 21   4. 24   5. $\dfrac{4}{7}$ 6. $\dfrac{8}{3}$ 7. $\dfrac{y + 3}{3}$ 8. $\dfrac{5}{x}$

9. $5x = 12$; $x = \dfrac{12}{5} = 2\dfrac{2}{5}$ 10. $8x = 21$; $x = \dfrac{21}{8} = 2\dfrac{5}{8}$

11. $8x = 15$; $x = \dfrac{15}{8} = 1\dfrac{7}{8}$ 12. $2x = 40$; $x = 20$

13. $2x + 10 = 4$; $2x = -6$; $x = -3$ 14. $3x + 9 = 8$; $3x = -1$; $x = -\dfrac{1}{3}$

15. $5x + 10 = 4x + 12$; $x = 2$ 16. $6x + 3 = 8x - 2$; $2x = 5$; $x = \dfrac{5}{2} = 2\dfrac{1}{2}$

17. $3x + 9 = 4x - 2$; $x = 11$ 18. $60x - 20 = 49x + 35$; $11x = 55$; $x = 5$

19. $4x + 20 = 7x - 35$; $3x = 55$; $x = \dfrac{55}{3} = 18\dfrac{1}{3}$

20. $28x - 35 = 80x + 4$; $52x = -39$; $x = -\dfrac{39}{52} = -\dfrac{3}{4}$

	KR	RT	KT	KS	SU	KU
21.	12	9	21	16	12	28
22.	8	2	10	12	3	15
23.	16	8	24	20	10	30
24.	6	2	8	9	3	12
B 25.	8	4	12	10	5	15
26.	12	4	16	15	5	20
27.	27	9	36	36	12	48
28.	20	10	30	28	14	42

29. By the means-extremes property, $\dfrac{a + b}{b} = \dfrac{c + d}{d}$ is equivalent to $(a + b)d = b(c + d)$;

   $ad + bd = bc + bd$; $ad = bc$; also, $\dfrac{a}{b} = \dfrac{c}{d}$ is equivalent to $ad = bc$. Since both

   proportions are equivalent to the same equation, they are equivalent to each other.

30. By the properties of proportions, $\dfrac{x + y}{y} = \dfrac{r}{s}$ is equivalent to $\dfrac{x + y}{r} = \dfrac{y}{s}$ and $\dfrac{r}{x + y} = \dfrac{s}{y}$;

   then $\dfrac{r}{x + y} = \dfrac{x - y}{x + y}$ and $r = x - y$.

<u>31.</u> By the means-extremes property, $\dfrac{a - b}{a + b} = \dfrac{c - d}{c + d}$ is equivalent to $(a - b)(c + d) =$

$(a + b)(c - d)$; $ac + ad - bc - bd = ac - ad + bc - bd$; $ad - bc = -ad + bc$;

$2ad = 2bc$; $ad = bc$; also, $\dfrac{a}{b} = \dfrac{c}{d}$ is equivalent to $ad = bc$. Since the two proportions

are equivalent to the same equation, they are equivalent to each other.

<u>32.</u> By the means-extremes property, $\dfrac{a + c}{b + d} = \dfrac{a - c}{b - d}$ is equivalent to $(a + c)(b - d) =$

$(b + d)(a - c)$; $ab - ad + bc - cd = ab - bc + ad - cd$; $-ad + bc = -bc + ad$;

$2bc = 2ad$; $ad = bc$; also, $\dfrac{a}{b} = \dfrac{c}{d}$ is equivalent to $ad = bc$. Since the two proportions

are equivalent to the same equation, they are equivalent to each other.

<u>33.</u> $x^2 = (x - 3)(x + 4)$; $x^2 = x^2 + x - 12$; $x - 12 = 0$; $x = 12$

<u>34.</u> $(x + 2)(x + 2) = (x + 6)(x - 1)$; $x^2 + 4x + 4 = x^2 + 5x - 6$; $x = 10$

<u>35.</u> $(x + 1)(x - 6) = (x - 2)(x + 5)$; $x^2 - 5x - 6 = x^2 + 3x - 10$; $8x = 4$; $x = \dfrac{1}{2}$

C <u>36.</u> $(x - 1)(x - 2) = (x - 5)(2x + 1)$; $x^2 - 3x + 2 = 2x^2 - 9x - 5$; $x^2 - 6x - 7 = 0$;

$(x - 7)(x + 1) = 0$; $x = 7$ or $x = -1$

<u>37.</u> $5x(x + 5) = 9(4x + 4)$; $5x^2 + 25x = 36x + 36$; $5x^2 - 11x - 36 = 0$;

$(5x + 9)(x - 4) = 0$; $x = -\dfrac{9}{5}$ or $x = 4$

<u>38.</u> $(3x - 2)(x - 1) = 10(x + 2)$; $3x^2 - 5x + 2 = 10x + 20$; $3x^2 - 15x - 18 = 0$;

$x^2 - 5x - 6 = 0$; $(x - 6)(x + 1) = 0$; $x = 6$ or $x = -1$

<u>39.</u> $2x = 3y + 3$; $x = \dfrac{1}{2}(3y + 3)$; $2x + 2y = 7x - 7y$; $5x - 9y = 0$; $5\left(\dfrac{1}{2}(3y + 3)\right) - 9y =$

0; $15y + 15 - 18y = 0$; $-3y = -15$; $y = 5$; $x = \dfrac{1}{2}(3 \cdot 5 + 3) = 9$

<u>40.</u> $2x - 6 = 4y + 8$; $2x = 4y + 14$; $x = 2y + 7$; $5x + 5y - 5 = 6x - 6y + 6$;

$x - 11y = -11$; $2y + 7 - 11y = -11$; $-9y = -18$; $y = 2$; $x = 2 \cdot 2 + 7 = 11$

<u>41.</u> Let $\dfrac{a}{b} = r$. Then $a = br$, $c = dr$, and $e = fr$; $\dfrac{a + c + e}{b + d + f} = \dfrac{br + dr + fr}{b + d + f} =$

$\dfrac{r(b + d + f)}{b + d + f} = r = \dfrac{a}{b}$

<u>42.</u> Suppose there are n terms, the last being $\dfrac{j}{k}$. Let $\dfrac{a}{b} = r$. Then $a = br$, $c = dr$,

$e = fr$, ..., and $j = kr$. Then $\dfrac{a + c + e + \cdots + j}{b + d + f + \cdots + k} = \dfrac{br + dr + fr + \cdots + kr}{b + d + f + \cdots + k} =$

$\dfrac{r(b + d + f + \cdots + k)}{b + d + f + \cdots + k} = r = \dfrac{a}{b}$

<u>43.</u> $b(4a - 9b) = 4a(a - 2b)$; $4ab - 9b^2 = 4a^2 - 8ab$; $4a^2 - 12ab + 9b^2 = 0$;

$(2a - 3b)^2 = 0$; $2a - 3b = 0$; $2a = 3b$; $\dfrac{a}{b} = \dfrac{3}{2}$; $a : b = 3 : 2$

Pages 214-216 · WRITTEN EXERCISES

<u>A</u> 1. always   2. sometimes   3. sometimes   4. sometimes   5. always

6. sometimes   7. sometimes   8. sometimes   9. never   10. never

11. sometimes   12. always   13. $\frac{9}{12} = \frac{3}{4}$

14. trap.; ABCD is a trap. (In a plane, 2 lines $\perp$ to the same line are $\parallel$.) and A'B'C'D' must have the same shape.

15. $m \angle D' = m \angle D = 45$ 16. $m \angle C' = m \angle C = 180 - 45 = 135$

17. $\frac{B'C'}{6} = \frac{4}{3}$; $B'C' = 8$ 18. $\frac{AD}{20} = \frac{3}{4}$; $AD = 15$ 19. $\frac{C'D'}{3k} = \frac{4}{3}$; $C'D' = 4k$

20. $\frac{\text{Per. (ABCD)}}{\text{Per. (A'B'C'D')}} = \frac{6 + 9 + 15 + 3k}{8 + 12 + 20 + 4k} = \frac{3(10 + k)}{4(10 + k)} = \frac{3}{4}$

<u>B</u> 21. scale factor $= \frac{8}{10} = \frac{4}{5}$; $\frac{13}{x} = \frac{4}{5}$; $4x = 65$; $x = 16\frac{1}{4}$; $\frac{y}{16} = \frac{4}{5}$; $5y = 64$; $y = 12\frac{4}{5}$;

$\frac{z}{14} = \frac{4}{5}$; $5z = 56$; $z = 11\frac{1}{5}$

22. scale factor $= \frac{15}{18} = \frac{5}{6}$; $\frac{21}{x} = \frac{5}{6}$; $5x = 126$; $x = 25\frac{1}{5}$; $\frac{18}{y} = \frac{5}{6}$; $5y = 108$; $y = 21\frac{3}{5}$;

$\frac{27}{z} = \frac{5}{6}$; $5z = 162$; $z = 32\frac{2}{5}$

23. scale factor $= \frac{10}{14} = \frac{5}{7}$; $\frac{5}{x} = \frac{5}{7}$; $x = 7$; $\frac{y}{7\sqrt{3}} = \frac{5}{7}$; $7y = 35\sqrt{3}$; $y = 5\sqrt{3}$

24. scale factor $= \frac{10}{24} = \frac{5}{12}$; $\frac{x}{15} = \frac{5}{12}$; $12x = 75$; $x = 6\frac{1}{4}$; $\frac{y}{16} = \frac{5}{12}$; $12y = 80$; $y = 6\frac{2}{3}$;

$\frac{z}{12} = \frac{5}{12}$; $z = 5$

25-26. Figures may vary.   Examples are given.

25.   26.

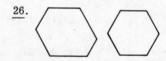

27. $\frac{AB}{DE} = \frac{BC}{EF} = \frac{AC}{DF}$; $AB = \frac{BC \cdot DE}{EF} = \frac{AC \cdot DE}{DF}$

28. $ZR > XR$ and $RS = RS$; then $\frac{ZR}{XR} \neq 1 = \frac{RS}{RS}$

29. C'(-6, 6) and D'(-10, 2) or
    C'(-6, -10) and D'(-10, -6)

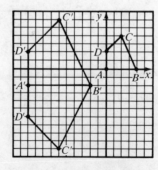

<u>30.</u> C'(9, 1) and D'(8, 2) or
C'(5, 1) and D'(6, 2)

<u>31.</u> $\dfrac{x}{40} = \dfrac{10}{x}$; $x^2 = 400$; $x = 20$

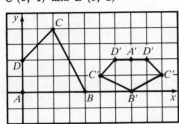

<u>C</u> 32. Answers may vary.   Quad. PQRS ~ Quad. TNZJ.   The sides are in proportion:

$\dfrac{PQ}{TN} = \dfrac{QR}{NZ} = \dfrac{RS}{ZJ} = \dfrac{SP}{JT} = \dfrac{2}{3}$.   Also, the $\angle$ are $\cong$ since $\angle R \cong \angle Z$; then $\overline{QR} \parallel \overline{NZ}$ and

$\angle Q \cong \angle N$; $\triangle$ POS and TOJ are similar isos. $\triangle$, with $\angle$ OPS $\cong \angle$ OSP $\cong \angle$ OTJ $\cong$

$\angle$ OJT; then $\angle$ QPS $\cong \angle$ NTJ $\cong \angle$ ZJT $\cong \angle$ RSP.

<u>33.</u> a. $\dfrac{x}{6} = \dfrac{6 - x}{x}$; $x^2 = 36 - 6x$; $x^2 + 6x - 36 = 0$; by the quadratic formula, $x =$

$\dfrac{-6 \pm \sqrt{6^2 - 4(-36)}}{2} = -3 \pm 3\sqrt{5}$; since $-3 - 3\sqrt{5}$ is negative, $x = -3 + 3\sqrt{5}$.

b. $\dfrac{6}{-3 + 3\sqrt{5}} = \dfrac{6(-3 - 3\sqrt{5})}{(-3 + 3\sqrt{5})(-3 - 3\sqrt{5})} = \dfrac{-18 - 18\sqrt{5}}{-36} = \dfrac{1 + \sqrt{5}}{2} \approx 1.62$

Page 217 · APPLICATION

<u>1.</u> length $= \dfrac{3}{4} \times 24 = 18$; 18 ft; width $= \dfrac{1}{2} \times 24 = 12$; 12 ft

<u>2.</u> $\dfrac{9}{24} = \dfrac{3}{8}$; $\dfrac{15}{2} \div 24 = \dfrac{5}{16}$; dim. on floor plan $= \dfrac{3}{8}$ in. $\times \dfrac{5}{16}$ in.; yes   <u>3.</u> 2.4

<u>4.</u> actual length of verandah $= 1 \times 24 = 24$ ft; $12x = 24$; $x = 2$; scale: 1 in. $= 2$ ft

Pages 221-224 · WRITTEN EXERCISES

<u>A</u> <u>1.</u> similar   <u>2.</u> not similar   <u>3.</u> similar   <u>4.</u> similar   <u>5.</u> similar

6. No conclusion is possible.   <u>7.</u> similar   8. No conclusion is possible.

<u>9.</u> similar   10. <u>a.</u> △VTJ   <u>b.</u> VJ; JT; VT

11. <u>a.</u> △MLN   <u>b.</u> 20; x; 20; y   <u>c.</u> 15x = 360; x = 24; 15y = 240; y = 16

<u>12.</u> $\dfrac{x}{8} = \dfrac{9}{12}$; 12x = 72; x = 6; $\dfrac{12}{12 + y} = \dfrac{9}{12}$; 144 = 108 + 9y; 9y = 36; y = 4

<u>13.</u> $\dfrac{8}{x} = \dfrac{6}{18}$; 6x = 144; x = 24; $\dfrac{y}{y + 11} = \dfrac{6}{18}$; 18y = 6y + 66; 12y = 66; y = $5\dfrac{1}{2}$

<u>14.</u> $\dfrac{x}{16} = \dfrac{24}{18} = \dfrac{4}{3}$; 3x = 64; x = $21\dfrac{1}{3}$; $\dfrac{12}{12 + y} = \dfrac{3}{4}$; 36 + 3y = 48; 3y = 12; y = 4

<u>B</u> 15. <u>a</u>. △ACD, △CBD   <u>b</u>. $\frac{16 + y}{20} = \frac{20}{16}$; 256 + 16y = 400; 16y = 144; y = 9;

$\frac{16}{12} = \frac{20}{x}$; 16x = 240; x = 15

16. $\frac{GF}{2} = \frac{4.4}{1.6}$; 1.6 · GF = 8.8; GF = 5.5; 5.5 m

17. $\frac{x}{2.2} = \frac{.06}{24}$; 24x = .132; x = .0055 m = .55 cm

18. $\frac{RI}{15} = \frac{36}{20}$; 20 · RI = 540; RI = 27; 27 m

19. $\frac{9}{y} = \frac{10}{6}$; 10y = 54; y = 5.4; $\frac{15}{x} = \frac{10}{6}$; 10x = 90; x = 9

20. $\frac{6}{24} = \frac{x}{8}$; 24x = 48; x = 2; y = 8 - 2 = 6

21. The girl and the flagpole are both ⊥ to the ground so ∠A ≅ ∠A' and the △ are ~ by the AA ~ Post.   Let h = height of pole in cm; $\frac{160}{h} = \frac{120}{450}$; 120h = 72000; h = 600; 600 cm or 6 m.

22. <u>a</u>. 1. $\overline{EF} \parallel \overline{RS}$ (Given)   2. ∠XFE ≅ ∠XSR; ∠XEF ≅ ∠XRS (If 2 ∥ lines are cut by a trans., then corr. △ are ≅.)   3. △ FXE ~ △ SXR (AA)

<u>b</u>. 1. △ FXE ~ △ SXR (Part <u>a</u>, above)   2. $\frac{FX}{SX} = \frac{EF}{RS}$ (Corr. sides of ~ △ are in prop.)

23. <u>a</u>. 1. ∠1 ≅ ∠2 (Given)   2. ∠J ≅ ∠J (Refl. Prop.)   3. △ JIG ~ △ JZY (AA)

<u>b</u>. 1. △ JIG ~ △ JZY (Part <u>a</u>, above)   2. $\frac{JG}{JY} = \frac{GI}{YZ}$ (Corr. sides of ~ △ are in prop.)

24. 1. ∠B ≅ ∠C (Given)   2. ∠1 ≅ ∠2 (Vert. △ are ≅.)   3. △ MLC ~ △ MNB (AA)

4. $\frac{NM}{LM} = \frac{BM}{CM}$ (Corr. sides of ~ △ are in prop.)   5. NM · CM = LM · BM

(Means-extremes Prop.)

25. 1. $\overline{BN} \parallel \overline{LC}$ (Given)   2. ∠C ≅ ∠B; ∠L ≅ ∠N (If 2 ∥ lines are cut by a trans., then alt. int. △ are ≅.)   3. △ MLC ~ △ MNB (AA)   4. $\frac{BN}{CL} = \frac{NM}{LM}$ (Corr. sides of ~ △ are in prop.)   5. BN · LM = CL · NM (Means-extremes prop.)

26. <u>a</u>. 1. ∠A ≅ ∠A (Refl. Prop.)   2. ∠D and ∠AHE are rt. △. (Given)

3. m∠D = 90 = m∠AHE (Def. of rt. ∠)   4. △ADG ~ △AHE (AA)

<u>b</u>. 1. △ADG ~ △AHE (Part <u>a</u>, above)   2. $\frac{AE}{AG} = \frac{HE}{DG}$ (Corr. sides of ~ △ are in prop.)   3. AE · DG = AG · HE (Means-extremes Prop.)

27. 1. $\overline{QT} \parallel \overline{RS}$ (Given)   2. ∠PQU ≅ ∠R; ∠PUQ ≅ ∠PVR; ∠PUT ≅ ∠PVS; ∠PTU ≅ ∠S (If 2 ∥ lines are cut by a trans., then corr. △ are ≅.)   3. △ PQU ~ △ PRV; △PUT ~ △ PVS (AA)   4. $\frac{QU}{RV} = \frac{PU}{PV}$; $\frac{UT}{VS} = \frac{PU}{PV}$ (Corr. sides of ~ △ are in prop.)   5. $\frac{QU}{RV} = \frac{UT}{VS}$ (Subst. Prop.)

<u>28.</u> First note that if 2 ∥ planes are cut by a third plane, then the lines of int. are ∥, so

$\overline{A'B'} \parallel \overline{AB}$, $\overline{A'C'} \parallel \overline{AC}$ and $\overline{C'B'} \parallel \overline{CB}$.   <u>a.</u> $\triangle VA'C' \sim \triangle VAC$; $\frac{15}{35} = \frac{18}{VC}$; $15 \cdot VC =$

630; VC = 42   <u>b.</u> $\frac{49 - BB'}{49} = \frac{15}{35} = \frac{3}{7}$; 343 - 7BB' = 147; 7BB' = 196; BB' = 28

<u>c.</u> $\frac{15}{35} = \frac{24}{AB}$; 15 · AB = 840; AB = 56

<u>29.</u> $\frac{10}{25} = \frac{A'B'}{20}$; 25 · A'B' = 200; A'B' = 8; $\frac{10}{25} = \frac{A'C'}{16}$; 25 · A'C' = 160; A'C' = 6.4;

$\frac{B'C'}{14} = \frac{10}{25}$; 25 · B'C' = 140; B'C' = 5.6.   Perimeter is 20.

<u>30.</u> Given: $\triangle ABC \sim \triangle A'B'C'$; $\overline{AD}$ and $\overline{A'D'}$

altitudes   Prove: $\frac{AD}{A'D'} = \frac{AB}{A'B'}$

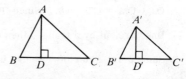

Proof: 1. $\triangle ABC \sim \triangle A'B'C'$ (Given)

2. $\angle A \cong \angle A'$ (Corr. ∠ of $\sim$ ⧌ are ≅.)   3. m∠ADB = 90 = m∠A'D'B' (Def. of alt.,

⊥ lines, rt. ∠)   4. $\triangle ADB \sim \triangle A'D'B'$ (AA)   5. $\frac{AD}{A'D'} = \frac{AB}{A'B'}$ (Corr. sides of $\sim$ ⧌

are in prop.)

C <u>31.</u> Given: $\triangle ABC$ and altitudes $\overline{AD}$ and $\overline{BE}$.

Prove: BC · AD = AC · BE.

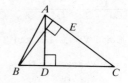

Proof: 1. $\overline{AD}$ and $\overline{BE}$ are alt. (Given)

2. m∠ADC = 90 = m∠BEC (Def. of alt.,

⊥ lines, rt. ∠)   3. $\angle C \cong \angle C$ (Refl. Prop.)   4. $\triangle ADC \sim \triangle BEC$ (AA)

5. $\frac{BC}{AC} = \frac{BE}{AD}$ (Corr. sides of $\sim$ ⧌ are in prop.)   6. BC · AD = AC · BE (Means-

extremes Prop.)

<u>32.</u> $\triangle CEF \sim \triangle CAD$ and $\triangle DFE \sim \triangle DCB$ so

$\frac{EF}{AD} = \frac{FC}{DC}$ and $\frac{EF}{BC} = \frac{DF}{DC}$; then $\frac{EF}{AD} + \frac{EF}{BC} =$

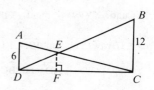

$\frac{FC}{DC} + \frac{DF}{DC}$; $\frac{EF}{6} + \frac{EF}{12} = \frac{FC + DF}{DC} = 1$;

2 · EF + EF = 12; 3 · EF = 12; EF = 4 ft.

<u>33.</u> Since $\overline{QN}$ and $\overline{RM}$ are medians, N and M are the midpts. of $\overline{SR}$ and $\overline{SQ}$.   The seg.

that joins the midpts. of 2 sides of a $\triangle$ is ∥ to the third side and has a length = to half

the length of the third side; $\overline{MN} \parallel \overline{QR}$ and MN = $\frac{1}{2}$QR; $\frac{QR}{MN} = \frac{2}{1}$.   Since $\overline{MN} \parallel \overline{QR}$,

$\angle PQR \cong \angle PNM$ and $\angle PRQ \cong \angle PMN$; $\triangle PQR \sim \triangle PNM$; $\frac{QP}{PN} = \frac{RP}{PM} = \frac{QR}{MN} = \frac{2}{1}$.

<u>34.</u> <u>a</u>, <u>b.</u> Check students' drawings; m∠ EAD = m∠ AEB = m∠ EDA = m∠ ADB = m∠ BDC

= m∠ CBD = m∠ DBE = m∠ EBA = 36; m∠ DAB = m∠ AKB = m∠ EKD = m∠ DEB = 72;

m∠EKA = m∠DKB = m∠C = 108   c. By the AA ~ Post., △DBA ~ △DEK and

△KBD ~ △KEA; then $\frac{DA}{DK} = \frac{DB}{DE}$ and $\frac{DK}{AK} = \frac{DB}{AE}$; ABCDE is reg. so DE = AE.   So

$\frac{DA}{DK} = \frac{DB}{DE} = \frac{DB}{AE} = \frac{DK}{AK}$, $\frac{DA}{DK} = \frac{DK}{AK}$

35. a. $\overline{TJ} \perp \overline{JO}$ and $\overline{PO} \perp \overline{JO}$ so $\overline{TJ} \parallel \overline{PO}$ and TJOP is a ▱. ∠J and ∠I are rt. ∠

and ∠TOJ ≅ ∠MOI (Vert. ∠ are ≅.) So by the AA ~ Post., △TJO ~ △MIO.   Since

corr. sides of ~ ∠ are in prop., $\frac{OM}{OT} = \frac{OI}{OJ}$ and by the Means-extremes Prop.,

OJ · OM = OT · OI.   Since $\overline{TP} \parallel \overline{JO}$, ∠PTO ≅ ∠IOM and ∠TPM ≅ ∠OFM. (If 2 ∥

lines are cut by a trans., then corr. ∠ are ≅.) So by the AA ~ Post., △TPM ~ △OFM.

Since corr. sides of ~ ∠ are in prop., $\frac{OF}{TP} = \frac{OM}{TM}$ and by the Means-extremes Prop.,

TM · OF = TP · OM.   TJOP is a ▱ so TP = OJ.   Then TM · OF = OJ · OM =

OT · OI.   By the Seg. Add. Post., OM + OT = TM and by the Div. Prop. of =,

$\frac{OM}{OJ \cdot OM} + \frac{OT}{OT \cdot OI} = \frac{TM}{TM \cdot OF}$ or $\frac{1}{OJ} + \frac{1}{OI} = \frac{1}{OF}$.   b. $\frac{1}{OJ} + \frac{1}{OI} = \frac{1}{OF}$;

$\frac{OI}{OJ \cdot OI} + \frac{OJ}{OJ \cdot OI} = \frac{1}{OF}$; $\frac{OJ + OI}{OJ \cdot OI} = \frac{1}{OF}$;   OF = $\frac{OJ \cdot OI}{OJ + OI}$

36. Since $\overline{VW} \perp \overline{UX}$ and $\overline{TY} \parallel \overline{UX}$, then $\overline{VW} \perp \overline{TY}$ and XYVW is a rect., and the ∠ of

XYVW are ≅ to the ∠ of YTUX.   ∠YVX ≅ ∠VXU since they are alt. int. ∠ of ∥

lines cut by transversal $\overline{VX}$.   ∠YXV is a comp. of ∠YVX; since $\overline{VZ} \perp \overline{UY}$,

∠UZX is a rt. ∠ and ∠ZUX is a comp. of ∠VXU.   Then ∠YXV ≅ ∠ZUX and

△YUX ~ △VXY (AA).   Since corr. sides of ~ ∠ are in prop., $\frac{YV}{XY} = \frac{XY}{UX}$.   YV = WX,

UX = YT, and XY = VW = TU, so by Subst. Prop., $\frac{WX}{XY} = \frac{XY}{YT} = \frac{YV}{TU} = \frac{VW}{UX}$.

Quad. XYVW ~ quad. YTUX.

37. a. Draw $\overline{HW}$ and $\overline{HX} \perp$ to $\overline{AB}$ and $\overline{DC}$, resp., and $\overline{HY}$ and $\overline{HZ} \perp$ to $\overline{AD}$ and $\overline{BC}$,

resp. $\overline{WX} \parallel \overline{AD}$ and $\overline{BC}$, and $\overline{YZ} \parallel \overline{AB}$ and $\overline{DC}$. If 3 ∥ lines cut off ≅ seg. on one

trans., then they cut off ≅ seg. on every trans.   Then HW =

HX and HW + HX = 16 so HW = HX = 8.   Also AY = YD

so Y is the midpt. of $\overline{AD}$ and H is the midpt. of $\overline{AG}$. (The

seg. that joins the midpts. of 2 sides of a △ has a length =

to half the length of the third side.) Then HY = $\frac{1}{2}$ · 12 = 6

and HZ = 16 - 6 = 10.

b. ∠AEH ≅ ∠HFZ so ∠YAH ≅ ∠ZHF and △YAH ~ △ZHF.   Then $\frac{10}{8} = \frac{ZF}{6}$;

8 · ZF = 60; ZF = 7.5; BF = 8 - 7.5 = 0.5; FC = 16 - 0.5 = 15.5;

CG = 16 - 12 = 4; $\triangle AHE \cong \triangle HZF$ by ASA so EH = ZF = 7.5. $\triangle YEH \sim \triangle ZFH$ and

$\frac{6}{10} = \frac{YE}{7.5}$; $10 \cdot YE = 45$; YE = 4.5; DE = 8 - 4.5 = 3.5; EA = 16 - 3.5 = 12.5.

Since $\triangle AYH \sim \triangle HZF$, $\frac{8}{10} = \frac{10}{HF}$; $8 \cdot HF = 100$; HF = 12.5

Page 225 · COMPUTER KEY-IN

1. a. Answers may vary.   A sample BASIC program is given.

```
10   PRINT "OBJECT DISTANCE: ";
20   INPUT OJ
30   PRINT "IMAGE DISTANCE: ";
40   INPUT OI
50   LET OF = (OJ * OI)/(OI + OJ)
60   PRINT "FOCAL DISTANCE: ";OF
70   END
```

b. Computer results may vary slightly; sample results shown below are rounded to

the nearest thousandth.

OJ	60	55	50	45	40	35	30	25	20
OI	20	20.5	21	22.5	24	26	30.5	42	61
OF	15	14.934	14.789	15	15	14.918	15.124	15.672	15.062

c. Answers may vary.   A sample BASIC program is given.

```
10   FOR Q = 1 TO 9
20   READ OJ
30   READ OI
50   LET OF = (OJ * OI)/(OI + OJ)
52   LET SUM = SUM + OF
53   NEXT Q
55   LET OF = SUM/9
60   PRINT "FOCAL DISTANCE: ";OF
65   DATA 60, 20, 55, 20.5, 50, 21, 45, 22.5
66   DATA 40, 24, 35, 26, 30, 30.5, 25, 42, 20, 61
70   END
```

Average focal distance $\approx$ 15.055

2. a. $\frac{1}{OJ} + \frac{1}{OI} = \frac{1}{15.1}$; $\frac{1}{OI} = \frac{1}{15.1} - \frac{1}{OJ}$; $\frac{1}{OI} = \frac{OJ - 15.1}{15.1(OJ)}$; $OI = \frac{15.1(OJ)}{OJ - 15.1}$

b. A sample BASIC program is given.

```
10   PRINT "OBJECT DISTANCE ";
20   INPUT OJ
30   LET OI = 15.1 * OJ/(OJ - 15.1)
40   PRINT "IMAGE DISTANCE: ";OI
50   END
```

Computer results may vary slightly; sample results shown below are rounded to

nearest thousandth.

OJ	100	90	80	70	65	15	10	5
OI	17.786	18.144	18.613	19.253	19.669	-2265.000	-29.608	-7.475

Pages 228-230 · WRITTEN EXERCISES

<u>A</u> <u>1</u>. △ABC ~ △GNK; SAS   <u>2</u>. △ABC ~ △THJ; AA

   <u>3</u>. △ABC ~ △XRN; SSS   <u>4</u>. △ABC ~ △MBL; SAS

   <u>5</u>. △ABC ~ △AEF; AA   <u>6</u>. △ABC ~ △ARS; SAS

   <u>7</u>. △ABC ~ △PKN; 2:3   <u>8</u>. △ABC ~ △KNP; 2:3

   <u>9</u>. no   <u>10</u>. △ABC ~ △NPK; 4:5

<u>11</u>. 1. $\frac{DE}{GH} = \frac{DF}{GI} = \frac{EF}{HI}$ (Given)   2. △DEF ~ △GHI (SSS)   3. ∠E ≅ ∠H (Corr. ∠ of

~ ▲ are ≅.)

<u>12</u>. 1. $\frac{DE}{GH} = \frac{EF}{HI}$; ∠E ≅ ∠H (Given)   2. △DEF ~ △GHI (SAS)   3. $\frac{EF}{HI} = \frac{DF}{GI}$ (Corr.

sides of ~ ▲ are in prop.)

<u>B</u> <u>13</u>. 1. $\frac{JL}{NL} = \frac{KL}{ML}$ (Given)   2. ∠MLN ≅ ∠KLJ (Vert. ∠ are ≅.)   3. △MLN ~ △KLJ

(SAS)   4. ∠J ≅ ∠N (Corr. ∠ of ~ ▲ are ≅.)

<u>14</u>. 1. $\frac{AB}{SR} = \frac{BC}{RA} = \frac{CA}{AS}$ (Given)   2. △ABC ~ △SRA (SSS)   3. ∠BCA ≅ ∠RAS (Corr. ∠

of ~ ▲ are ≅.)   4. $\overline{BC} \parallel \overline{AR}$ (If 2 lines are cut by a trans. and alt. int. ∠ are ≅,

then the lines are ∥.)

<u>15</u>. 1. $\frac{VW}{VX} = \frac{VZ}{VY}$ (Given)   2. ∠V ≅ ∠V (Refl. Prop.)   3. △VWZ ~ △VXY (SAS)

∠1 ≅ ∠2 (Corr. ∠ of ~ ▲ are ≅.)   5. $\overline{WZ} \parallel \overline{XY}$ (If 2 lines are cut by a trans. and

corr. ∠ are ≅, then the lines are ∥.)

<u>16</u>. (3) ∠1 ≅ ∠Y

<u>17</u>. WD = WC = 4 · VA = 4 · VB; $\frac{VA}{WD} = \frac{VB}{WC}$ and m∠BVA = m∠CWD = 90;

△AVB ~ △DWC; $\frac{AB}{CD} = \frac{VA}{WD} = \frac{1}{4}$; CD = 4 · AB; length of median of trap. ABCD =

$\frac{1}{2}$(AB + 4 · AB) = $\frac{5}{2}$ · AB

<u>18</u>. 1. OR' = 2 · OR; OS' = 2 · OS; OT' = 2 · OT (Given)   2. OR = $\frac{1}{2}$ · OR';

OS = $\frac{1}{2}$ · OS'; OT = $\frac{1}{2}$ · OT' (Div. Prop. of =)   3. R, S, and T are the midpts.

of OR', OS', and OT', resp. (Def. of midpt.)   4. RS = $\frac{1}{2}$ · R'S'; ST = $\frac{1}{2}$ · S'T',

RT = $\frac{1}{2}$ · R'T' (The seg. that joins the midpts. of 2 sides of a △ has a length = half

the length of the third side.)   5. $\frac{RS}{R'S'} = \frac{ST}{S'T'} = \frac{RT}{R'T'} = \frac{1}{2}$ (Div. Prop. of =, Trans.

Prop.)   6. △RST ~ △R'S'T' (SSS)

<u>19</u>. Assume that AB < DE.   1. Take X on $\overline{DE}$ so that DX = AB (Ruler Post.)

2. Through X draw a line ∥ to $\overline{EF}$, int. $\overline{DF}$ at Y. (Through a pt. outside a line there is

exactly one line $\parallel$ to the given line.)   3. $\angle DXY \cong \angle E$; $\angle DYX \cong \angle F$ (If 2 $\parallel$ lines are

cut by a trans., then corr. $\angle$ are $\cong$.)   4. $\triangle DXY \sim \triangle DEF$ (AA)   5. $\dfrac{DX}{DE} = \dfrac{DY}{DF}$

(Corr. sides of $\sim \triangle$ are in prop.)   6. $DY = \dfrac{DX \cdot DF}{DE}$ (By algebra)

7. $\dfrac{AB}{DE} = \dfrac{AC}{DF}$ (Given)   8. $AC = \dfrac{AB \cdot DF}{DE} = \dfrac{DX \cdot DF}{DE}$ (By algebra; Subst. Prop.)

9. $DY = AC$ (Subst. Prop.)   10. $\angle A \cong \angle D$ (Given)   11. $\triangle ABC \cong \triangle DXY$ (SAS)

12. $\angle B \cong \angle DXY$ (Corr. parts of $\cong \triangle$ are $\cong$.)   13. $\angle B \cong \angle E$ (Trans. Prop.)

14. $\triangle ABC \sim \triangle DEF$ (AA)

20. Assume $AB < DE$.   1. Take X on $\overline{DE}$ so that $DX = AB$. (Ruler Post.)   2. Draw

a line through X $\parallel$ to $\overline{EF}$, int. $\overline{DF}$ at Y. (Through a pt. outside a line, there is exactly

one line $\parallel$ to the given line.)   3. $\angle DXY \cong \angle E$; $\angle DYX \cong \angle F$ (If 2 $\parallel$ lines are cut by

a trans., corr. $\angle$ are $\cong$.)   4. $\triangle DXY \sim \triangle DEF$ (AA)   5. $\dfrac{DX}{DE} = \dfrac{XY}{EF} = \dfrac{DY}{DF}$ (Corr.

sides of $\sim \triangle$ are in prop.)   6. $\dfrac{AB}{DE} = \dfrac{XY}{EF} = \dfrac{DY}{DF}$ (Subst. Prop.)   7. $\dfrac{AB}{DE} = \dfrac{BC}{EF} = \dfrac{AC}{DF}$

(Given)   8. $\dfrac{XY}{EF} = \dfrac{BC}{EF}$; $\dfrac{DY}{DF} = \dfrac{AC}{DF}$ (Trans. Prop.)   9. $BC = XY$; $AC = DY$ (By

algebra)   10. $\triangle ABC \cong \triangle DXY$ (SSS)   11. $\angle B \cong \angle DXY$ (Corr. parts of $\cong \triangle$ are $\cong$.)

12. $\angle E \cong \angle B$ (Trans. Prop.)   13. $\triangle ABC \sim \triangle DEF$ (SAS)

21. Given: Isos. $\triangle ABC$ with $AB = AC$; isos. $\triangle DEF$ with

DE = DF; $\angle A \cong \angle D$ Prove: $\triangle ABC \sim \triangle DEF$.

Proof: 1. $AB = AC$; $DE = DF$ (Given)   2. $\dfrac{AB}{DE} = \dfrac{AC}{DF}$

(Div. Prop. of =)   3. $\angle A \cong \angle D$ (Given)   4. $\triangle ABC \sim \triangle DEF$ (SAS)

22. 1. M and N are the midpts. of $\overline{AB}$ and $\overline{AC}$, resp. (Given)   2. $AM = \dfrac{1}{2} \cdot AB$;

$AN = \dfrac{1}{2} \cdot AC$ (Midpt. Thm.)   3. $\dfrac{AM}{AB} = \dfrac{1}{2} = \dfrac{AN}{AC}$ (Div. Prop. of =; Trans. Prop.)

4. $\angle A \cong \angle A$ (Refl. Prop.)   5. $\triangle AMN \sim \triangle ABC$ (SAS)   6. $\angle AMN \cong \angle B$ (Corr. $\angle$

of $\sim \triangle$ are $\cong$.)   7. $\overline{MN} \parallel \overline{BC}$ (If 2 lines are cut by a trans. and corr. $\angle$ are $\cong$,

then the lines are $\parallel$.)   8. $\dfrac{MN}{BC} = \dfrac{AM}{AB} = \dfrac{1}{2}$ (Corr. sides of $\sim \triangle$ are in prop.)

9. $MN = \dfrac{1}{2} \cdot BC$ (Mult. Prop. of =)

C 23. Given: $\triangle ABC \sim \triangle DEF$; medians $\overline{AM}$ and $\overline{DN}$.

Prove: $\dfrac{AM}{DN} = \dfrac{AB}{DE}$ Proof: 1. $\triangle ABC \sim \triangle DEF$

(Given)   2. $\angle B \cong \angle E$ (Corr. $\angle$ of $\sim \triangle$ are $\cong$.)

3. $\dfrac{AB}{DE} = \dfrac{BC}{EF}$ (Corr. sides of $\sim \triangle$ are in prop.)   4. $\overline{AM}$ and $\overline{DN}$ are medians.

(Given)   5. M and N are the midpts. of $\overline{BC}$ and $\overline{EF}$, resp. (Def. of median)

6. $BM = \frac{1}{2} \cdot BC$; $EN = \frac{1}{2} \cdot EF$ (Midpt. Thm.)   7. $\dfrac{BM}{EN} = \dfrac{\frac{1}{2} \cdot BC}{\frac{1}{2} \cdot EF} = \dfrac{BC}{EF} = \dfrac{AB}{DE}$

(Subst. Prop.; algebra)   8. $\triangle ABM \sim \triangle DEN$ (SAS)

9. $\dfrac{AM}{DN} = \dfrac{AB}{DE}$ (Corr. sides of $\sim \triangle$ are in prop.)

<u>24</u>. 1. WXYZ is a $\square$; $\overline{WX} \parallel \overline{ZY}$ (Given; def. of $\square$)   2. $\angle WAT \cong \angle YAT$; $\angle BWT \cong$

$\angle B'YT$ (If 2 $\parallel$ lines are cut by a trans., alt. int. $\angle$ are $\cong$.)   3. $\angle WTA' \cong \angle YTA'$;

$\angle BTW \cong \angle B'TY$ (Vert. $\angle$ are $\cong$.)   4. $\triangle WTA \sim \triangle YTA'$; $\triangle BTW \sim \triangle B'TY$ (AA)

5. $\dfrac{TW}{TY} = \dfrac{AT}{A'T}$; $\dfrac{TW}{TY} = \dfrac{BT}{B'T}$ (Corr. sides of $\sim \triangle$ are in prop.)   6. $\dfrac{AT}{A'T} = \dfrac{BT}{B'T}$ (Trans.

Prop.)   7. $\angle ATB \cong \angle A'TB$ (Vert. $\angle$ are $\cong$.)   8. $\triangle ATB \sim \triangle A'TB$ (SAS)

<u>25</u>. <u>a</u>. Draw $\overline{QS} \parallel \overline{CP}$. $\triangle KMP \sim \triangle KRQ$ so

$\dfrac{QK}{PK} = \dfrac{QR}{PM}$. $\triangle AQR \sim \triangle ACM$ so $\dfrac{QR}{CM} = \dfrac{AQ}{AC}$.

Then $\dfrac{QK}{PK} = \dfrac{QR}{PM} = \dfrac{QR}{CM} = \dfrac{AQ}{AC} = \dfrac{\frac{3}{5} \cdot AP}{AC} = \dfrac{15}{20} = \dfrac{3}{4}$

<u>b</u>. Draw $\overline{QS} \parallel \overline{CT}$ int. $\overline{AM}$ at R and $\overline{UP} \parallel \overline{CT}$ int.

$\overline{AM}$ at V. $\triangle KVP \sim \triangle KRQ$ so $\dfrac{QK}{PK} = \dfrac{QR}{VP}$.

$\triangle AQR \sim \triangle ACM$ and $\triangle ARS \sim \triangle AMT$ so

$\dfrac{QR}{CM} = \dfrac{AR}{AM}$ and $\dfrac{RS}{MT} = \dfrac{AR}{AM}$.   Then $\dfrac{QR}{CM} = \dfrac{RS}{MT}$;

but $CM = MT$ so $QR = RS$.   We now have

$\dfrac{QK}{PK} = \dfrac{RS}{VP}$.   Since $\triangle AVP \sim \triangle ARS$, $\dfrac{RS}{VP} = \dfrac{AS}{AP}$, and $\dfrac{QK}{PK} = \dfrac{AS}{AP}$. $\triangle AQS \sim \triangle ACT$ so

$\dfrac{AQ}{AC} = \dfrac{AS}{AT}$; $\dfrac{\frac{3}{5} \cdot AP}{20} = \dfrac{AS}{25}$; $15 \cdot AP = 20 \cdot AS$; $\dfrac{AS}{AP} = \dfrac{3}{4}$; $\dfrac{QK}{PK} = \dfrac{3}{4}$

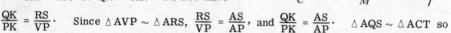

<u>Page 230 · CHALLENGE</u>

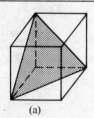 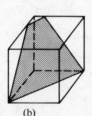 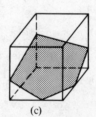 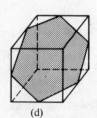

(a)   (b)   (c)   (d)

<u>Page 231 · CALCULATOR KEY-IN</u>

<u>1</u>. $\dfrac{AD}{AC} \approx 1.62$; $\dfrac{AC}{AB} \approx 1.62$; $\dfrac{AB}{BC} \approx 1.63$ <u>2</u>. ≈ 1.618 <u>3</u>. ≈ 0.618

Page 232 · COMPUTER KEY-IN

<u>1</u>. Ratios approach 1.61803399   <u>2</u>. Ratios approach 1.61803399

<u>3</u>. Ratios always approach 1.61803399 regardless of the pair of starting numbers.

Pages 236-238 · WRITTEN EXERCISES

<u>1</u>. a. no   b. yes   c. yes   d. no   e. yes   f. yes

<u>2</u>. a. no   b. no   c. yes   d. yes

	<u>3.</u>	<u>4.</u>	<u>5.</u>	<u>6.</u>
AB	6	15	21	37.5
BC	10	25	35	62.5
AC	16	40	56	100

<u>7</u>. $\frac{4}{5} = \frac{6}{x}$; $4x = 30$; $x = 7.5$ <u>8</u>. $\frac{x}{48} = \frac{16}{36}$; $36x = 768$; $x = \frac{64}{3}$

<u>9</u>. $\frac{10}{x} = \frac{15}{39}$; $15x = 390$; $x = 26$ <u>10</u>. $\frac{8}{x} = \frac{14}{21}$; $14x = 168$; $x = 12$

<u>11</u>. $\frac{x}{14 - x} = \frac{10}{15}$; $15x = 140 - 10x$; $25x = 140$; $x = 5.6$

<u>12</u>. $\frac{x}{18} = \frac{25}{15}$; $15x = 450$; $x = 30$ <u>13</u>. $\frac{22}{11} = \frac{29}{x}$; $22x = 319$; $x = \frac{319}{22} = 14.5$

<u>14</u>. $\frac{24 - x}{x} = \frac{18}{9} = \frac{2}{1}$; $2x = 24 - x$; $3x = 24$; $x = 8$

<u>15</u>. $\frac{3x}{18} = \frac{2x}{4x} = \frac{1}{2}$; $6x = 18$; $x = 3$

		AR	RT	AT	AN	NP	AP	RN	TP
B	<u>16.</u>	6	4	10	9	6	15	9	15
	<u>17.</u>	?	?	?	10	6	16	?	?
	<u>18.</u>	18	6	24	?	?	?	30	40
	<u>19.</u>	12	8	20	18	12	30	15	25
	<u>20.</u>	18	9	27	26	13	39	24	36
	<u>21.</u>	18	15	33	24	20	44	27.$\overline{27}$	50

<u>22</u>. 1. Draw $\overline{TX}$ int. $\overleftrightarrow{SY}$ at N. (Through any 2 pts. there is exactly one line.)

   2. $\overleftrightarrow{RX} \parallel \overleftrightarrow{SY} \parallel \overleftrightarrow{TZ}$ (Given)   3. $\frac{RS}{ST} = \frac{XN}{NT}$; $\frac{XN}{NT} = \frac{XY}{YZ}$ ($\triangle$ Prop. Thm.)

   4. $\frac{RS}{ST} = \frac{XY}{YZ}$ (Trans. Prop.)

<u>23</u>. 1. Draw a line through E $\parallel$ to $\overrightarrow{DG}$. (Through a pt. outside a line there is exactly one

   line $\parallel$ to the given line.)   2. Extend $\overrightarrow{FD}$ to int. the line at K. (Through a pt. outside a line there is exactly one line ∥ to the given line; if 2 lines int., then they int. in

exactly one pt.)   3. $\dfrac{GF}{GE} = \dfrac{DF}{DK}$ (△ Prop. Thm.)   4. $\overrightarrow{DG}$ bisects ∠ FDE. (Given)

5. ∠1 ≅ ∠2 (Def. of ∠ bis.)   6. ∠3 ≅ ∠1 (If 2 ∥ lines are cut by a trans., then

alt. int. ∠s are ≅.)   7. ∠2 ≅ ∠4 (If 2 ∥ lines are cut by a trans., then corr. ∠s

are ≅.)   8. ∠3 ≅ ∠4 (Trans. Prop.)   9. DK = DE (If 2 ∠s of a △ are ≅, then

the sides opp. those ∠s are ≅.)   10. $\dfrac{GF}{GE} = \dfrac{DF}{DE}$ (Subst. Prop.)

24. $\dfrac{AB}{25 - AB} = \dfrac{21}{14} = \dfrac{3}{2}$; $2 \cdot AB = 75 - 3 \cdot AB$; $5 \cdot AB = 75$; $AB = 15$

25. $\dfrac{BC}{60 - BC} = \dfrac{30}{50} = \dfrac{3}{5}$; $5 \cdot BC = 180 - 3 \cdot BC$; $8 \cdot BC = 180$; $BC = 22.5$

26. $\dfrac{x}{27} = \dfrac{\frac{4}{3}x}{x} = \dfrac{4}{3}$; $3x = 108$; $x = 36$; $BC = 36$; $AC = 27 + 36 = 63$

27. $\dfrac{2x - 12}{x} = \dfrac{2x - 4}{x + 5}$; $2x^2 - 2x - 60 = 2x^2 - 4x$; $2x = 60$; $x = 30$; $2x - 12 = 48$;

AC = 48 + 30 = 78

28. The frontages of the lots on Martin Luther King Ave. are prop. to their resp. frontages

on Lakeview Rd.   Let the frontages on Martin Luther King Ave. be 40x, 30x and 35x.

Then $40x + 30x + 35x = 140$; $x = \dfrac{4}{3}$.   The frontages are $40x = 53.3$ m, $30x = 40$ m,

and $35x = 46.7$ m.

29. $\dfrac{AP}{13 - AP} = \dfrac{14}{12} = \dfrac{7}{6}$; $6 \cdot AP = 91 - 7 \cdot AP$; $13 \cdot AP = 91$; $AP = 7$; $AM = \dfrac{1}{2} \cdot 13 =$

6.5; MP = 7 - 6.5 = 0.5

30. Given: △ABC; $\overleftrightarrow{AX}$ bis. ∠A; $\overleftrightarrow{AX}$ bis. $\overline{BC}$.

Prove: AB = AC   Proof: 1. $\overleftrightarrow{AX}$ bis. ∠A. (Given)

2. $\dfrac{XB}{XC} = \dfrac{AB}{AC}$ (△ Angle-Bisector Thm.)   3. $\overleftrightarrow{AX}$ bis.

$\overline{BC}$. (Given)   4. XB = XC (Def. of seg. bis.)   5. $\dfrac{XB}{XC} = 1$ (Div. Prop. of =)

6. $\dfrac{AB}{AC} = 1$ or AB = AC (Subst. Prop.; Mult. Prop. of =)

C 31. If 3 ∥ planes int. 2 trans., then they divide the trans.

proportionally.   Given: Plane P ∥ plane Q ∥

plane R; trans. $\overleftrightarrow{AE}$ and $\overleftrightarrow{BF}$.   Prove: $\dfrac{AC}{CE} = \dfrac{BD}{DF}$.

Proof: 1. Draw $\overline{EB}$, int. Q at G.   Draw $\overline{AB}$, $\overline{CG}$, $\overline{GD}$,

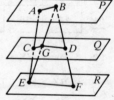

and $\overline{EF}$. (Through any 2 pts. there is exactly one line.)

2. Exactly one plane contains $\overleftrightarrow{AE}$ and $\overleftrightarrow{BE}$; exactly one plane contains $\overleftrightarrow{BE}$ and $\overleftrightarrow{BF}$. (If

2 lines int., then exactly one plane contains them.)   3. $\overline{AB} \parallel \overline{CG}$; $\overline{GD} \parallel \overline{EF}$ (If 2 ∥

planes are cut by a third plane, then the lines of int. are ∥.)

4. $\dfrac{AC}{CE} = \dfrac{BG}{GE}$; $\dfrac{BD}{DF} = \dfrac{BG}{GE}$ ($\triangle$ Prop. Thm.)   5. $\dfrac{AC}{CE} = \dfrac{BD}{DF}$ (Subst. Prop.)

32. Assume temporarily that $\overrightarrow{AD}$ and $\overrightarrow{AE}$ trisect $\angle BAC$

and BD = DE = EC. Then $\overrightarrow{AD}$ bisects $\angle BAE$ and

$\overrightarrow{AE}$ bisects $\angle DAC$, so $\dfrac{BD}{DE} = \dfrac{AB}{AE}$ and $\dfrac{DE}{EC} = \dfrac{AD}{AC}$.

Since $\dfrac{BD}{DE} = \dfrac{DE}{EC} = 1$, then AB = AE and AD = AC.

Also, $m\angle BAE = 2 \cdot m\angle DAE = m\angle DAC$; since $\triangle BAE$ and $\triangle DAC$ are isos.,

$m\angle ABE = m\angle AEB = m\angle ADC = m\angle ACD$.   BE = DC and $\triangle BAE \cong \triangle DAC$ (ASA).

Then AB = AD = AE = AC and $\triangle ABD \cong \triangle ADE$, so $m\angle ABD = m\angle ADE = 90$.

This contradicts the fact that in a plane, 2 lines $\perp$ to the same line are $\parallel$. Our temp.

assumption must be incorrect; it follows that $\overrightarrow{AD}$ and $\overrightarrow{AE}$ cannot trisect both

$\angle BAC$ and $\overline{BC}$.

33. No.   By $\triangle$ Angle-Bisector Thm., in $\triangle ROE$, $\dfrac{1}{2} = \dfrac{OR}{OE}$;

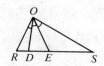

OE = 2 $\cdot$ OR.   In $\triangle ODS$, $\dfrac{2}{4} = \dfrac{OD}{OS}$; OS = 2 $\cdot$ OD.

Then $\triangle ROE \sim \triangle DOS$ (SAS) and $\angle ORD \cong \angle ODE$.

This contradicts the fact that the measure of $\angle ODE$, an ext. $\angle$ of $\angle ORD$, is = to

$m\angle ORD + m\angle ROD$.

34. ZNKJ is a trap.   Proof: 1. $\overrightarrow{EX}$ bis. $\angle E$. (Given)   2. $\dfrac{ZX}{NX} = \dfrac{ZE}{NE}$ ($\triangle$ Angle-Bisector

Thm.)   3. $\dfrac{ZX}{ZE} = \dfrac{NX}{NE}$ (A property of proportions)   4. ZJ = ZX; NK = NX (Given)

5. $\dfrac{ZJ}{ZE} = \dfrac{NK}{NE}$ (Subst. Prop.)   6. $\angle E \cong \angle E$ (Refl. Prop.)   7. $\triangle JEK \sim \triangle ZEN$ (SAS)

8. $\angle EJK \cong \angle EZN$ (Corr. $\angle$ of $\sim$ $\triangle$ are $\cong$.)   9. $\overline{JK} \parallel \overline{ZN}$ (If 2 lines are cut by a

trans. and corr. $\angle$ are $\cong$, then the lines are $\parallel$.)   10. $\overleftrightarrow{JZ}$ and $\overleftrightarrow{KN}$ intersect. (Given)

11. ZNKJ is a trap. (Def. of trap.)

35. Draw lines $\parallel$ to $\overline{ST}$ through R, M, and V.

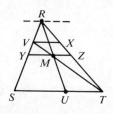

$\dfrac{RY}{YS} = \dfrac{RZ}{ZT} = \dfrac{RM}{MU}$; since M is the midpt. of $\overline{RU}$,

Y and Z are the midpts. of $\overline{RS}$ and $\overline{RT}$, and YM =

$\dfrac{1}{2} \cdot SU = \dfrac{1}{2} \cdot \dfrac{3}{5} \cdot ST = \dfrac{3}{10} \cdot ST$; $\dfrac{YM}{ST} = \dfrac{3}{10}$;

$\triangle VYM \sim \triangle VST$ so $\dfrac{VY}{VS} = \dfrac{YM}{ST} = \dfrac{3}{10}$; then $\dfrac{VY}{VY + YS} = \dfrac{3}{10}$ and $\dfrac{VY}{YS} = \dfrac{3}{7}$.   RV =

RS $-$ (VY $+$ YS) $=$ RS $-$ ($\frac{10}{3} \cdot$ VY) $=$ RS $-$ ($\frac{10}{3} \cdot \frac{3}{7}$ YS) $=$ RS $-$ ($\frac{10}{7} \cdot$ YS) $=$

RS $-$ ($\frac{10}{7} \cdot \frac{1}{2} \cdot$ RS) $=$ RS $- \frac{5}{7} \cdot$ RS $= \frac{2}{7} \cdot$ RS; RV : RS $= 2 : 7$

<u>36</u>. 1. Draw $\overline{AN}$ and $\overline{BM}$ || to $\overline{CX}$. (Through a pt. outside a line there is exactly one line ||

to the given line.)   2. $\frac{AX}{XB} = \frac{AP}{PM}$ ($\triangle$ Prop. Thm.)   3. $\overline{AN}$ || $\overline{BM}$ (Two lines || to a

third line are || to each other.)   4. $\angle$ ANP $\cong$ $\angle$ MBP; $\angle$ MBY $\cong$ $\angle$ PCY; $\angle$ BMY $\cong$

$\angle$ CPY; $\angle$ PCZ $\cong$ $\angle$ NAZ; $\angle$ ANZ $\cong$ $\angle$ CPZ (If 2 || lines are cut by a trans., then alt.

int. $\angle$ are $\cong$.)   5. $\angle$ NPA $\cong$ $\angle$ BPM (Vert. $\angle$ are $\cong$.)   6. $\triangle$ APN $\sim$ $\triangle$ MPB;

$\triangle$ BYM $\sim$ $\triangle$ CYP; $\triangle$ CZP $\sim$ $\triangle$ AZN (AA)   7. $\frac{AP}{PM} = \frac{AN}{MB}$; $\frac{BY}{YC} = \frac{MB}{PC}$; $\frac{CZ}{ZA} = \frac{PC}{AN}$

(Corr. sides of $\sim$ $\triangle$ are in prop.)   8. $\frac{AX}{XB} \cdot \frac{BY}{YC} \cdot \frac{CZ}{ZA} = \frac{AN}{MB} \cdot \frac{MB}{PC} \cdot \frac{PC}{AN} = 1$

(Subst. Prop.; algebra)

<u>Page 238 · CHALLENGE</u>

$\overline{FB}$ || $\overline{EC}$ so $\frac{FE}{AF} = \frac{BC}{AB}$ ($\triangle$ Prop. Thm.) and $\overline{BD}$ || $\overline{AE}$ so $\frac{BC}{AB} = \frac{CD}{DE}$.   Then $\frac{FE}{AF} = \frac{CD}{DE}$.

$\overline{FD}$ || $\overline{AC}$ so $\frac{FE}{AF} = \frac{DE}{CD}$; by subst., $\frac{CD}{DE} = \frac{DE}{CD}$; $(CD)^2 = (DE)^2$; CD $=$ DE; D is the midpt.

of $\overline{CE}$.   Then $\frac{BC}{AB} = 1$, so B is the midpt. of $\overline{AC}$; $\frac{FE}{AF} = 1$, and F is the midpt. of $\overline{AE}$.

<u>Page 240 · EXTRA</u>

<u>1</u>. c   <u>2</u>. d   <u>3</u>. b   <u>4</u>. a   <u>5</u>. d

<u>6</u>. {1, 2̂, 3, 5, 7}, {0, 4, 6, 9}, {8}   <u>7</u>. <u>a</u>, <u>b</u>. Check students' drawings.

<u>Pages 241-242 · CHAPTER REVIEW</u>

<u>1</u>. 3 : 5   <u>2</u>. 2 : 4 : 3   <u>3</u>. $\frac{2y}{3x}$

<u>4</u>. Let 4x, 4x, and 7x rep. the meas.; 4x $+$ 4x $+$ 7x $=$ 180; 15x $=$ 180; x $=$ 12;

48, 48, and 84.

<u>5</u>. no   <u>6</u>. yes   <u>7</u>. yes   <u>8</u>. yes   <u>9</u>. $\angle$ J   <u>10</u>. SP

<u>11</u>. $\frac{20}{ET} = \frac{5}{3}$; 5 $\cdot$ ET $=$ 60; ET $=$ 12

<u>12</u>. scale factor $= \frac{8}{12} = \frac{2}{3}$; $\frac{6}{x} = \frac{2}{3}$; 2x $=$ 18; x $=$ 9; $\frac{9}{y} = \frac{2}{3}$; 2y $=$ 27; y $=$ $13\frac{1}{2}$

<u>13</u>. <u>a</u>. $\triangle$ UVH   <u>b</u>. AA Similarity Postulate   <u>14</u>. UV; VH; UH

<u>15</u>. $\frac{RS}{UH} = \frac{RT}{UV}$ <u>16</u>. $\triangle$ NCD $\sim$ $\triangle$ NBA   <u>17</u>. $\triangle$ NCD $\sim$ $\triangle$ NAB

18. $\triangle NCD \sim \triangle NAB$ 19. no   20. no

21. 2   22. $\frac{8}{20} = \frac{10}{OW}$; $8 \cdot OW = 200$; $OW = 25$

23. $\frac{VW}{24} = \frac{12}{20} = \frac{3}{5}$; $5 \cdot VW = 72$; $VW = 14\frac{2}{5}$

24. $\frac{AK}{28 - AK} = \frac{18}{24} = \frac{3}{4}$; $4 \cdot AK = 84 - 3 \cdot AK$; $7 \cdot AK = 84$; $AK = 12$

Page 243 · CHAPTER TEST

1. a. $\frac{20}{32} = \frac{5}{8}$ b. $\frac{2 \cdot 20 + 2 \cdot 32}{32} = \frac{104}{32} = \frac{13}{4}$ 2. a. $\angle C$ b. TS

3. $5 \cdot 4 = 20$; $5 \cdot 6 = 30$ 4. $9x = 120$; $x = 13\frac{1}{3}$

5. b; c + 10   6. AA Similarity Postulate

7. VN   8. $\frac{2 \cdot 5}{VN} = \frac{5}{8}$; $5 \cdot VN = 20$; $VN = 4$

9. $\frac{15}{TU} = \frac{10}{6} = \frac{5}{3}$; $5 \cdot TU = 45$; $TU = 9$ 10. $\frac{PR}{10} = \frac{32}{16} = \frac{2}{1}$; $PR = 20$

11. $\frac{26}{SU} = \frac{14}{21} = \frac{2}{3}$; $2 \cdot SU = 78$; $SU = 39$ 12. $\frac{EB}{7} = \frac{8}{5}$; $5 \cdot EB = 56$; $EB = 11\frac{1}{5}$

13. $\frac{GK}{30 - GK} = \frac{14}{21} = \frac{2}{3}$; $3 \cdot GK = 60 - 2 \cdot GK$; $5 \cdot GK = 60$; $GK = 12$

14. $\triangle ABC \sim \triangle XOT$

15. 1. $\overleftrightarrow{DE} \parallel \overleftrightarrow{FG} \parallel \overleftrightarrow{HJ}$ (Given)   2. $\frac{DF}{FH} = \frac{EG}{GJ}$ (If 3 $\parallel$ lines int. 2 trans., then they divide them proportionally.)   3. $DF \cdot GJ = FH \cdot EG$ (Means-extremes Prop.)

16. 1. $BX = 6$; $AX = 8$; $CX = 9$; $DX = 12$ (Given)   2. $\frac{BX}{CX} = \frac{6}{9} = \frac{2}{3} = \frac{8}{12} = \frac{AX}{DX}$ (By algebra)   3. $\angle BXA \cong \angle CXD$ (Vert. $\angle$ are $\cong$.)   4. $\triangle BXA \sim \triangle CXD$ (SAS) 5. $\angle ABX \cong \angle DCX$ (Corr. $\angle$ of $\sim \triangle$ are $\cong$.)   6. $\overline{AB} \parallel \overline{CD}$ (If 2 lines are cut by a trans. and alt. int. $\angle$ are $\cong$, then the lines are $\parallel$.)

Page 244 · MIXED REVIEW

1. $5x + 3 = 10x - 32$; $5x = 35$; $x = 7$; $XY = XZ = 10(7) - 32 = 38$; $YZ = 4(7) + 2 = 30$

2. a. SAS Similarity Thm.   b. $\frac{x}{45} = \frac{65}{39} = \frac{5}{3}$; $3x = 225$; $x = 75$; perimeter = $40 + 65 + 75 = 180$

3. Coord. of midpt. = $\frac{-13 + 4}{2} = \frac{-9}{2} = -4\frac{1}{2}$

4. a. isos.   b. $3x + 3x + 4x = 180$; $10x = 180$; $x = 18$; $3x = 54$; $4x = 72$; acute c. $\overline{AB}$

5. Two planes either intersect in a line or are ∥.   6. conclusion

7. corresponding; alternate interior; same-side interior

8. 1. RSTWYZ is a reg. hexagon (Given)   2. m∠R =

m∠S = m∠T = m∠W = m∠Y = m∠Z = 120 (The

meas. of each ∠ of a reg. n-gon is $\frac{(n - 2)180}{n}$.)

3. m∠ZRY = m∠ZYR; m∠TSW = m∠TWS (Def. of

a reg. polygon; if 2 sides of a △ are ≅, then the ∠ opp. those sides are ≅.)

4. 2m∠ZRY + 120 = 180; 2m∠TSW + 120 = 180 (The sum of the meas. of the ∠

of a △ = 180; Subst. Prop.)   5. m∠ZRY = m∠ZYR = 30; m∠TSW = m∠TWS =

30 (By algebra and Subst. Prop.)   6. m∠ZRY + m∠YRS = m∠R or m∠YRS =

m∠R - m∠ZRY; m∠RSW = m∠S - m∠TSW; m∠SWY = m∠W - m∠TWS;

m∠RYW = m∠Y - m∠ZYR (Angle Add. Post.)   7. m∠YRS = m∠RSW =

m∠SWY = m∠RYW = 90 (Subst. Prop.)   8. RSWY is a rect. (Def. of rect.)

9. $\frac{x - 5}{x - 2} = \frac{x}{x + 4}$; $x^2 - x - 20 = x^2 - 2x$; x = 20

10. Assume temporarily that x, y, and x + y are the lengths of the sides of a △. By the

△ Ineq. Thm., x + y > x + y, which is false. Our temp. assumption must be

incorrect. It follows that x, y, and x + y cannot be the lengths of the sides of a △.

11. (8 - 2)180 = 6 · 180 = 1080

12. 1. ∠WXY ≅ ∠XZY (Given)   2. ∠Y ≅ ∠Y (Refl. Prop.)   3. △WXY ∼ △XZY (AA)

4. $\frac{XY}{ZY} = \frac{WY}{XY}$ (Corr. sides of ∼ ∠ are in prop.)   5. $(XY)^2$ = WY · ZY (Means-

extremes Prop.)

13. a. no   b. yes   c. no

Page 245 · ALGEBRA REVIEW

1. $\sqrt{81}$ = 9   2. $\sqrt{0}$ = 0   3. $\sqrt{24} = \sqrt{4 \cdot 6} = 2\sqrt{6}$

4. $\sqrt{13^2}$ = 13   5. $(\sqrt{7})^2$ = 7

6. $\sqrt{600} = \sqrt{100 \cdot 6} = 10\sqrt{6}$ 7. $\sqrt{245} = \sqrt{49 \cdot 5} = 7\sqrt{5}$

8. $\frac{1}{\sqrt{5}} = \frac{\sqrt{5}}{\sqrt{5} \cdot \sqrt{5}} = \frac{\sqrt{5}}{5}$ 9. $\frac{12}{\sqrt{2}} = \frac{12\sqrt{2}}{\sqrt{2} \cdot \sqrt{2}} = \frac{12\sqrt{2}}{2} = 6\sqrt{2}$

10. $\sqrt{\frac{2}{3}} = \frac{\sqrt{2}}{\sqrt{3}} = \frac{\sqrt{2} \cdot \sqrt{3}}{\sqrt{3} \cdot \sqrt{3}} = \frac{\sqrt{6}}{3}$ 11. $\sqrt{4} \cdot \sqrt{7} = 2\sqrt{7}$

12. $\sqrt{8} \cdot \sqrt{15} = \sqrt{4 \cdot 2 \cdot 15} = 2\sqrt{30}$ 13. $\frac{\sqrt{45}}{\sqrt{5}} = \frac{\sqrt{45} \cdot \sqrt{5}}{\sqrt{5} \cdot \sqrt{5}} = \frac{\sqrt{9 \cdot 5 \cdot 5}}{5} = \frac{15}{5} = 3$

14. $\dfrac{\sqrt{12}}{\sqrt{24}} = \dfrac{\sqrt{12} \cdot \sqrt{24}}{\sqrt{24} \cdot \sqrt{24}} = \dfrac{\sqrt{12 \cdot 12 \cdot 2}}{24} = \dfrac{12\sqrt{2}}{24} = \dfrac{\sqrt{2}}{2}$ $\qquad$ 15. $\dfrac{\sqrt{5}}{\sqrt{3}} = \dfrac{\sqrt{5} \cdot \sqrt{3}}{\sqrt{3} \cdot \sqrt{3}} = \dfrac{\sqrt{15}}{3}$

16. $\dfrac{\sqrt{21}}{\sqrt{18}} = \dfrac{\sqrt{7 \cdot 3} \cdot \sqrt{3 \cdot 6}}{\sqrt{18} \cdot \sqrt{18}} = \dfrac{\sqrt{7 \cdot 3 \cdot 3 \cdot 6}}{18} = \dfrac{3\sqrt{42}}{18} = \dfrac{\sqrt{42}}{6}$

17. $\dfrac{12}{\sqrt{15}} = \dfrac{12\sqrt{15}}{\sqrt{15} \cdot \sqrt{15}} = \dfrac{12\sqrt{15}}{15} = \dfrac{4\sqrt{15}}{5}$ $\qquad$ 18. $\sqrt{\dfrac{80}{25}} = \dfrac{\sqrt{80}}{\sqrt{25}} = \dfrac{\sqrt{16 \cdot 5}}{5} = \dfrac{4\sqrt{5}}{5}$

19. $\sqrt{\dfrac{25}{80}} = \dfrac{\sqrt{25}}{\sqrt{80}} = \dfrac{\sqrt{25} \cdot \sqrt{80}}{\sqrt{80} \cdot \sqrt{80}} = \dfrac{5\sqrt{16 \cdot 5}}{80} = \dfrac{20\sqrt{5}}{80} = \dfrac{\sqrt{5}}{4}$

20. $3\sqrt{27} = 3\sqrt{9 \cdot 3} = 9\sqrt{3}$ $\qquad$ 21. $\dfrac{1}{2}\sqrt{121} = \dfrac{1}{2} \cdot 11 = \dfrac{11}{2}$

22. $\dfrac{4\sqrt{125}}{5} = \dfrac{4\sqrt{25 \cdot 5}}{5} = \dfrac{4 \cdot 5\sqrt{5}}{5} = 4\sqrt{5}$ $\qquad$ 23. $\dfrac{12}{5\sqrt{6}} = \dfrac{12\sqrt{6}}{5\sqrt{6}\,\sqrt{6}} = \dfrac{12\sqrt{6}}{30} = \dfrac{2\sqrt{6}}{5}$

24. $\dfrac{15\sqrt{2}}{\sqrt{5}} = \dfrac{15\sqrt{2} \cdot \sqrt{5}}{\sqrt{5} \cdot \sqrt{5}} = \dfrac{15\sqrt{10}}{5} = 3\sqrt{10}$ $\qquad$ 25. $(9\sqrt{2})^2 = 9^2 \cdot 2 = 81 \cdot 2 = 162$

26. $\left(\dfrac{\sqrt{10}}{2}\right)^2 = \dfrac{10}{2^2} = \dfrac{10}{4} = \dfrac{5}{2}$ $\qquad$ 27. $5(2\sqrt{3})^2 = 5 \cdot 2^2 \cdot 3 = 60$

28. $\dfrac{3}{4}(3\sqrt{8})^2 = \dfrac{3}{4} \cdot 3^2 \cdot 8 = \dfrac{3}{4} \cdot 9 \cdot 8 = 54$ $\qquad$ 29. $x^2 = 16; \quad x = 4$

30. $x^2 = 27; \quad x = \sqrt{27} = \sqrt{9 \cdot 3} = 3\sqrt{3}$ $\qquad$ 31. $x^2 = 35; \quad x = \sqrt{35}$

32. $x^2 = 4900; \quad x = 70$ $\qquad$ 33. $x^2 = 128; \quad x = \sqrt{128} = \sqrt{64 \cdot 2} = 8\sqrt{2}$

34. $x^2 = 180; \quad x = \sqrt{180} = \sqrt{36 \cdot 5} = 6\sqrt{5}$ $\qquad$ 35. $x^2 = 9 + 16 = 25; \quad x = 5$

36. $x^2 + 9 = 16; \quad x^2 = 7; \quad x = \sqrt{7}$

37. $25 + x^2 = 81; \quad x^2 = 56; \quad x = \sqrt{56} = \sqrt{4 \cdot 14} = 2\sqrt{14}$

38. $4^2 \cdot 2 + x^2 = 4^2 \cdot 3; \quad 16 \cdot 2 + x^2 = 16 \cdot 3; \quad x^2 + 32 = 48; \quad x^2 = 16; \quad x = 4$

39. $3x^2 + 6x = x^2 + 6x + 8; \quad 2x^2 = 8; \quad x^2 = 4; \quad x = 2$

40. $4x^2 + 225 = 9x^2; \quad 5x^2 = 225; \quad x^2 = 45; \quad x = \sqrt{45} = \sqrt{9 \cdot 5} = 3\sqrt{5}$

CHAPTER 6 · Right Triangles

Pages 250-251 · WRITTEN EXERCISES

A 1. $\sqrt{49} = 7$

2. $3\sqrt{64} = 3 \cdot 8 = 24$

3. $\frac{2}{5}\sqrt{9} = \frac{2}{5} \cdot 3 = \frac{6}{5}$

4. $\frac{2}{5}\sqrt{25} = \frac{2}{5} \cdot 5 = 2$

5. $\sqrt{12} = \sqrt{4 \cdot 3} = 2\sqrt{3}$

6. $\sqrt{50} = \sqrt{25 \cdot 2} = 5\sqrt{2}$

7. $5\sqrt{28} = 5\sqrt{4 \cdot 7} = 10\sqrt{7}$

8. $\frac{1}{2}\sqrt{300} = \frac{1}{2}\sqrt{100 \cdot 3} = \frac{10}{2}\sqrt{3} = 5\sqrt{3}$

9. $\sqrt{\frac{1}{2}} = \sqrt{\frac{1}{2} \cdot \frac{2}{2}} = \sqrt{\frac{2}{4}} = \frac{\sqrt{2}}{2}$

10. $\frac{1}{\sqrt{2}} = \frac{1}{\sqrt{2}} \cdot \frac{\sqrt{2}}{\sqrt{2}} = \frac{\sqrt{2}}{2}$

11. $\sqrt{\frac{2}{27}} = \sqrt{\frac{2}{27} \cdot \frac{3}{3}} = \sqrt{\frac{6}{81}} = \frac{\sqrt{6}}{9}$

12. $6\sqrt{\frac{1}{3}} = 6\sqrt{\frac{1}{3} \cdot \frac{3}{3}} = 6\sqrt{\frac{3}{9}} = 2\sqrt{3}$

13. $\frac{18}{\sqrt{3}} = \frac{18}{\sqrt{3}} \cdot \frac{\sqrt{3}}{\sqrt{3}} = \frac{18\sqrt{3}}{3} = 6\sqrt{3}$

14. $\frac{15}{\sqrt{30}} = \frac{15}{\sqrt{30}} \cdot \frac{\sqrt{30}}{\sqrt{30}} = \frac{15\sqrt{30}}{30} = \frac{\sqrt{30}}{2}$

15. $\frac{3\sqrt{32}}{4} = \frac{3\sqrt{16 \cdot 2}}{4} = \frac{3 \cdot 4\sqrt{2}}{4} = 3\sqrt{2}$

16. $\frac{5}{2\sqrt{10}} = \frac{5}{2\sqrt{10}} \cdot \frac{\sqrt{10}}{\sqrt{10}} = \frac{5\sqrt{10}}{20} = \frac{\sqrt{10}}{4}$

17. $\frac{2}{x} = \frac{x}{8}$; $x^2 = 16$; $x = 4$

18. $\frac{3}{x} = \frac{x}{27}$; $x^2 = 81$; $x = 9$

19. $\frac{13}{x} = \frac{x}{25}$; $x^2 = 25 \cdot 13$; $x = \sqrt{25 \cdot 13} = 5\sqrt{13}$

20. $\frac{1}{x} = \frac{x}{50}$; $x^2 = 50$; $x = \sqrt{50} = \sqrt{25 \cdot 2} = 5\sqrt{2}$

21. $\frac{6}{x} = \frac{x}{10}$; $x^2 = 60$; $x = \sqrt{60} = \sqrt{4 \cdot 15} = 2\sqrt{15}$

22. $\frac{\frac{1}{10}}{x} = \frac{x}{2}$; $x^2 = \frac{2}{10} = \frac{1}{5}$; $x = \sqrt{\frac{1}{5}} = \sqrt{\frac{1}{5} \cdot \frac{5}{5}} = \frac{\sqrt{5}}{5}$

B 23. $\frac{4}{x} = \frac{x}{25}$; $x^2 = 100$; $x = 10$; $\frac{29}{y} = \frac{y}{4}$; $y^2 = 29 \cdot 4$; $y = \sqrt{29 \cdot 4} = 2\sqrt{29}$; $\frac{29}{z} = \frac{z}{25}$; $z^2 = 25 \cdot 29$; $z = \sqrt{25 \cdot 29} = 5\sqrt{29}$

24. $\frac{9}{x} = \frac{x}{7}$; $x^2 = 9 \cdot 7$; $x = \sqrt{9 \cdot 7} = 3\sqrt{7}$; $\frac{16}{y} = \frac{y}{9}$; $y^2 = 144$; $y = 12$; $\frac{16}{z} = \frac{z}{7}$; $z^2 = 16 \cdot 7$; $z = \sqrt{16 \cdot 7} = 4\sqrt{7}$

25. $\frac{\frac{1}{6}}{x} = \frac{x}{\frac{1}{3}}$; $x^2 = \frac{1}{18}$; $x = \sqrt{\frac{1}{18}} = \sqrt{\frac{2}{36}} = \frac{\sqrt{2}}{6}$; $\frac{\frac{1}{2}}{y} = \frac{y}{\frac{1}{6}}$; $y^2 = \frac{1}{12}$; $y = \sqrt{\frac{1}{12}} = \sqrt{\frac{3}{36}} = \frac{\sqrt{3}}{6}$; $\frac{\frac{1}{2}}{z} = \frac{z}{\frac{1}{3}}$; $z^2 = \frac{1}{6}$; $z = \sqrt{\frac{1}{6}} = \sqrt{\frac{6}{36}} = \frac{\sqrt{6}}{6}$

26. $\frac{8}{x} = \frac{x}{8}$; $x^2 = 64$; $x = 8$ (x can also be determined immediately using the midpt. of the

94

hyp. of a rt. $\triangle$.); $\dfrac{16}{y} = \dfrac{y}{8}$; $y^2 = 128$; $y = \sqrt{128} = \sqrt{64 \cdot 2} = 8\sqrt{2}$; $z = y = 8\sqrt{2}$

27. $\dfrac{15}{9} = \dfrac{9}{15 - y}$; $225 - 15y = 81$; $15y = 144$; $y = 9.6$; $\dfrac{y}{x} = \dfrac{x}{15}$; $x^2 = 15 \cdot y = 15(9.6) =$

144; $x = 12$; $\dfrac{y}{z} = \dfrac{z}{15 - y}$; $z^2 = y(15 - y) = 9.6(5.4) = 51.84$; $z = \sqrt{51.84} = 7.2$

28. $\dfrac{2}{6} = \dfrac{6}{x}$; $2x = 36$; $x = 18$; $\dfrac{18}{y} = \dfrac{y}{16}$; $y^2 = 18 \cdot 16$; $y = \sqrt{18 \cdot 16} = 12\sqrt{2}$; $\dfrac{16}{z} = \dfrac{z}{2}$;

$z^2 = 16 \cdot 2$; $z = \sqrt{16 \cdot 2} = 4\sqrt{2}$

29. $\dfrac{4 + y}{8} = \dfrac{8}{4}$; $16 + 4y = 64$; $4y = 48$; $y = 12$; $x = 4 + 12 = 16$; $\dfrac{16}{z} = \dfrac{z}{12}$;

$z^2 = \sqrt{192}$; $z = 8\sqrt{3}$

30. $\dfrac{25}{10} = \dfrac{10}{x}$; $25x = 100$; $x = 4$; $\dfrac{25}{y} = \dfrac{y}{21}$; $y^2 = 25 \cdot 21$; $y = \sqrt{25 \cdot 21} = 5\sqrt{21}$; $\dfrac{4}{z} = \dfrac{z}{21}$;

$z^2 = 4 \cdot 21$; $z = \sqrt{4 \cdot 21} = 2\sqrt{21}$

31. $\dfrac{x + \sqrt{2}}{2} = \dfrac{2}{\sqrt{2}}$; $x\sqrt{2} + 2 = 4$; $x\sqrt{2} = 2$; $x = \dfrac{2}{\sqrt{2}} = \dfrac{2\sqrt{2}}{2} = \sqrt{2}$; $\dfrac{2\sqrt{2}}{y} = \dfrac{y}{\sqrt{2}}$;

$y^2 = 4$; $y = 2$; $\dfrac{\sqrt{2}}{z} = \dfrac{z}{\sqrt{2}}$; $z^2 = 2$; $z = \sqrt{2}$ (z may be found more simply because

the midpt. of the hyp. of a rt. $\triangle$ is equidistant from the vert.)

32. 1. $\angle$ SUT is a rt. $\angle$ (Given)   2. $\angle 2$ and $\angle 1$ are comp. $\angle$ (Def. of rt. $\angle$; if the ext.

sides of 2 acute adj. $\angle$ are $\perp$, then the $\angle$ are comp.)   3. $\triangle$ SUT is rt. $\triangle$ (Def. of

rt. $\triangle$)   4. $\angle$ S and $\angle 1$ are comp. $\angle$ (The acute $\angle$ of a rt. $\triangle$ are comp.)

5. $\angle$ S $\cong \angle 2$ (If 2 $\angle$ are comp. of the same $\angle$, then the 2 $\angle$ are $\cong$.)   6. $\angle$ S $\cong \angle$ S

(Refl. Prop.)   7. $\overline{UN} \perp \overline{ST}$ (Given)   8. m$\angle$ SNU = m$\angle$ UNT = 90 (Def. of $\perp$

lines)   9. m$\angle$ SUT = 90 (Def. of rt. $\angle$)   10. m$\angle$ SNU = m$\angle$ SUT = m$\angle$ UNT

(Trans. Prop.)   11. $\triangle$ SNU $\sim \triangle$ SUT $\sim \triangle$ UNT (AA)

C 33. Given: $\triangle$ ABC with rt. $\angle$ C; $\overline{CD}$ an alt.

Prove: AB $\cdot$ CD = AC $\cdot$ BC.   Proof: 1. $\overline{CD}$ is the

alt. to the hyp. of $\triangle$ ABC. (Given)   2. $\triangle$ ABC $\sim \triangle$ ACD

(If the alt. is drawn to the hyp. of a rt. $\triangle$, the 2 $\angle$

formed are $\sim$ to the orig. $\triangle$ and to each other.)   3. $\dfrac{AB}{AC} = \dfrac{BC}{CD}$ (Corr. sides of $\sim \triangle$

are in prop.)   4. AB $\cdot$ CD = AC $\cdot$ BC (Means-extremes Prop.)

34. a. The midpt. of the hyp. of a rt. $\triangle$ is equidistant from the three vertices; CM = AM

$= \dfrac{AB}{2} = \dfrac{AH + BH}{2}$; CM is the arith. mean between AH and BH.   CH is the geom.

mean between AH and BH. (When the alt. is drawn to the hyp. of a rt. $\triangle$, the length of the alt. is the geom. mean between the segments of the hyp.)   Since the $\perp$ seg. from

a pt. to a line is the shortest seg. from the pt. to the line, CM > CH; the arith.

mean > geom. mean.

<u>b.</u> $(r - s)^2 > 0$; $r^2 - 2rs + s^2 > 0$; $r^2 + 2rs + s^2 > 4rs$; $\dfrac{r^2 + 2rs + s^2}{4} > rs$;

$\dfrac{(r + s)^2}{4} > rs$; $\dfrac{r + s}{2} > \sqrt{rs}$

<u>35.</u> <u>a.</u> 1 and 36; 2 and 18; 3 and 12; 4 and 9; 6 and 6

<u>b.</u> 1 and p^2q^2; p and pq^2; q and p^2q; p^2 and q^2; pq and pq

<u>c.</u> 14; 1 and $p^2q^2r^2$; p and pq^2r^2; p^2 and q^2r^2; q and p^2qr^2; q^2 and p^2r^2;

r and p^2q^2r; r^2 and p^2q^2; pr and pq^2r; qr and p^2qr; p^2q and qr^2; p^2r and q^2r;

pq^2 and pr^2; pqr and pqr; pq and pqr^2 <u>d.</u> 122

Page 251 · CHALLENGE

Answers may vary.   Example:

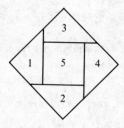

Pages 254-255 · WRITTEN EXERCISES

<u>A</u>

	<u>1.</u>	<u>2.</u>	<u>3.</u>	<u>4.</u>	<u>5.</u>	<u>6.</u>	<u>7.</u>	<u>8.</u>
a	3	6	5	8	11	3n	$3\sqrt{2}$	6
b	4	8	12	15	60	4n	$3\sqrt{2}$	$6\sqrt{3}$
c	5	10	13	17	61	5n	6	12

<u>9-12.</u> Check students' drawings.

<u>9.</u> $d^2 = 6^2 + 8^2 = 100$; d = 10   <u>10.</u> $d^2 = (0.8)^2 + (0.6)^2 = 1$; d = 1

<u>11.</u> $d^2 = 80^2 + 60^2 = 10{,}000$; d = 100   <u>12.</u> $d^2 = (\sqrt{3})^2 + 1^2 = 4$; d = 2

<u>13-16.</u> $s^2 = d^2 - s^2$; $2s^2 = d^2$; $s^2 = \dfrac{d^2}{2}$; $s = \sqrt{\dfrac{d^2}{2}} = \dfrac{d\sqrt{2}}{2}$

<u>13.</u> $s = \dfrac{d\sqrt{2}}{2} = \dfrac{2\sqrt{2}}{2} = \sqrt{2}$ <u>14.</u> $s = \dfrac{d\sqrt{2}}{2} = \dfrac{10\sqrt{2}}{2} = 5\sqrt{2}$

<u>15.</u> $s = \dfrac{d\sqrt{2}}{2} = \dfrac{20k\sqrt{2}}{2} = 10k\sqrt{2}$ <u>16.</u> $s = \dfrac{d\sqrt{2}}{2} = \dfrac{7n\sqrt{2}\,\sqrt{2}}{2} = 7n$

B 17. $x^2 = 5^2 - 4^2 = 9$; $x = 3$ 18. $x^2 = 12^2 + 5^2 = 169$; $x = 13$

19. $x^2 = 13^2 - 5^2 = 144$; $x = 12$ 20. $x^2 = 3^2 + 4^2 = 25$; $x = 5$

21. $x^2 = 2^2 + (2\sqrt{3})^2 = 16$; $x = 4$ 22. $x^2 = 3^2 - (\sqrt{5})^2 = 4$; $x = 2$

23. $x^2 = 25^2 - (9^2 + 12^2) = 400$; $x = 20$

24. $x^2 = (17^2 - 8^2) + (10^2 - 8^2) = 261$; $x = \sqrt{261} = 3\sqrt{29}$

25. $a^2 = 12^2 + 4^2 = 160$; $d^2 = 160 + 3^2 = 169$; $d = 13$

26. $a^2 = 5^2 + 5^2 = 50$; $d^2 = 50 + 2^2 = 54$; $d = \sqrt{54} = 3\sqrt{6}$

27. $a^2 = (\sqrt{7})^2 + (\sqrt{6})^2 = 13$; $d^2 = 13 + (\sqrt{5})^2 = 18$; $d = \sqrt{18} = 3\sqrt{2}$

28. $a^2 = e^2 + e^2 = 2e^2$; $d^2 = 2e^2 + e^2 = 3e^2$; $d = \sqrt{3e^2} = e\sqrt{3}$

29. $a^2 = \ell^2 + w^2$; $d^2 = \ell^2 + w^2 + h^2$; $d = \sqrt{\ell^2 + w^2 + h^2}$

30. $a^2 = (n + 2)^2 + (\sqrt{2n + 1})^2 = n^2 + 4n + 4 + 2n + 1 = n^2 + 6n + 5$;

$d^2 = n^2 + 6n + 5 + 2^2 = n^2 + 6n + 9 = (n + 3)^2$; $d = n + 3$

31. The square of the side opp. an acute $\angle$ in
any $\triangle$ is less than the sum of the squares
of the other 2 sides.   Given: $\triangle ABC$;
$\angle C$ acute; $CB = a$, $AC = b$, and $AB = c$

 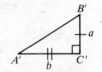

Prove: $c^2 < a^2 + b^2$ Proof: 1. Draw rt. $\triangle A'B'C'$ with $C'B' = a$, $A'C' = b$, and
$\angle C'$ a rt. $\angle$. (Ruler Post.; Protractor Post.; through any 2 pts. there is exactly one
line.)   2. $(A'B')^2 = a^2 + b^2$ (Pyth. Thm.)   3. $\angle C$ is acute (Given)
4. $m\angle C < m\angle C'$ (Def. of acute and rt. $\angle$)   5. $c < A'B'$; $c^2 < (A'B')^2$ (SAS
Ineq. Thm.; algebra)   6. $c^2 < a^2 + b^2$ (Subst. Prop.)

C 32. 1. a, b, and c are the sides of a rt. $\triangle$ (hyp. = c) (Given)   2. $a^2 + b^2 = c^2$ (Pyth.
Thm.)   3. b is the arith. mean of a and c. (Given)   4. $b = \dfrac{a + c}{2}$ (Def. of arith.
mean)   5. $a = 2b - c$ (By algebra)   6. $b^2 + (2b - c)^2 = c^2$; $b^2 + 4b^2 - 4bc +$
$c^2 = c^2$; $5b^2 = 4bc$; $5b = 4c$; $\dfrac{b}{c} = \dfrac{4}{5}$ or $b : c = 4 : 5$ (Subst. Prop.; by algebra)
7. $\dfrac{4}{5}c = \dfrac{a + c}{2}$ (Subst. Prop.)   8. $8c = 5a + 5c$; $3c = 5a$; $\dfrac{a}{c} = \dfrac{3}{5}$ or $a : c = 3 : 5$
(By algebra)   9. $a : b = (\dfrac{3}{5}c) : (\dfrac{4}{5}c) = 3 : 4$ (Subst. Prop.; by algebra)
10. $a : b : c = 3 : 4 : 5$ (Def. of extended proportion)

33. Let $PQ = x$; $QR = 21 - x$; $h = \sqrt{20^2 - x^2} = \sqrt{13^2 - (21 - x)^2}$; $20^2 - x^2 =$
$13^2 - (21 - x)^2$; $400 - x^2 = 169 - 441 + 42x - x^2$; $42x = 672$; $x = 16$;
$h = \sqrt{400 - 16^2} = \sqrt{144} = 12$

<u>34.</u> Let TU = x; SU = x + 11; h = $\sqrt{25^2 - x^2}$ = $\sqrt{30^2 - (x+11)^2}$; 625 - x^2 =

900 - x^2 - 22x - 121; 22x = 154; x = 7; h = $\sqrt{25^2 - 7^2}$ = $\sqrt{576}$ = 24

<u>35.</u> $\overline{OE}$ is the alt. to the hyp. of a rt. $\triangle$; length of hyp. = $\sqrt{20^2 + 15^2}$ = $\sqrt{625}$ = 25;

$\frac{25}{20} = \frac{20}{VE}$; 25 · VE = 400; VE = 16; OE = $\sqrt{20^2 - 16^2}$ = $\sqrt{144}$ = 12

<u>36.</u> 1. $\overline{FG}$ is a median. (Given)   2. G is the midpt. of $\overline{DE}$. (Def. of median)

3. DG = GE = $\frac{1}{2}$ · DE (Midpt. Thm.)   4. Draw $\overline{FH} \perp \overline{DE}$ and let GH = x and

FH = y. (Through a pt. outside a line there is exactly one line $\perp$ to the given line.)

5. $\triangle$ FHE and $\triangle$ FHD are rt. $\triangle$. (Def. of $\perp$ lines, rt. $\triangle$)   6. $y^2 = s^2 - (\frac{1}{2}t - x)^2$;

$y^2 = r^2 - (\frac{1}{2}t + x)^2$; $s^2 - (\frac{1}{2}t - x)^2 = r^2 - (\frac{1}{2}t + x)^2$ (Pyth. Thm.; Subst. Prop.)

7. $s^2 - r^2 = (\frac{t}{2} - x)^2 - (\frac{t}{2} + x)^2 = \frac{1}{4}t^2 - tx + x^2 - \frac{1}{4}t^2 - tx - x^2 = -2tx$;

$x = \frac{r^2 - s^2}{2t}$; $x^2 = \frac{r^4 - 2r^2s^2 + s^4}{4t^2}$; $y^2 = s^2 - (\frac{t}{2} - x)^2 = s^2 - (\frac{t^2 - r^2 + s^2}{2t})^2 =$

$\frac{4s^2t^2 + 2r^2t^2 - 2s^2t^2 + 2r^2s^2 - t^4 - r^4 - s^4}{4t^2}$; $y^2 + x^2 = \frac{2r^2t^2 + 2s^2t^2 - t^4}{4t^2} =$

$\frac{2r^2 + 2s^2 - t^2}{4}$ (By algebra)   8. $\triangle$ FGH is a rt. $\triangle$ (Def. of $\perp$ lines, rt. $\triangle$)

9. $m^2 = y^2 + x^2$ (Pyth. Thm.)   9. $m^2 = \frac{2r^2 + 2s^2 - t^2}{4}$ (Subst. Prop.)

10. m = $\frac{1}{2}\sqrt{2r^2 + 2s^2 - t^2}$ (By algebra)

Pages 259-260 · WRITTEN EXERCISES

<u>A</u>   <u>1.</u> $11^2 + 11^2 = 242 > 225 = 15^2$; acute   <u>2.</u> $9^2 + 9^2 = 162 < 169 = 13^2$; obtuse

<u>3.</u> $8^2 + (8\sqrt{3})^2 = 256 = 16^2$; right

<u>4.</u> $(0.03)^2 + (0.04)^2 = 0.0025 = (0.05)^2$; right

<u>5.</u> $300^2 + 400^2 = 250,000 < 251,001 = 501^2$; obtuse

<u>6.</u> $(0.6)^2 + (0.8)^2 = 1 = 1^2$; right   <u>7.</u> $(5n)^2 + (12n)^2 = 169n^2 = (13n)^2$; right

<u>8.</u> $(n + 4)^2 + (n + 5)^2 = 2n^2 + 18n + 41$; $(n + 6)^2 = n^2 + 12n + 36$;

$(n + 4)^2 + (n + 5)^2 - (n + 6)^2 = n^2 + 6n + 5 \geq 12$. Then $(n + 4)^2 + (n + 5)^2 >$

$(n + 6)^2$ and the $\triangle$ is acute.

<u>9.</u> $(7 - n)^2 + 7^2 = 98 - 14n + n^2$; $(7 + n)^2 = 49 + 14n + n^2$; $(7 + n)^2 - ((7 - n)^2 + 7^2) =$

$-49 + 28n$; if $0 < n \leq 3$, $-49 < -49 + 28n \leq 35$; can't tell.

<u>10.</u> $(ST)^2 = 13^2 - 12^2 = 25$; $(ST)^2 = (RS)^2 + (RT)^2 = 25$. By the converse of the Pyth.

Thm., $\triangle$ TRS is a rt. $\triangle$.

<u>11</u>. $(BC)^2 = 10^2 - 8^2 = 36$; $(BD)^2 = 121 > (BC)^2 + (CD)^2$. If the square of the longest

side of a $\triangle$ is greater than the sum of the squares of the other 2 sides, the $\triangle$ is obtuse.

<u>B</u> <u>12</u>. ABCD is a rhombus. Let X be the int. of $\overline{AC}$

and $\overline{BD}$. Then since the diag. bisect each other,

AX = 12 and BX = 5. $5^2 + 12^2 = 13^2$, so $\angle AXB$

is a rt. $\angle$; $\overline{AC} \perp \overline{BD}$, so ABCD is a rhombus.

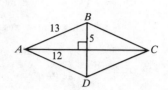

<u>13</u>. $\overline{RM}$; the diag. of a $\square$ bisect each other, so

RT = 22 and $(RT)^2 = 484 > (RS)^2 + (ST)^2$.

Then $\triangle$ RST is obtuse, and $\angle$ RST is obtuse; its

supp., $\angle$ SRU must be acute. By the SAS Ineq.

Thm. applied to $\triangle$ RST and $\triangle$ SRU, RT > SU, and RM > SM.

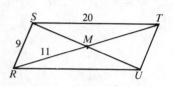

<u>14</u>. 1. $a = n^2 - 1$; $b = 2n$ (Given)   2. $a^2 + b^2 = (n^2 - 1)^2 + (2n)^2 =$

$n^4 - 2n^2 + 1 + 4n^2 = n^4 + 2n^2 + 1 = (n^2 + 1)^2$ (Subst. Prop.; by algebra)

3. $c = n^2 + 1$ (Given)   4. $a^2 + b^2 = c^2$ (Subst. Prop.)   5. The $\triangle$ is a rt. $\triangle$.

(If the square of one side of a $\triangle$ = the sum of the squares of the other 2 sides, then

the $\triangle$ is a rt. $\triangle$.)

<u>15</u>. $x^2 + (x + 4)^2 > 20^2$; $x^2 + x^2 + 8x + 16 > 400$; $2x^2 + 8x - 384 > 0$;

$x^2 + 4x - 192 > 0$; $(x + 16)(x - 12) > 0$. Either $[(x + 16) > 0$ and $(x - 12) > 0]$ or

$[(x + 16) < 0$ and $(x - 12) < 0]$. Then $x > 12$ or $x < -16$ (reject), and since 20 is

the longest side of the $\triangle$, $12 < x \leq 16$.

<u>16</u>. Obtuse; Proof: 1. $\triangle$ ADC and $\triangle$ BDC are rt. $\triangle$. (Given)   2. AD = $\sqrt{4^2 - 3^2} = \sqrt{7}$;

DB = $\sqrt{5^2 - 3^2} = \sqrt{16} = 4$ (Pyth. Thm.)   3. AB = AD + DB = $4 + \sqrt{7}$ (Seg. Add.

Post.; Subst. Prop.)   4. $(AB)^2 = (4 + \sqrt{7})^2 = 23 + 8\sqrt{7} \approx 44.2 > 41 =$

$(AC)^2 + (BC)^2$ (By algebra; Subst. Prop.)   5. $\triangle$ ABC is an obtuse $\triangle$. (If the square

of the longest side of a $\triangle$ is greater than the sum of the squares of the other 2 sides,

then the $\triangle$ is obtuse.)

<u>C</u> <u>17</u>. Draw rt. $\triangle$ UVW with UV = j, VW = k, and hyp. UW = n. By the Pyth. Thm.,

$n^2 = j^2 + k^2$. Then $\ell^2 > n^2$ and ℓ and n are both > 0, so $\ell > n$. Then by the SSS

Ineq. Thm., $m\angle S > m\angle V = 90$ and $\triangle$ RST is an obtuse $\triangle$.

__18.__ Given: $\triangle$ RST, RS = j, ST = k, and RT, the length of the longest side, = ℓ;

$\ell^2 < j^2 + k^2$.   Prove: $\triangle$ RST is acute.   Plan of proof: Draw rt. $\triangle$ UVW with

UV = j, VW = k, and hyp. UW = n.   By the Pyth. Thm. $n^2 = j^2 + k^2$.   Then

$\ell^2 < n^2$ and ℓ and n are both > 0, so $\ell < n$.   Then by the SSS Ineq. Thm.,

m$\angle$S $<$ m$\angle$V = 90 and $\angle$RST is an acute $\angle$. $\angle$RST is the largest $\angle$ of $\triangle$RST so

$\triangle$RST is an acute $\triangle$.

__19.__ 1. $\triangle$ABC is a rt. $\triangle$. (Given)   2. $\ell^2 = j^2 + k^2$ (Pyth. Thm.)   3. $\ell < j + k$ ($\triangle$

Ineq. Thm.)   4. $(\ell + 1)^2 = \ell^2 + 2\ell + 1 = j^2 + k^2 + 2\ell + 1 < j^2 + k^2 + 2\ell + 1 +$

$1 < j^2 + k^2 + 2(j + k) + 1 + 1 = j^2 + 2j + 1 + k^2 + 2k + 1 = (j + 1)^2 + (k + 1)^2$

(By algebra)   5. $\triangle$RST is an acute $\triangle$. (If the square of the longest side of a $\triangle$ is

less than the sum of the squares of the other 2 sides, then the $\triangle$ is an acute $\triangle$.)

__20.__ Since $5^2 + 12^2 = 13^2$, $\triangle$GBC and $\triangle$GFE are rt. $\triangle$.

Then $\triangle$CFE is a rt. $\triangle$ and CE = $\sqrt{18^2 + 12^2}$ =

$\sqrt{468}$ = $6\sqrt{13}$. $\triangle$ABG and $\triangle$AFG are also rt. $\triangle$

and $\triangle$ABG $\cong$ $\triangle$AFG (HL), so $\angle$CAD $\cong$ $\angle$EAD.

Then $\triangle$CAD $\cong$ $\triangle$EAD (SAS) and thus x =

$\frac{1}{2}$ · CE = $3\sqrt{13}$.   Also, $\triangle$AFC is a rt. $\triangle$ and

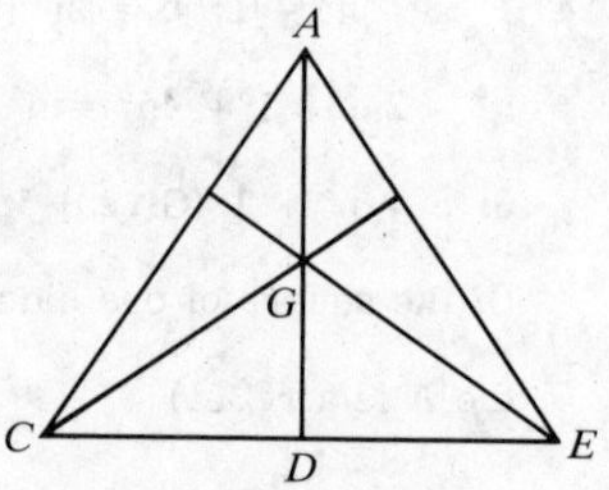

$(y + 12)^2 = y^2 + 18^2$; $y^2 + 24y + 144 = y^2 + 324$; $24y = 180$; y = 7.5; s = 9, j = 6;

$9 \geq 2 \cdot 6 - 3$ so the scissors truss is stable. (For the frame shown at the left, s = 12,

j = 7; 2j - 3 = 11, so s $\geq$ 2j - 3 and the frame is also stable.)

Page 261 · COMPUTER KEY-IN

__1.__ (3, 4, 5), (6, 8, 10), (5, 12, 13), (8, 15, 17), (12, 16, 20), (7, 24, 25), (10, 24, 26),

(20, 21, 29), (16, 30, 34), (9, 40, 41), (12, 35, 37), (24, 32, 40), (27, 36, 45),

(20, 48, 52), (11, 60, 61), (14, 48, 50), (28, 45, 53), (40, 42, 58), (33, 56, 65),

(24, 70, 74), (13, 84, 85)   Primitive: (3, 4, 5), (5, 12, 13), (8, 15, 17),

(7, 24, 25), (20, 21, 29), (9, 40, 41), (12, 35, 37), (11, 60, 61), (28, 45, 53),

(33, 56, 65), (13, 84, 85)

__2.__ $(2xy)^2 + (x^2 - y^2)^2 = 4x^2y^2 + x^4 - 2x^2y^2 + y^4 = x^4 + 2x^2y^2 + y^4 = (x^2 + y^2)^2$

__3.__ If Y = X then B = $X^2 - Y^2$ = 0

4. (101, 5100, 5101), (204, 5200, 5204), (103, 5304, 5305), (309, 5300, 5309),

(208, 5406, 5410), (105, 5512, 5513), (416, 5400, 5416), (315, 5508, 5517),

(212, 5616, 5620), (107, 5724, 5725), (525, 5500, 5525), (424, 5610, 5626),

(321, 5720, 5729), (216, 5830, 5834), (109, 5940, 5941)

5. $1 + 2 + \cdots + 9 = 45$ 6. $1 + 2 + \cdots + 99 = 4950$

Page 261 · CHALLENGE

Picture the room opened flat, as shown at the right.
(You may want to copy the model, draw $\overline{AB}$, and
fold the model up to convince yourself that the
model is correct and to see in three dimensions
the path taken by the spider.)   The fly is at B
and the spider is at A.   AC = 24 and BC =
$30 + 1 + 1 = 32$. $(AB)^2 = 24^2 + 32^2$,
so AB = 40.

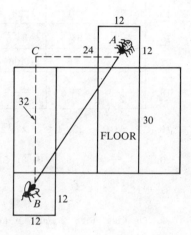

Pages 264-265 · WRITTEN EXERCISES

A   1. a. $a = 5\sqrt{3}$ b. $a = \sqrt{10^2 - 5^2} = \sqrt{75} = 5\sqrt{3}$

2. a. $s = \dfrac{13}{\sqrt{2}} = \dfrac{13\sqrt{2}}{2}$

b. $2s^2 = 13^2;\ s^2 = \dfrac{169}{2};\ s = \sqrt{\dfrac{169}{2}} = \sqrt{\dfrac{169 \cdot 2}{4}} = \dfrac{13\sqrt{2}}{2}$

	3.	4.	5.	6.	7.	8.
a	6	$\dfrac{4}{5}$	$\sqrt{5}$	8	$3\sqrt{2}$	$\sqrt{11}$
b	6	$\dfrac{4}{5}$	$\sqrt{5}$	8	$3\sqrt{2}$	$\sqrt{11}$
c	$6\sqrt{2}$	$\dfrac{4\sqrt{2}}{5}$	$\sqrt{10}$	$8\sqrt{2}$	6	$\sqrt{22}$

	9.	10.	11.	12.	13.	14.
d	7	$\frac{1}{5}$	5	$2\sqrt{3}$	6	$\frac{5}{2}$
e	$7\sqrt{3}$	$\frac{\sqrt{3}}{5}$	$5\sqrt{3}$	6	$6\sqrt{3}$	$\frac{5\sqrt{3}}{2}$
f	14	$\frac{2}{5}$	10	$4\sqrt{3}$	12	5

		TU	UV	TV	WT	WU	WV
B	15.	7	21	28	14	$7\sqrt{3}$	$14\sqrt{3}$
	16.	$2\sqrt{3}$	$6\sqrt{3}$	$8\sqrt{3}$	$4\sqrt{3}$	6	12
	17.	25	75	100	50	$25\sqrt{3}$	$50\sqrt{3}$
	18.	$\frac{7\sqrt{3}}{3}$	$7\sqrt{3}$	$\frac{28\sqrt{3}}{3}$	$\frac{14\sqrt{3}}{3}$	7	14

19. GF = GD = 22; DF = $22\sqrt{2}$; FE = $\frac{22\sqrt{2}}{2}$ = $11\sqrt{2}$; DE = $11\sqrt{2} \cdot \sqrt{3}$ = $11\sqrt{6}$

20. GI = $\frac{12}{2}$ = 6; JG = $6\sqrt{3}$; GH = GI = 6; HI = $6\sqrt{2}$; JH = $\sqrt{(6\sqrt{3})^2 + 6^2}$ = $\sqrt{144}$ = 12

21. MN = NL = $\frac{8}{\sqrt{2}}$ = $\frac{8\sqrt{2}}{2}$ = $4\sqrt{2}$; KL = $8\sqrt{2}$; KN = $4\sqrt{2} \cdot \sqrt{3}$ = $4\sqrt{6}$

22. The diag. form 2 acute △ and 2 obtuse △. The acute △ are equilateral with side 4. Then each half of the rect. is a rt. △ with hyp. 8 and leg 4; $\sqrt{8^2 - 4^2}$ = $\sqrt{48}$ = $4\sqrt{3}$; length = $4\sqrt{3}$, width = 4.

23. Each diag. of a rhombus bis. 2 △ of the rhombus. Draw both diag.; four 30-60-90 △ with hyp. 16 are formed. The △ have legs 8 and $8\sqrt{3}$ so lengths of diag. = 2 · 8 = 16 and 2 · $8\sqrt{3}$ = $16\sqrt{3}$.

24. 1. The △ has △ of meas. 45, 45, and 90 (Given)   2. The △ is a rt. △ (Def. of rt. △)   3. Let M be the length of one leg, and c the length of the hyp.; then the other leg has length n. (If 2 △ of a △ are ≅, then the sides opp. those △ are ≅.) 4. $c^2 = n^2 + n^2$ (Pyth. Thm.)   5. c = $n\sqrt{2}$ (By algebra)

25. Consider the 30-60-90 △ ABC with sides 1, $\sqrt{3}$, and 2 and any △ DEF having sides in the ratio $1:\sqrt{3}:2$. Then DE = 2x, EF = x, and DF = $x\sqrt{3}$. $\frac{DE}{AB}$ = $\frac{EF}{BC}$ = $\frac{DF}{AC}$, so △ DEF ~ △ ABC (SSS). But corr. △ of ~ △ are ≅, so △ DEF is a 30-60-90 △.

<u>C</u>   26. $\overline{QS}$ is the hyp. of a 45-45-90 $\triangle$ with legs 8 so $QS = 8\sqrt{2}$.

$\triangle QRS$ is an isos. $\triangle$ with vertex $\angle$ of meas. 60 so

$\triangle QRS$ is equilateral.   Let $\overline{RT}$ and $\overline{QS}$ int. at X.

Then $QX = 4\sqrt{2} \cdot \sqrt{3} = 4\sqrt{6}$.   Since X is equidistant

from Q, T, and S, $TX = 4\sqrt{2}$.   Then $RT =$

$4\sqrt{6} + 4\sqrt{2} > 8\sqrt{2} = QS$; the length of the longer diag. is $4\sqrt{6} + 4\sqrt{2}$.

27. Draw $\overline{BD} \perp \overline{AC}$. $m\angle DBC = 90 - 30 = 60$; $m\angle ABD =$

105 - 60 = 45; $\triangle ABD$ is a 45-45-90 $\triangle$; $AD = BD =$

$\dfrac{8}{\sqrt{2}} = 4\sqrt{2}$; $\triangle BDC$ is a 30-60-90 $\triangle$; $BC = 8\sqrt{2}$; $DC =$

$4\sqrt{2} \cdot \sqrt{3} = 4\sqrt{6}$; $AC = 4\sqrt{2} + 4\sqrt{6}$.   Perimeter of $\triangle ABC = 8 + 4\sqrt{2} + 4\sqrt{6} =$

$8 + 12\sqrt{2} + 4\sqrt{6}$.

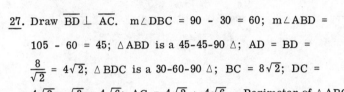

28. Draw $\overline{TX}$ and $\overline{YA}$ both $\perp$ to $\overline{PA}$. $\triangle TPX$ is a

30-60-90 $\triangle$ so $TX = \dfrac{j\sqrt{3}}{2}$ and $PX = \dfrac{j}{2}$.   Then

$TY = XA = \dfrac{j}{2}$. $\triangle AYR$ is a 45-45-90 $\triangle$ so

$YR = YA = TX = \dfrac{j\sqrt{3}}{2}$ and $TR = \dfrac{j}{2} + \dfrac{j\sqrt{3}}{2} =$

$\dfrac{j + j\sqrt{3}}{2}$.   The length of the median of the trap. is $\dfrac{1}{2}(TR + PA) = \dfrac{1}{2}(\dfrac{j + j\sqrt{3}}{2} + j) =$

$\dfrac{3j + j\sqrt{3}}{4}$.

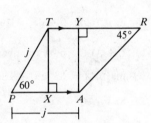

29. Let ABCDEF be a reg. hexagon with AB = 1.   Then x = AE.   If $\overline{FG}$ is the $\perp$

from F to $\overline{AE}$, $\triangle AFG$ and $\triangle EFG$ are $\cong$ 30-60-90 $\triangle$; $AE = 2 \cdot AG = 2(\dfrac{1}{2} \cdot \sqrt{3}) = \sqrt{3}$.

$x = \sqrt{3}$ cm

30. Draw $\overline{BY}$ and $\overline{BZ}$. $\triangle XBY$ and $\triangle XBZ$ are 30-60-90 $\triangle$;

$BY = BZ = 8\sqrt{3}$. $\triangle BYZ$ is an isos. $\triangle$ with $\overline{BA}$ the

median to the base. $\triangle BAY$ is a rt. $\triangle$ and $AB =$

$\sqrt{(8\sqrt{3})^2 - 4^2} = \sqrt{176} = 4\sqrt{11}$.

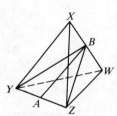

Pages 269-270 · WRITTEN EXERCISES

<u>A</u>   1. $\tan 32° = \dfrac{x}{22}$; $x \approx 22(0.6249) \approx 13.7$ <u>2.</u> $\tan 63° = \dfrac{x}{12}$; $x \approx 12(1.9626) \approx 23.6$

  <u>3.</u> $\tan 44° = \dfrac{x}{50}$; $x \approx 50(0.9657) \approx 48.3$ <u>4.</u> $\tan 50° = \dfrac{x}{1.2}$; $x \approx 1.2(1.1918) \approx 1.4$

  <u>5.</u> $\tan 29° = \dfrac{x}{100}$; $x \approx 100(0.5543) \approx 55.4$ <u>6.</u> $\tan 25° = \dfrac{x}{7.1}$; $x \approx 7.1(0.4663) \approx 3.3$

7. $\tan y° = \dfrac{6.1}{4} = 1.5250$; $y° \approx 57°$ 8. $\tan y° = \dfrac{8}{15} \approx 0.5333$; $y° \approx 28°$

9. $\tan y° = \dfrac{n}{2n} = 0.5000$; $y° \approx 27°$

B 10. $\tan 20° = \dfrac{w}{221}$; $w \approx 221(0.3640) \approx 80$; $z = 2w \approx 160$

11. $w = \dfrac{1}{2} \cdot 120 = 60$; $\tan 42° = \dfrac{z}{60}$; $z \approx 60(0.9004) \approx 54$

12. $w = 82$; $\tan 62° = \dfrac{z}{82}$; $z \approx 82(1.8807) \approx 154$

13. Let ABCD be a rhombus with AC = 4 and BD = 10. $\tan \angle BAC = \dfrac{5}{2} = 2.5$; $m\angle BAC \approx 68$; each diag. of a rhombus bis. 2 $\angle$ of the rhombus so $m\angle A = m\angle C \approx 136$; $m\angle B = m\angle D \approx 44$

14. Let ABCD be a rect. with diag. int. at X, AB = 40, and AD = 20.   Draw $\overline{XE} \perp \overline{AD}$. $m\angle AXE = \dfrac{1}{2}m\angle AXD$; $\tan \angle AXE = \dfrac{10}{20} = \dfrac{1}{2}$; $m\angle AXE \approx 27$, $m\angle AXD \approx 54$

15. a. 0.7002; 0.4663; 1.1665   b. 60; 1.7321   c. no

16. Let ABCD be a rhombus with diag. int. at X, $m\angle A = 70$, and BD = 124; $m\angle BAX = 35$, $m\angle AXB = 90$, and $m\angle ABX = 55$; $\tan 55° = \dfrac{AX}{62}$; $AX \approx 62(1.4281) \approx$ 88.5, $AC \approx 177$ cm

17. 1. The acute $\angle$ of a rt. $\triangle$ are comp.   2. Given   3. If 2 $\angle$ are comp. of the same $\angle$, then the 2 $\angle$ are $\cong$.   4. If $m\angle A = m\angle B$, then $\tan A = \tan B$ 5. $\dfrac{n}{m}$ 7. Subst. Prop.

C 18. HB = 40; $\tan 53° = \dfrac{WH}{40}$; $WH \approx 40(1.3270) \approx 53$; $\tan 61° = \dfrac{TH}{WH} \approx \dfrac{TH}{53}$; $TH \approx$ $53(1.8040) \approx 96$; $TB = TH + HB \approx 96 + 40 = 136$; approx. 136 ft.

19. $\tan 32° = \dfrac{GF}{355}$; $GF \approx 355(0.6249) \approx 222$; $\tan 46° = \dfrac{EF}{GF} \approx \dfrac{EF}{222}$; $EF \approx 222(1.0355) \approx$ 230

20. Draw $\overline{AE} \perp \overline{BC}$. $\triangle ABC$ is isos. so $\overline{AE}$ is also the median to $\overline{BC}$ and E is the midpt. of $\overline{BC}$. Draw $\overline{DE}$. $\triangle DBC$ is an isos. rt. $\triangle$ so $\overline{DE}$ is an alt. and DE = EC.

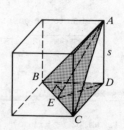

Then DE $= \dfrac{s}{\sqrt{2}} = \dfrac{s\sqrt{2}}{2}$. The meas. of the dihedral $\angle$ is $m\angle AED$; $\tan \angle AED = \dfrac{AD}{DE} = \dfrac{s\sqrt{2}}{s} = \sqrt{2} \approx 1.4142$;

$m\angle AED \approx 55$.

Pages 275-276 · WRITTEN EXERCISES

<u>A</u> <u>1</u>. sin 37° = $\frac{x}{35}$; x ≈ 35(0.6018) ≈ 21; cos 37° = $\frac{y}{35}$; y ≈ 35(0.7986) ≈ 28

<u>2</u>. sin 58° = $\frac{x}{120}$; x ≈ 120(0.8480) ≈ 102; cos 58° = $\frac{y}{120}$; y ≈ 120(0.5299) ≈ 64

<u>3</u>. tan 50° = $\frac{x}{75}$; x ≈ 75(1.1918) ≈ 89; cos 50° = $\frac{75}{y}$; y ≈ $\frac{75}{0.6428}$ ≈ 117

<u>4</u>. sin 40° = $\frac{x}{84}$; x ≈ 84(0.6428) ≈ 54; cos 40° = $\frac{y}{84}$; y ≈ 84(0.7660) ≈ 64

<u>5</u>. sin 70° = $\frac{x}{30}$; x ≈ 30(0.9397) ≈ 28; cos 70° = $\frac{y}{30}$; y ≈ 30(0.3420) ≈ 10

<u>6</u>. cos 65° = $\frac{12}{x}$; x ≈ $\frac{12}{0.4226}$ ≈ 28; tan 65° = $\frac{y}{12}$; y ≈ 12(2.1445) ≈ 26

<u>7</u>. sin v° = $\frac{14}{50}$ ≈ 0.2800; v° ≈ 16°   <u>8</u>. cos v° = $\frac{11}{61}$ ≈ 0.1803; v° ≈ 80°

<u>9</u>. Draw the alt. to the base; sin $(\frac{v}{2})$° = $\frac{6}{10}$ = 0.6000; $(\frac{v}{2})$° ≈ 37°; v° ≈ 74°

<u>10</u>. <u>a</u>. x² = 14² - 9² = 115; x = $\sqrt{115}$ ≈ 10.7   <u>b</u>. sin v° = $\frac{9}{14}$ ≈ 0.6429, v° ≈ 40°

<u>c</u>. cos 40° = $\frac{x}{14}$; x ≈ 14(0.7660) ≈ 10.7   <u>d</u>. yes

<u>B</u> <u>11</u>. Let △ABC have AB = AC = 24 and BC = 32. Draw $\overline{AD}$ ⊥ $\overline{BC}$; BD = $\frac{BC}{2}$ = 16;

cos B = $\frac{16}{24}$ ≈ .6667; m∠B ≈ 48

<u>12</u>. Let △ABC be such that AB = AC = 25 and BC = 42. Draw $\overline{AD}$ ⊥ $\overline{BC}$; BD =

$\frac{1}{2}$ · BC = 21, and m∠A = 2 · m∠BAD; sin ∠BAD = $\frac{21}{25}$ = 0.8400; m∠BAD ≈ 57;

m∠A ≈ 114

<u>13</u>. alt. = 60 sin 42° ≈ 40 cm; base = 2(60 sin 48°) ≈ 89 cm

<u>14</u>. Draw $\overline{BD}$ ⊥ $\overline{AC}$; △ABD is isos. so △ABD and △CBD are ≅ rt. △ ; m∠BAD =

$\frac{1}{2}$(180 - 144) = 18; cos 18° = $\frac{AD}{AB}$ = $\frac{AD}{16}$; AD ≈ 16(0.9511) ≈ 15; AC = 2 · AD ≈

30 cm

<u>15</u>. Let x = length of wire; sin 65° = $\frac{75}{x}$; x ≈ $\frac{75}{0.9063}$ ≈ 83 m

<u>16</u>. sin 25° = $\frac{AB}{352}$; AB ≈ 352(0.4226) ≈ 149 m

<u>17</u>. Let x = alt. gain in meters; sin 20° = $\frac{x}{1000}$; x ≈ 1000(0.3420) ≈ 350; approx. 350 m

<u>18</u>. Let j = height ladder reaches at 75° ∠, k = height ladder reaches at 65° ∠; sin 65° =

$\frac{k}{6}$; k ≈ 6(0.9063) ≈ 5.4; sin 75° = $\frac{j}{6}$; j ≈ 6(0.9659) ≈ 5.8; 5.8 - 5.4 = 0.4;

approx. 0.4 m

C 19. 1. Draw a $\perp$ from the third vertex to $\overline{AB}$; label it p.   2. $\sin A = \frac{p}{b}$; $\sin B = \frac{p}{a}$

3. $\sin A \cdot b = p = \sin B \cdot a$ 4. $\frac{a}{\sin A} = \frac{b}{\sin B}$

20. 1. Choose a pt. D on one side of $\angle E$ and draw $\overline{DF} \perp$ to the other side of $\angle E$.

2. $\triangle DEF$ is a rt. $\triangle$.   3. $(DF)^2 + (EF)^2 = (ED)^2$ 4. $\sin E = \frac{DF}{ED}$;

$(\sin E)^2 = \frac{(DF)^2}{(ED)^2}$; $\cos E = \frac{EF}{ED}$; $(\cos E)^2 = \frac{(EF)^2}{(ED)^2}$ 5. $(\sin E)^2 + (\cos E)^2 =$

$\frac{(DF)^2 + (EF)^2}{(ED)^2} = \frac{(ED)^2}{(ED)^2} = 1$

21. $\sin 35° = \frac{p}{300}$; $p \approx 300(0.5736) \approx 172$; $q + 40 = 90 - 35 = 55$; $q° = 15°$; $\sin 15° =$

$\frac{p}{r} \approx \frac{172}{r}$; $r \approx \frac{172}{0.2588} \approx 665$; $\sin 50° = \frac{x}{r} \approx \frac{x}{665}$; $x \approx 665(.7660) \approx 509$ m

22. Because of folding, $\angle DCE \cong \angle ECD$ and $m\angle DCD' = 2n$. $\cos n° = \frac{DC}{k}$; $k = \frac{DC}{\cos n°}$;

since $\overline{AB} \parallel \overline{CD}$, $m\angle CD'B = m\angle DCD' = (2n)°$; $\sin (2n)° = \sin \angle CDB' = \frac{10}{D'C} =$

$\frac{10}{DC}$; $DC = \frac{10}{\sin (2n°)}$; substituting, $k = \frac{\frac{10}{\sin (2n°)}}{\cos n°} = \frac{10}{\sin (2n)° \cos n°}$

Pages 278-280 · WRITTEN EXERCISES

A 1. Let h = height of building in meters; $\tan 57° = \frac{h}{21}$; $h \approx 21(1.5399) \approx 32$ m.

2. $\tan x° = \frac{3}{4} = 0.7500$; $x° \approx 37°$

3. Let h = height of kite in meters; $\sin 40° = \frac{h}{80}$; $h \approx 80(0.6428) \approx 50$ m

4. Let d = dist. in meters; $\tan 82° = \frac{d}{125}$; $d \approx 125(7.1154) \approx 889$; about 900 m

5. Let x° be the meas. of the $\angle$ and d the length of the diag. in meters   a. $\tan x° =$

$\frac{10}{20} = 0.5000$; $x° \approx 27°$ b. $\cos x° = \frac{20}{d}$; $d \approx \frac{20}{0.8910} \approx 22$ m

c. $d = \sqrt{10^2 + 20^2} = \sqrt{500} = 10\sqrt{5} \approx 22$m

6. Let h = length of Heidi's shadow and m = length of Martha's shadow; $\tan 55° = \frac{h}{90}$;

$h \approx 90(1.4281) \approx 129$; $\tan 20° = \frac{m}{180}$; $m \approx 180(0.3640) \approx 66$; $129 - 66 = 63$;

Heidi's shadow is about 63 cm longer.

B 7. $\sin 25° = \frac{x}{32}$; $x \approx 32(0.4226) \approx 13.5232 \approx 14$; $\tan 32° = \frac{y}{x} \approx \frac{y}{13.5232}$; $y \approx$

$13.5232(0.6249) \approx 8.4506 \approx 8$; $\cos 32° = \frac{x}{z}$; $z \approx \frac{13.5232}{0.8480} \approx 15.947 \approx 16$

8. $\sin 42° = \frac{u}{58}$; $u \approx 58(0.6691) \approx 39$; $\tan 28° = \frac{v}{u} \approx \frac{v}{39}$; $v \approx 39(0.3517) \approx 21$;

$\sin 62° = \frac{u}{w} \approx \frac{39}{w}$; $w \approx \frac{39}{0.8829} \approx 44$

<u>9.</u> Let ABCDE be the reg. pentagon of side 20.   Draw $\overline{AC}$ and draw $\overline{BF} \perp \overline{AC}$.

$m \angle BAC = \frac{1}{2}(180 - 108) = 36$; $\cos 36° = \frac{AF}{20}$; $AF \approx 20(0.8090) \approx 16$;

$AC = 2 \cdot AD \approx 32$

<u>10.</u> First draw $\overline{AD}$, $\overline{AC}$, and $\overline{BD}$. $\triangle ABC$ and $\triangle BCD$ are $\cong$ isos. $\triangle$ (SAS) so $\angle CAB \cong$

$\angle CBD \cong \angle BCA \cong \angle CDB$.   Then $\angle ABD \cong \angle DCA$ and $\triangle ABD \cong \triangle DCA$ (SAS);

$m \angle BAD = m \angle CDA = \frac{1}{2}(360 - 2 \cdot 140) = 40$ and $\overline{BC} \parallel \overline{AD}$.   Draw $\overline{BX}$ and $\overline{CY}$ both

$\perp$ to $\overline{AD}$; BCYX is a rect. so $XY = 25$. $\triangle AXB \cong \triangle DYC$ and $DY = AX$; $\cos 40° =$

$\frac{AX}{25}$; $AX \approx 25(0.7660) \approx 19$; $AD = AX + XY + DY \approx 2 \cdot 19 + 25 = 63$;

approx. 63 mm

<u>11.</u> <u>a.</u> $\tan A = \frac{1}{4} = 0.25$; $m \angle A \approx 14$ <u>b.</u> $\sin A \approx 0.2419$; force of car $\approx$

$(0.2419)(2500) \approx 605$; approx. 600 lb   <u>c.</u> no

<u>12.</u> $t = \sqrt{61^2 - 11^2} = \sqrt{3600} = 60$; $\cos A = \frac{60}{61}$; $\tan A = \frac{11}{60}$

<u>13.</u> $t = \sqrt{5^2 + 8^2} = \sqrt{89}$; $\sin A = \frac{5}{\sqrt{89}} = \frac{5\sqrt{89}}{89}$; $\cos A = \frac{8}{\sqrt{89}} = \frac{8\sqrt{89}}{89}$

<u>C</u> <u>14.</u> $t = \sqrt{k^2 - j^2}$; $\sin A = \frac{\sqrt{k^2 - j^2}}{k}$; $\tan A = \frac{\sqrt{k^2 - j^2}}{j}$

<u>15.</u> $t = \sqrt{(2uv)^2 + (u^2 - v^2)^2} = \sqrt{u^4 + 2u^2v^2 + v^4} = \sqrt{(u^2 + v^2)^2} = u^2 + v^2$; $\sin A =$

$\frac{2uv}{u^2 + v^2}$; $\cos A = \frac{u^2 - v^2}{u^2 + v^2}$

<u>16.</u> $m \angle C = 180 - (53 + 61) = 66$; from Ex. 19 on page 276, $\frac{BC}{\sin 53°} = \frac{142}{\sin 66°}$;

$BC = \frac{142 \sin 53°}{\sin 66°} \approx \frac{142(0.7986)}{0.9135} \approx 124$ m; $\frac{AC}{\sin 61°} = \frac{142}{\sin 66°}$; $AC = \frac{142 \sin 61°}{\sin 66°} \approx$

$\frac{142(0.8746)}{0.9135} \approx 136$ m

<u>17.</u> ABCD is a rect. and $\triangle ADC$ and $\triangle BCD$ are

$\cong$ rt. $\triangle$; $m \angle ACD = m \angle BDC$; let e = edge

of cube; $\tan \angle ACD = \frac{e\sqrt{2}}{e} = \sqrt{2}$; $m \angle ACD =$

$m \angle BDC \approx 54.7$; $m \angle DXC = 180 -$

$(m \angle ACD + m \angle BDC) \approx 70\frac{1}{2}°$

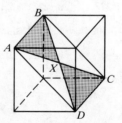

<u>18.</u> $\tan 19° = \frac{x}{d}$; $d = \frac{x}{\tan 19°}$; $\tan 29° = \frac{x + 6.3}{d}$; $d = \frac{x + 6.3}{\tan 29°}$; $\frac{x}{\tan 19°} = \frac{x + 6.3}{\tan 29°}$;

$x(\tan 29°) = x(\tan 19°) + 6.3(\tan 19°)$; $x = \frac{6.3(\tan 19°)}{\tan 29° - \tan 19°} \approx$

$\frac{6.3(0.3443)}{0.5543 - 0.3443} \approx 10.3$; approx. 10.3 m

Page 281 · APPLICATION

1. longest: $90° - 47\frac{1}{2}^° + 23\frac{1}{2}^° = 66°$; shortest: $90° - 47\frac{1}{2}^° - 23\frac{1}{2}^° = 19°$

2. longest: $90° - 42° + 23\frac{1}{2}^° = 71\frac{1}{2}^°$; shortest: $90° - 42° - 23\frac{1}{2}^° = 24\frac{1}{2}^°$

3. longest: $90° - 30° + 23\frac{1}{2}^° = 83\frac{1}{2}^°$; shortest: $90° - 30° - 23\frac{1}{2}^° = 36\frac{1}{2}^°$

4. longest: $90° - 34° + 23\frac{1}{2}^° = 79\frac{1}{2}^°$; shortest: $90° - 34° - 23\frac{1}{2}^° = 32\frac{1}{2}^°$

5. longest: $90° - 64\frac{1}{2}^° + 23\frac{1}{2}^° = 49°$; shortest: $90° - 64\frac{1}{2}^° - 23\frac{1}{2}^° = 2°$

6. longest: $90° - 26° + 23\frac{1}{2}^° = 87\frac{1}{2}^°$; shortest: $90° - 26° - 23\frac{1}{2}^° = 40\frac{1}{2}^°$

7. If the $\angle$ of elevation is $> 90°$, then at noon on the summer solstice the sun is in the northern sky rather than to the south ($\angle$ of elevation $< 90°$) or directly overhead ($\angle$ of elevation $= 90°$).

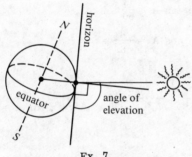

Ex. 7

Ex. 8

8. The sun is below the horizon (and is not visible).

9. $\tan(16°) = \frac{x}{7}$; $x = 7\tan(16°) \approx 7(0.2867) \approx 2$ ft.

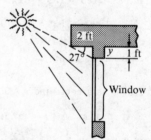

10. $\angle$ of elevation of sun at the winter solstice is $27°$. $\tan(27°) = \frac{y}{2}$; $y = 2\tan(27°) \approx 2(0.5095) \approx 1$ ft. Since the window is 1 ft. below the overhang, all of the window is in the sun.

Pages 283-284 · CHAPTER REVIEW

1. $\frac{12}{x} = \frac{x}{3}$; $x^2 = 36$; $x = \sqrt{36} = 6$

2. $\frac{10}{x} = \frac{x}{5}$; $x^2 = 50$; $x = \sqrt{50} = \sqrt{25 \cdot 2} = 5\sqrt{2}$

3. $\frac{15}{y} = \frac{y}{10}$; $y^2 = 150$; $y = \sqrt{150} = \sqrt{25 \cdot 6} = 5\sqrt{6}$

4. $\frac{15}{z} = \frac{z}{5}$; $z^2 = 75$; $z = \sqrt{75} = \sqrt{25 \cdot 3} = 5\sqrt{3}$

5. $c = \sqrt{3^2 + 6^2} = \sqrt{45} = \sqrt{9 \cdot 5} = 3\sqrt{5}$

6. $d = \sqrt{10^2 + 8^2} = \sqrt{164} = \sqrt{4 \cdot 41} = 2\sqrt{41}$ 7. $s = \frac{14}{\sqrt{2}} = \frac{14\sqrt{2}}{2} = 7\sqrt{2}$

8. $\frac{b}{2} = \sqrt{10^2 - 8^2} = \sqrt{36} = 6$; $b = 12$ 9. $6^2 = 36 < 25 + 16 = 5^2 + 4^2$; acute

10. $8 + 8 < 17$; not possible

11. $61^2 = 3721 = 3600 + 121 = 60^2 + 11^2$; right

12. $6^2 = 36 > 12 + 18 = (2\sqrt{3})^2 + (3\sqrt{2})^2$; obtuse 13. $x = 5\sqrt{3}$

14. $x = 7\sqrt{2}$ (45-45-90 $\triangle$) 15. $x = 16$ (30-60-90 $\triangle$)

16. alt. of large $\triangle = 2\sqrt{3}$; longer leg of medium $\triangle = 2\sqrt{3} \cdot \sqrt{3} = 6$; $x = 6 + 2 = 8$

17. $x = 2k \cdot \sqrt{2}$ (45-45-90 $\triangle$) 18. $\frac{9}{6} = 1.5$ 19. $\frac{6}{9} = \frac{2}{3}$ 20. 3.0777

21. 24° 22. $\frac{10}{26} = \frac{5}{13}$ 23. $\frac{10}{26} = \frac{5}{13}$ 24. 75° 25. 0.6820

26. $\tan 50° = \frac{x}{75}$; $x \approx 75(1.1918) \approx 89$ 27. $\cos y° = \frac{13}{24} \approx 0.5417$; $y° \approx 57°$

28. Let a = length of alt.; $\sin 76° = \frac{a}{20}$; $a = 20(\sin 76°)$; $\tan 53° = \frac{x}{a}$; $x = a(\tan 53°) =$

$20(\sin 76°)(\tan 53°) \approx 20(0.9703)(1.3270) \approx 26$

Pages 284-285 · CHAPTER TEST

1. $\frac{5}{x} = \frac{x}{20}$; $x^2 = 100$; $x = \sqrt{100} = 10$

2. $\frac{6}{x} = \frac{x}{8}$; $x^2 = 48$; $x = \sqrt{48} = \sqrt{16 \cdot 3} = 4\sqrt{3}$

3. $\triangle$DEN; $\triangle$NEF 4. DE; EF 5. DF; EF

6. $\frac{25}{ND} = \frac{ND}{10}$; $(ND)^2 = 250$; $ND = \sqrt{250} = \sqrt{25 \cdot 10} = 5\sqrt{10}$

7. $x = \sqrt{2^2 + 3^2} = \sqrt{13}$; $y = \sqrt{(\sqrt{13})^2 - 1^2} = \sqrt{12} = 2\sqrt{3}$

8. $3 + 4 < 8$; not possible 9. $13^2 = 169 < 121 + 144 = 11^2 + 12^2$; acute

10. $10^2 = 100 > 49 + 49 = 7^2 + 7^2$; obtuse

11. $1^2 = 1 = \frac{9}{25} + \frac{16}{25} = (\frac{3}{5})^2 + (\frac{4}{5})^2$; right 12. $x = 11\sqrt{2}$ (45-45-90 $\triangle$)

13. $x = 9$ (30-60-90 $\triangle$) 14. $x = 14$ (30-60-90 $\triangle$)

15. $x = \frac{\sqrt{6}}{\sqrt{2}} = \frac{\sqrt{2} \cdot \sqrt{3}}{\sqrt{2}} = \sqrt{3}$ (45-45-90 $\triangle$)

16. $(x + 1)^2 = x^2 + 7^2$; $x^2 + 2x + 1 = x^2 + 49$; $2x + 1 = 49$; $2x = 48$; $x = 24$

17. $\frac{4}{2\sqrt{6}} = \frac{2\sqrt{6}}{x}$; $4x = (2\sqrt{6})^2 = 24$; $x = 6$

18. __a__. right   __b__. $(TS)^2 = 17^2 - 8^2 = 225$; $225 = 144 + 81 = (TV)^2 + (VS)^2$ so $\triangle$ TVS is

a rt. $\triangle$.   The largest $\angle$ of a $\triangle$ is opp. the longest side so $\angle$ V is a rt. $\angle$.

19. $\sin 41° = \dfrac{x}{32}$; $x \approx 32(0.6561) \approx 21$ 20. $\tan 48° = \dfrac{x}{28}$; $x \approx 28(1.1106) \approx 31$

21. $\cos 50° = \dfrac{x}{44}$; $x \approx 44(0.6428) \approx 28$

22. Method may vary; $\cos x° = \dfrac{4}{5} = 0.8000$; $x° \approx 37°$

23. Draw the alt. to the base of this isos. $\triangle$; the alt. is also the $\perp$ bis. of the base, so

$\cos x° = \dfrac{17}{20} = .85$; $x° \approx 32°$

24. Let a = length of leg opp. 58° $\angle$; a = 50 (30-60-90 $\triangle$); $\tan 32° = \dfrac{x}{a}$;

$x = a(\tan 32°) \approx 50(0.6249) \approx 31$

Page 286 · PREPARING FOR COLLEGE ENTRANCE EXAMS

__1__. A   __2__. C   __3__. B   __4__. C   __5__. E   __6__. A   __7__. C   __8__. A

__9__. B   __10__. C

Pages 287-291 · CUMULATIVE REVIEW: CHAPTERS 1-6

True-False Exercises

__A__   __1__. F   __2__. F   __3__. T   __4__. F   __5__. T   __6__. T   __7__. T   __8__. F

__B__   __9__. T   __10__. T   __11__. F   __12__. F   __13__. T   __14__. T   __15__. F

Multiple-Choice Exercises

__A__   __1__. d   __2__. c   __3__. e   __4__. d   __5__. b

__B__   __6__. a   __7__. e   __8__. c

Always-Sometimes-Never Exercises

__A__   __1__. S   __2__. N   __3__. A   __4__. N   __5__. S   __6__. A   __7__. S   __8__. N

__9__. S   __10__. N   __11__. A

__B__ __12__. S   __13__. N   __14__. N   __15__. S   __16__. S   __17__. A   __18__. N

Algebraic Exercises

__A__   __1__. $7x - 13 = 2x + 17$; $5x = 30$; $x = 6$

__2__. $(x + 38) + (2x - 5) = 90$; $3x + 33 = 90$; $3x = 57$; $x = 19$

__3__. $6x + (2x + 20) = 180$; $8x + 20 = 180$; $8x = 160$; $x = 20$

__4__. $(x + 12) + (2x - 7) + (3x + 1) = 180$; $6x + 6 = 180$; $6x = 174$; $x = 29$

<u>5.</u> $\frac{-8 + x}{2} = -1$; $-8 + x = -2$; $x = 6$ <u>6.</u> $x^2 + 18x = x^2 + 54$; $18x = 54$; $x = 3$

<u>7.</u> $x + (x + 4) + (x + 8) + (x + 12) = 360$; $4x + 24 = 360$; $x + 6 = 90$; $x = 84$

<u>8.</u> $2(\frac{4x}{\sqrt{3}}) = 8\sqrt{3}$; $\frac{8x}{\sqrt{3}} = 8\sqrt{3}$; $x = \sqrt{3} \cdot \sqrt{3} = 3$

<u>9.</u> $15 = \frac{1}{2}(x + x + 8)$; $15 = \frac{1}{2}(2x + 8)$; $x + 4 = 15$; $x = 11$

<u>10.</u> $9x - 3 = 8x + 4$; $x = 7$ <u>11.</u> $8x - 8 = 30$; $8x = 38$; $x = \frac{38}{8} = \frac{19}{4}$

<u>12.</u> $x^2 + 9x = x^2 + 7x + 12$; $2x = 12$; $x = 6$

B <u>13.</u> Let x = meas. of the $\angle$; $180 - x = 3(90 - x) + 8$; $180 - x = 270 - 3x + 8$;

$2x = 98$; $x = 49$

<u>14.</u> $4x + 5x + 7x = 64$; $16x = 64$; $x = 4$; lengths of sides = 16 cm, 20 cm, and 28 cm

<u>15.</u> $m\angle Z = m\angle X$; $5x + 5x + 2x = 180$; $12x = 180$; $x = 15$; $m\angle Z = 5x = 75$

<u>16.</u> Let n = number of vertices = number of sides; $\frac{\frac{360}{n}}{\frac{(n - 2)180}{n}} = \frac{2}{13}$; $\frac{2}{n - 2} = \frac{2}{13}$;

$2n - 4 = 26$; $n = 15$

<u>17.</u> $\frac{SU}{9 - SU} = \frac{8}{12} = \frac{2}{3}$; $3 \cdot SU = 18 - 2 \cdot SU$; $5 \cdot SU = 18$; $SU = 3\frac{3}{5}$

<u>18.</u> By the $\triangle$ Ineq. Thm., $x + 2x + 2 > 2x + 3$; $3x + 2 > 2x + 3$; $x > 1$; since the $\triangle$

is obtuse, $(2x + 3)^2 > (2x + 2)^2 + x^2$; $4x^2 + 12x + 9 > 4x^2 + 8x + 4 + x^2$;

$x^2 - 4x - 5 < 0$; $(x - 5)(x + 1) < 0$; either $x - 5 > 0$ and $x + 1 < 0$ (reject) or

$x - 5 < 0$ and $x + 1 > 0$; $x < 5$ and $x > -1$; $0 < x < 5$

<u>19.</u> perimeter $= 2(12 + 15) = 54$; ratio of lengths of sides = ratio of perimeters =

$\frac{54}{90} = \frac{3}{5}$; $\frac{12}{w} = \frac{3}{5}$; $3w = 60$; $w = 20$; $\frac{15}{\ell} = \frac{3}{5}$; $3\ell = 75$; $\ell = 25$; 20 cm and 25 cm

<u>20.</u> Let x and y be the lengths of the sides; $x + y + 10 = 24$; $x + y = 14$; $y = 14 - x$;

$x^2 + (14 - x)^2 = 100$; $x^2 + 196 - 28x + x^2 = 100$; $2x^2 - 28x + 96 = 0$;

$x^2 - 14x + 48 = 0$; $(x - 6)(x - 8) = 0$; $x = 6$ or $x = 8$; if $x = 6$, $y = 8$; if

$x = 8$, $y = 6$; length = 8, width = 6

<u>21.</u> $\cos X = \frac{XY}{XZ}$; $\frac{XY}{24} = \frac{7}{10}$; $10 \cdot XY = 168$; $XY \approx 17$

<u>22.</u> $\tan X = \frac{15}{10} = 1.5$; $m\angle X \approx 56$; $m\angle Z = 90 - 56 = 34$

<u>23.</u> $\frac{24}{18} = \frac{18}{24 - XM}$; $324 = 576 - 24 \cdot XM$; $24 \cdot XM = 252$; $XM = 10.5$

<u>24.</u> $\angle DAF \cong \angle GBF$, $\angle ADF \cong \angle BGF$; $\triangle ADF \sim \triangle BGF$; $\frac{y}{7} = \frac{4}{8}$; $8y = 28$; $y = 3\frac{1}{2}$;

$\angle EAD \cong \angle ECG$, $\triangle EDA \sim \triangle EGC$; $\frac{x}{9} = \frac{7}{7 + y} = \frac{7}{10\frac{1}{2}}$; $10\frac{1}{2}x = 63$; $x = 6$

25. right; $(x - y)^2 + (2\sqrt{xy})^2 = x^2 - 2xy + y^2 + 4xy = x^2 + 2x + y^2 = (x + y)^2$

26. Let x be the length of the sides of the square; two $\sim$ rt. $\triangle$ are formed; $\dfrac{8 - x}{x} = \dfrac{x}{12 - x}$; $x^2 = 96 - 20x + x^2$; $20x = 96$; $x = 4\dfrac{4}{5}$

Completion Exercises

A   1. 120   2. complementary   3. obtuse   4. $\perp$ 5. 108   6. $1 : \sqrt{2}$

   7. $\sim$ 8. $\dfrac{4}{5}$; $\dfrac{4}{5}$; $\dfrac{3}{4}$ 9. 24   10. 36

B   11. $\dfrac{s}{u}$ 12. $10\sqrt{3}$ 13. $\dfrac{15}{17}$ 14. rectangle   15. 45°

Proof Exercises

A   1. 1. $\overline{AD} \cong \overline{BC}$; $\overline{AD} \parallel \overline{BC}$ (Given)   2. ABCD is a $\square$. (If one pair of opp. sides of a quad. is both $\cong$ and $\parallel$, then the quad. is a $\square$.)   3. $\angle D \cong \angle B$ (Opp. $\angle$ of a $\square$ are $\cong$.)

2. 1. $\overline{CE} \perp \overline{AB}$; $\overline{AF} \perp \overline{CD}$ (Given)   2. $\angle AFD$ and $\angle CEB$ are rt. $\angle$; $\triangle AFD$ and $\triangle CEB$ are rt. $\triangle$ (Def. of rt. $\angle$, rt. $\triangle$)   3. ABCD is a $\square$; $\overline{AB} \parallel \overline{DC}$ (Given; Def. of $\square$)   4. AF = CE (If 2 lines are $\parallel$, then all pts. on one line are equidistant from the other line.)   5. $\overline{DA} \cong \overline{CB}$ (Opp. sides of a $\square$ are $\cong$.)   6. $\triangle AFD \cong \triangle CEB$ (HL)   6. $\overline{BE} \cong \overline{DF}$ (Corr. parts of $\cong$ $\triangle$ are $\cong$.)

3. 1. $\triangle DAF \cong \triangle BCE$ (Given)   2. $\overline{DA} \cong \overline{CB}$ (Corr. parts of $\cong$ $\triangle$ are $\cong$.)   3. $\overline{CD} \cong \overline{AB}$ (Given)   4. ABCD is a $\square$. (If both pairs of opp. sides of a quad. are $\cong$, then the quad. is a $\square$.)

4. 1. $\overline{CE} \perp \overline{AB}$; $\overline{AF} \perp \overline{AB}$ (Given)   2. $\overline{CE} \parallel \overline{AF}$ (In a plane, 2 lines $\perp$ to the same line are $\parallel$.)   3. $\overline{DC} \parallel \overline{AB}$ (Given)   4. AECF is a $\square$. (If both pairs of opp. sides of a quad. are $\parallel$, then the quad. is a $\square$.)   5. $\angle FAE$ is a rt. $\angle$. (Def. of $\perp$ lines)   6. AECF is a rect. (If one $\angle$ of a $\square$ is a rt. $\angle$, then the $\square$ is a rect.)

5. 1. $\overline{SU} \cong \overline{SV}$; $\angle 1 \cong \angle 2$ (Given)   2. $\overline{SQ} \cong \overline{SQ}$ (Refl. Prop.)   3. $\triangle SQU \cong \triangle SQV$ (SAS)   4. $\overline{UQ} \cong \overline{VQ}$ (Corr. parts of $\cong$ $\triangle$ are $\cong$.)

6. 1. $\overrightarrow{QS}$ bisects $\angle RQT$. (Given)   2. $\angle RQS \cong \angle TQS$ (Def. of $\angle$ bis.)   3. $\angle R \cong \angle T$ (Given)   4. $\overline{QS} \cong \overline{QS}$ (Refl. Prop.)   5. $\triangle QRS \cong \triangle QTS$ (AAS)   6. $\angle 1 \cong \angle 2$ (Corr. parts of $\cong$ $\triangle$ are $\cong$.)   7. $\overrightarrow{SQ}$ bisects $\angle RST$. (Def. of $\angle$ bis.)

B   7. 1. $\triangle QRU \cong \triangle QTV$ (Given)   2. QR = QT; RU = TV; $\angle R \cong \angle T$ (Corr. parts of $\cong$ $\triangle$ are $\cong$.)   3. US = VS (Given)   4. RU + US = TV + VS (Add. Prop. of =)   5. RU + US = RS; TV + VS = TS (Seg. Add. Post.)   6. RS = TS (Subst. Prop.)

7. $\triangle$ QRS $\cong$ $\triangle$ QTS (SAS)

__8.__ 1. $\overrightarrow{QS}$ bisects $\angle$ UQV and $\angle$ USV. (Given)   2. $\angle$ UQS $\cong$ $\angle$ VQS; $\angle 1 \cong \angle 2$ (Def. of $\angle$

bis.)   3. $\overline{QS} \cong \overline{QS}$ (Refl. Prop.)   4. $\triangle$ UQS $\cong$ $\triangle$ VQS (ASA)   5. $\overline{QU} \cong \overline{QV}$;

$\angle$ QUS $\cong$ $\angle$ QVS (Corr. parts of $\cong$ $\triangle$ are $\cong$.)   6. $\angle$ QUR $\cong$ $\angle$ QVT (If 2 $\angle$ are supp.

of $\cong$ $\angle$, then the 2 $\angle$ are $\cong$.)   7. $\angle$ R $\cong$ $\angle$ T (Given)   8. $\triangle$ QRU $\cong$ $\triangle$ QTV (AAS)

9. $\overline{RQ} \cong \overline{TQ}$ (Corr. parts of $\cong$ $\triangle$ are $\cong$.)

__9.__ 1. $\overline{EF} \parallel \overline{JK}$; $\overline{JK} \parallel \overline{HI}$ (Given)   2. $\overline{EF} \parallel \overline{HI}$ (Two lines $\parallel$ to a third line are $\parallel$ to

each other.)   3. $\angle 2 \cong \angle 3$; $\angle$ F $\cong$ $\angle$ H (If 2 $\parallel$ lines are cut by a trans., then alt.

int. $\angle$ are $\cong$.)   4. $\triangle$ EFG $\sim$ $\triangle$ IHG (AA)

__10.__ 1. $\dfrac{JG}{HG} = \dfrac{KG}{IG}$ (Given)   2. $\angle$ KGJ $\cong$ $\angle$ KGJ (Refl. Prop.)   3. $\triangle$ GJK $\sim$ $\triangle$ GHI (SAS)

4. $\angle 1 \cong \angle 3$ (Corr. $\angle$ of $\sim$ $\triangle$ are $\cong$.)   5. $\angle 1 \cong \angle 2$ (Given)   6. $\angle 2 \cong \angle 3$ (Trans.

Prop.)   7. $\overline{EF} \parallel \overline{HI}$ (If 2 lines are cut by a trans. and alt. int. $\angle$ are $\cong$, then the

lines are $\parallel$.)

__11.__ 1. XZ = YW; VZ = VW (Given)   2. XV + VZ = XZ; YV + VW = YW (Seg. Add.

Post.)   3. XV + VZ = YV + VW (Subst. Prop.)   4. XV = YV (Subtr. Prop. of =)

5. $\angle$ WVX $\cong$ $\angle$ ZVY (Vert. $\angle$ are $\cong$.)   6. $\triangle$ WVX $\cong$ $\triangle$ ZVY (SAS)   6. XW = YZ

(Corr. parts of $\cong$ $\triangle$ are $\cong$.)

__12.__ 1. $\overline{XW} \cong \overline{YZ}$; $\angle$ XWZ $\cong$ $\angle$ YZW (Given)   2. $\overline{WZ} \cong \overline{WZ}$ (Refl. Prop.)

3. $\triangle$ XWZ $\cong$ $\triangle$ YZW (SAS)   4. m$\angle$ WZX = m$\angle$ ZWY (Corr. parts of $\cong$ $\triangle$ are $\cong$.)

5. m$\angle$ XWZ = m$\angle$ XWV + m$\angle$ ZWY; m$\angle$ YZW = m$\angle$ YZV + m$\angle$ WZX (Angle Add.

Post.)   6. m$\angle$ XWV + m$\angle$ ZWY = m$\angle$ YZV + m$\angle$ WZX (Subst. Prop.)

7. m$\angle$ XWV = m$\angle$ YZV (Subtr. Prop. of =)   8. $\angle$ XVW $\cong$ $\angle$ YVZ (Vert. $\angle$ are $\cong$.)

9. $\triangle$ XVW $\cong$ $\triangle$ YVZ (AAS)

__13.__ 1. WXYZ is an isos. trap. (Given)   2. $\overline{XW} \cong \overline{YZ}$ (Given)   3. $\angle$ XWZ $\cong$ $\angle$ YZW

(Base $\angle$ of an isos. trap. are $\cong$.)   4. $\overline{WZ} \cong \overline{WZ}$ (Refl. Prop.)   4. $\triangle$ XWZ $\cong$

$\triangle$ YZW (SAS)   5. $\overline{XZ} \cong \overline{YW}$ (Corr. parts of $\cong$ $\triangle$ are $\cong$.)

__14.__ 1. VW = VZ; VX = VY (Given)   2. $\dfrac{VW}{VX} = \dfrac{VZ}{VY}$ (Div. Prop. of =)   3. $\angle$ WVZ $\cong$

$\angle$ XVY (Vert. $\angle$ are $\cong$)   4. $\triangle$ WVZ $\sim$ $\triangle$ XVY (SAS)   5. $\dfrac{XY}{WZ} = \dfrac{VX}{VW}$ (Corr. sides

of $\sim$ $\triangle$ are in prop.)   6. XY $\cdot$ VW = WZ $\cdot$ VX (Means-extremes Prop.)

__15.__ 1. $\angle$ G $\cong$ $\angle 1$ (Given)   2. $\angle$ J $\cong$ $\angle$ J (Refl. Prop.)   3. $\triangle$ HGJ $\sim$ $\triangle$ KHJ (AA)

4. $\dfrac{GJ}{JH} = \dfrac{JH}{KJ}$ (Corr. sides of $\sim$ $\triangle$ are in prop.)   5. JH is the geom. mean between

GJ and KJ. (Def. of geom. mean)

<u>16.</u> 1. $\overline{GH} \perp \overline{JH}$; $\overline{HK} \perp \overline{GJ}$ (Given)   2. $\triangle$ HGJ and $\triangle$ HGK are rt. $\triangle$. (Def. of $\perp$, rt. $\triangle$)

3. $\overline{HK}$ is the alt. to the hyp. of rt. $\triangle$ HGJ. (Def. of alt.)   4. $\dfrac{GK}{HK} = \dfrac{HK}{KJ}$ (When the alt.

is drawn to the hyp. of a rt. $\triangle$, the length of the alt. is the geom. mean between the

lengths of the seg. of the hyp.)   5. $(HK)^2 = GK \cdot KJ$ (Means-extremes Prop.)

6. $(GH)^2 = (GK)^2 + (HK)^2$; $(HK)^2 = (GH)^2 - (GK)^2$ (Pyth. Thm.; Subtr. Prop. of =)

7. $(GH)^2 - (GK)^2 = GK \cdot KJ$ (Subst. Prop.)

<u>17.</u> 1. $\overline{QS} \perp$ plane P (Given)   2. $\overline{QS} \perp \overline{SR}$; $\overline{QS} \perp \overline{ST}$ (Def. of line $\perp$ to plane)

3. $\angle$ QSR and $\angle$ QST are rt. $\angle$; $\triangle$ QSR and $\triangle$ QST are rt. $\triangle$. (Def. of $\perp$ lines; def.

of rt. $\triangle$)   4. $\overline{QS} \cong \overline{QS}$ (Refl. Prop.)   5. $\triangle$ QRT is equilateral. (Given)

6. $\overline{QR} \cong \overline{QT}$ (Def. of equilateral $\triangle$)   7. $\triangle$ QSR $\cong$ $\triangle$ QST (HL)   8. $\overline{SR} \cong \overline{ST}$ (Corr.

parts of $\cong$ $\triangle$ are $\cong$.)   9. $\angle$ SRT $\cong$ $\angle$ STR (If 2 sides of a $\triangle$ are $\cong$, then the $\angle$ opp.

those sides are $\cong$.)

Page 295 · WRITTEN EXERCISES

<u>A</u> <u>1.</u> 1   <u>2.</u> 2   <u>3.</u> 1   <u>4.</u> 0   <u>5.</u> 1   <u>6.</u> 2   <u>7.</u> 1   <u>8.</u> 0

<u>9.</u> P is the ctr.; radius = 12   <u>10.</u> P is not the ctr.; radius < 12

<u>11-13.</u> Check students' drawings   <u>14.</u> not possible

<u>15-16.</u> Check students' drawings

<u>B</u> <u>17-20.</u> Check students' drawings   <u>17.</u> AB = $12\sqrt{2}$ <u>18.</u> AB = 24

<u>19.</u> AB = 12   <u>20.</u> AB = $12\sqrt{3}$

<u>21.</u> The radius of a sphere is the distance from the ctr. to any pt. on the sphere.   A seg. that joins the ctr. to a pt. on the sphere is called a radius.

<u>22.</u> ≅ spheres are spheres that have ≅ radii.

<u>23.</u> r = $\sqrt{10^2 - 6^2} = \sqrt{64}$ = 8   <u>24.</u> r = $\sqrt{15^2 + 8^2} = \sqrt{289}$ = 17

<u>C</u> <u>25.</u> △XPQ ≅ △ZPQ; △XPY ≅ △ZPY; $\overline{XZ} \perp \overline{PQ}$;

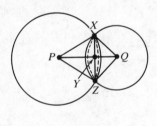

XY = $\sqrt{6^2 - (PY)^2} = \sqrt{4^2 - (YQ)^2} = \sqrt{4^2 - (8 - PY)^2}$;

$36 - (PY)^2 = 16 - 64 + 16 \cdot PY - (PY)^2$; $16 \cdot PY =$

84; PY = $\frac{21}{4}$; XY = $\sqrt{36 - (\frac{21}{4})^2} = \sqrt{\frac{576 - 441}{16}} =$

$\sqrt{\frac{135}{16}} = \frac{3\sqrt{15}}{4}$; radius = $\frac{3\sqrt{15}}{4}$

<u>26.</u> Let $\overleftrightarrow{AB}$ be a line such that A and B are on ⊙O.   Let C be

a third pt. on $\overleftrightarrow{AB}$ and assume temp. that C is on ⊙O.

Draw $\overline{OA}$, $\overline{OB}$, $\overline{OC}$ and draw $\overline{OD} \perp \overline{AB}$.   Since OA =

OB = OC, △AOB and △BOC are isos. △.   Then $\overline{OD}$ is the ⊥ bis. of both $\overline{BC}$ and

$\overline{AB}$.   BD = DC = AD, contradicting the Seg. Add. Post.   Our temp. assumption that

C is on ⊙O must be incorrect.   It follows that a line intersects a ⊙ in at most 2 pts.

<u>27.</u> Case I (Z passes through Q): Let R and S be any 2 pts. in the int.   Since R and S are

on the sphere, $\overline{QR} \cong \overline{QS}$.   By def., the int. is a ⊙ with ctr. Q and radius the radius

of sphere Q.   Case II (Z does not pass through Q): Draw a ⊥ from Q to Z int. Z

in P.   Let R and S be any 2 pts. in the int.   Since R and S are on the sphere,

$\overline{QR} \cong \overline{QS}$. Also, $\overline{QP} \cong \overline{QP}$. Since $\overline{QP} \perp Z$, $\overline{QP} \perp \overline{PR}$ and $\overline{QP} \perp \overline{PS}$, so $\triangle QPR$ and $\triangle QPS$ are $\cong$ rt. $\triangle$. Then $\overline{PR} \cong \overline{PS}$ and by def., the int. is a $\odot$ with center P.

Pages 298-301 · WRITTEN EXERCISES

<u>A</u>   <u>1</u>. 1. exactly one line   2. Seg. Add. Post.   3. Tan. to a $\odot$ from a pt. are $\cong$.
   4. Subst. Prop.   5. Tan. to a $\odot$ from a pt. are $\cong$.   6. Subtr. Prop. of =

<u>2</u>. 1. If a line is tan. to a $\odot$, then the line is $\perp$ to the radius drawn to the pt. of tangency.
   2. In a plane, 2 lines $\perp$ to the same line are $\parallel$.   3. Def. of $\cong$ ⑤.   4. If one pair
   of opp. sides of a quad. are both $\parallel$ and $\cong$, then the quad. is a $\square$.   5. Opp. sides of
   a $\square$ are $\cong$.   6. Trans. Prop.

<u>3</u>.   <u>4</u>.   <u>5</u>.   <u>6</u>.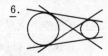

<u>7</u>. infinitely many   <u>8</u>. The new circle and $\odot$O are tan. at Z.   <u>9</u>. 10; 10

<u>10</u>. $\overline{JT} \perp \overline{OT}$; JT = $\sqrt{13^2 - 5^2}$ = $\sqrt{144}$ = 12

<u>11</u>. $10\sqrt{3}$ <u>12</u>. JT = $\sqrt{17^2 - 8^2}$ = $\sqrt{225}$ = 15

<u>B</u> <u>13</u>. Thm.: 2 lines tan. to a $\odot$ at the endpts. of a diam. are $\parallel$.
   Given: $\overline{AB}$, a diam. of $\odot$O; j tan. to $\odot$O at A, k tan.
   to $\odot$O at B.   Prove: j $\parallel$ k   Proof: 1. j is tan. to
   $\odot$O at A; k is tan. to $\odot$O at B. (Given)   2. j $\perp \overline{AB}$; k $\perp \overline{AB}$ (If a line is tan. to
   a $\odot$, then it is $\perp$ to the radius drawn to the pt. of tangency.)   3. j $\parallel$ k (In a plane,
   2 lines $\perp$ to the same line are $\parallel$.)

<u>14</u>. 2 planes tan. to a sphere at the endpts. of a diam. are $\parallel$.

<u>15</u>. AB + DC = AD + BC; Proof: 1. Let W, X, Y, and Z be the pts. of tangency of $\overline{AB}$,
   $\overline{BC}$, $\overline{CD}$, and $\overline{AD}$, resp. (Def. of fig. circumscribed about a $\odot$)   2. AW = AZ;
   BW = BX; CX = CY; DY = DZ (Tan. to a $\odot$ from a pt. are $\cong$.)   3. AW + BW +
   DY + YC = AZ + DZ + BX + CX (Add. Prop. of =)   4. AB + DC = AD + BC
   (Seg. Add. Post.; Subst. Prop.)

<u>16</u>. $\overrightarrow{AO}$ bis. $\angle$BAC.   Proof: 1. $\overrightarrow{OB} \perp \overrightarrow{AB}$; $\overrightarrow{OC} \perp \overrightarrow{AC}$ (If a line is tan. to a $\odot$, then the
   line is $\perp$ to the radius drawn to the pt. of tangency.)   2. $\overline{AB} \cong \overline{AC}$ (Tan. to a $\odot$
   from a pt. are $\cong$.)   3. $\overline{AO} \cong \overline{AO}$ (Refl. Prop.)   4. $\triangle$OBA $\cong \triangle$OCA (HL)
   5. $\angle$BAO $\cong \angle$CAO (Corr. parts of $\cong \triangle$ are $\cong$.)   6. $\overrightarrow{AO}$ bis. $\angle$BAC. (Def. of $\angle$ bis.)

17. $\triangle RTQ \sim \triangle RSP$; $QR = \sqrt{8^2 + 6^2} = \sqrt{100} = 10$; $\frac{PS}{6} = \frac{30}{10}$; $10 \cdot PS = 180$; $PS = 18$;

PQ = 30 - 10 = 20; $\frac{10}{20} = \frac{8}{ST}$; $10 \cdot ST = 160$; $ST = 16$

18. JPQK is a trap. Let X be on $\overline{JP}$ such that JX = KQ; $JK = XQ = \sqrt{17^2 - 8^2} =$

$\sqrt{225} = 15$.

19. Let X be on $\overline{AP}$ such that AX = BQ; $AB = XQ = \sqrt{8^2 - 4^2} = \sqrt{48} = 4\sqrt{3}$

20. 1. $\overline{GE} \cong \overline{GH}$; $\overline{GF} \cong \overline{GH}$ (Tan. to a $\odot$ from a pt. are $\cong$.)   2. $\angle GEH \cong \angle EHG$;

$\angle GFH \cong \angle GHF$ (Isos. $\triangle$ Thm.)   3. $m\angle EGH = 180 - 2 \cdot m\angle EHG$; $m\angle FGH =$

$180 - 2 \cdot m\angle GHF$ (The sum of the meas. of the $\angle$ of a $\triangle$ is 180.)

4. $m\angle EGH + m\angle FGH = 180 = 180 - 2 \cdot m\angle EHG + 180 - 2 \cdot m\angle GHF$ ($\angle$ Add.

Post.; Subst. Prop.)   5. $2 \cdot m\angle EHG + 2 \cdot m\angle GHF = 180$; $m\angle EHG + m\angle GHF =$

90 (By algebra)   6. $m\angle EHF = 90$ ($\angle$ Add. Post.; Subst. Prop.)   7. $\angle EHF$ is a

rt. $\angle$. (Def. of rt. $\angle$)

21. 8

    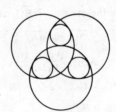

22. Let the 3 spheres be A, B, and C.   a. There are 2 $\parallel$ tan. planes, X and X', with

spheres A, B, and C between them, as shown.

There are also 2 tan. planes, Y and Y', between

sphere A and spheres B and C, as shown below.

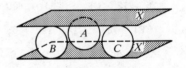

Similarly, sphere B can be separated from

spheres A and C by 2 tan. planes, and sphere C

can be separated from spheres A and B by 2 tan. planes, for a total of 8 planes tan.

to the 3 spheres.

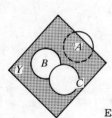 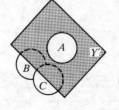 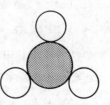 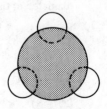

Ex. 22a   Ex. 22b

<u>b</u>. Any sphere with a large enough radius can be placed so that it is tangent to the 3 given spheres.   The figures show top views of two such arrangements.

C 22. a. Think of the ctrs. of the ≅ spheres as lying in the plane of the page.   There are 2 planes tan. to all 3 spheres; each is ∥ to the plane of the page.   <u>b</u>. 8

<u>23</u>. Let ℓ be in the plane of $\odot$ Q, $\ell \perp \overline{QR}$, and assume temp. that ℓ is not tan. to $\odot$ Q. Since ℓ int. $\odot$ Q but is not tan. to $\odot$ Q, it must int. Q in some other pt., say S. $\overline{QR}$ and $\overline{QS}$ are radii of $\odot$ Q so $\overline{QR} \cong \overline{QS}$, and m∠ QSR = m∠ QRS = 90. This contradicts the fact that △ QRS can have at most one rt. ∠. Our temp. assumption must be false; it follows that ℓ is tan. to $\odot$ Q.

<u>24</u>. Let O be the ctr. of the $\odot$ and D, E, and F the pts.
of tangency of $\overline{BC}$, $\overline{AB}$, and $\overline{AC}$, resp.   AE = AF so
BE = CF; but BE = BD and CF = CD so BD = DC
and D is the midpt. of $\overline{BC}$, the base of isos. △ ABC.

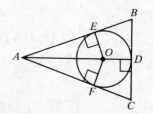

Then $\overline{AD} \perp \overline{BC}$ and $\overline{OD} \perp \overline{BC}$ so O is on $\overline{AD}$.
△ AEO ~ △ ADB; $\frac{AO}{12} = \frac{OE}{4}$; 4 · AO = 12 · OE; AO = 3 · OE; $\frac{8}{AD} = \frac{OE}{4}$;
AD = AO + OD = AO + OE = 4 · OE; $\frac{8}{4 \cdot OE} = \frac{OE}{4}$; $4(OE)^2 = 32$; $(OE)^2 = 8$;
OE = $\sqrt{8}$ = $2\sqrt{2}$

<u>25</u>. Let O be the ctr. of the $\odot$ and D and E the pts. of tangency of $\overline{AC}$ and $\overline{BC}$, resp.
BE = BK = 6; AD = AK = 20; CD = CE; $26^2 = (6 + CE)^2 + (20 + CE)^2 =$
$36 + 12 \cdot CE + (CE)^2 + 400 + 40 \cdot CE + (CE)^2 = 676$; $2(CE)^2 + 52 \cdot CE - 240 = 0$;
$(CE)^2 + 26 \cdot CE - 120 = 0$; (CE + 30)(CE - 4) = 0; CE = 30 (reject) or CE = 4;
AC = 20 + 4 = 24; BC = 6 + 4 = 10; AB = 26

<u>26</u>. Let the rt. △ be △ ABC with ∠ C a rt. ∠, and let E,
F, and G be the pts. of tangency of $\overline{AB}$, $\overline{BC}$, and $\overline{AC}$,
resp.   Since ∠ C is an inscribed rt. ∠, $\overline{AB}$ is a
diameter of the circumscribed $\odot$ and AB = 17;
let AE = x; AG = AE = x; BE = BF = 17 - x;

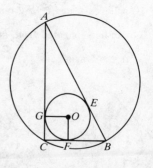

let O be the ctr. of the inscribed $\odot$; GOFC is a
square; CG = CF = OF = 3; $17^2 = (x + 3)^2 +$
$(20 - x)^2$; $x^2 + 6x + 9 + 400 - 40x + x^2 = 289$; $2x^2 - 34x + 120 = 0$; $x^2 - 17x + 60 = 0$; (x - 5)(x - 12) = 0; x = 5 or x = 12. If x = 5, AC = 8 and BC = 15;
if x = 12, AC = 15 and BC = 8.   The sides of the rt. △ have lengths 8, 15, and 17.

Pages 304-306 · WRITTEN EXERCISES

A **1.** 85   **2.** 360 - 280 = 80   **3.** 150   **4.** 180 - 130 = 50

5. 360 - (115 + 125) = 360 - 240 = 120   **6.** 90 - 35 = 55

7. $\frac{360}{12}$ = 30   **8.** 4; 8

9. **a.** Draw A, B, and C so that $\overparen{AB}$ and $\overparen{BC}$ are overlapping arcs.   **b.** no

10. 1. $\overparen{AC} \cong \overparen{CE}$ (Given)   2. $\angle 1 \cong \angle 2$ (In the same $\odot$ 2 minor arcs are $\cong$ if and only if their central $\angle$ are $\cong$.)   3. $\angle 1 \cong \angle 4$; $\angle 2 \cong \angle 3$ (Vert. $\angle$ are $\cong$.)

4. $\angle 3 \cong \angle 4$ (Trans. Prop.)

11. 1. $\angle 4 \cong \angle 1$; $\angle 2 \cong \angle 3$ (Vert. $\angle$ are $\cong$.)   2. $\angle 1 \cong \angle 2$ (Given)   3. $\angle 4 \cong \angle 3$ (Trans. Prop.)   4. $\overparen{BD} \cong \overparen{DF}$ (In the same $\odot$, minor arcs are $\cong$ if and only if their central $\angle$ are $\cong$.)

12. 1. $m\angle 5 = m\angle 7$ (Given)   2. $m\angle 5 + m\angle 6 = m\angle 6 + m\angle 7$ (Add. Prop. of =)   3. $m\angle ROT = m\angle SOU$ (Angle Add. Post.; Subst. Prop.)   4. $\overparen{RT} \cong \overparen{SU}$ (In the same $\odot$, minor arcs are $\cong$ if and only if their central $\angle$ are $\cong$.)

B **13.** 1. Draw $\overline{OY}$. (Through any 2 pts. there is exactly one line.)   2. $\overline{OY} \cong \overline{OZ}$ (All radii of a $\odot$ are $\cong$.)   3. $\angle OZY \cong \angle OYZ$ (If 2 sides of a $\triangle$ are $\cong$, then the $\angle$ opp. those sides are $\cong$.)   4. $\overline{OX} \parallel \overline{ZY}$ (Given)   5. $\angle XOY \cong \angle OYZ$ (If 2 $\parallel$ lines are cut by a trans., then alt. int. $\angle$ are $\cong$.)   6. $\angle WOX \cong \angle OZY$ (If 2 $\parallel$ lines are cut by a trans., then corr. $\angle$ are $\cong$.)   7. $\angle WOX \cong \angle XOY$ (Trans. Prop.)

8. $\overparen{WX} \cong \overparen{XY}$ (In the same $\odot$, 2 minor arcs are $\cong$ if and only if their central $\angle$ are $\cong$.)

14. 1. Draw $\overline{OY}$. (Through any 2 pts. there is exactly one line.)   2. $\overline{OY} \cong \overline{OZ}$ (All radii of a $\odot$ are $\cong$.)   3. $m\angle Z = m\angle OYZ$ (If 2 sides of a $\triangle$ are $\cong$, then the $\angle$ opp. those sides are $\cong$.)   4. $m\angle ZOY = 180 - (m\angle Z + m\angle OYZ) = (180 - 2 \cdot m\angle Z)$ (The sum of the meas. of the $\angle$ of a $\triangle$ is 180; Subst. Prop.)   5. $m\overparen{WX} = m\overparen{XY} = n$; $m\angle WOX = m\angle XOY = n$ (Given; Def. of arc meas.)   6. $m\angle ZOY = 180 - (m\angle WOX + m\angle XOY) = 180 - 2n$ (Angle Add. Post., Trans. Prop.)

7. $180 - 2 \cdot m\angle Z = 180 - 2n$ (Trans. Prop.)   8. $m\angle Z = n$ (By algebra)

15. **a.** 35; 35 + 35 = 70   **b.** 2n   **c.** 3k

16. Draw $\overline{PF}$. $\triangle FPE$ is isos. with $\angle PFE \cong \angle FEP$. $m\angle FPE = m\overparen{EF} = n$; $m\angle DEF = \frac{1}{2}(180 - n) = 90 - \frac{1}{2}n$

C 17. $\cos \frac{n°}{2} \approx \frac{6400}{6700} \approx 0.9552$; $\frac{n°}{2} \approx 17°$; $n° \approx 34°$; $m\widehat{XTY} \approx \frac{34}{360} \cdot 40{,}200 \approx 3800$ km

18. $\cos \frac{n°}{2} \approx \frac{6400}{7000} \approx 0.9143$; $\frac{n°}{2} \approx 24°$; $n° \approx 48°$; $m\widehat{XTY} \approx \frac{48}{360} \cdot 40{,}200 \approx 5400$ km

19. 1. Draw $\overline{OQ}$. (Through any 2 pts. there is exactly one line.)   2. $\overline{OQ} \cong \overline{OQ}$ (Refl. Prop.)   3. $\overline{OR} \cong \overline{OS}$; $\overline{QR} \cong \overline{QS}$ (All radii of a $\odot$ are $\cong$.)   4. $\triangle ORQ \cong \triangle OSQ$ (SSS)   5. $m\angle ROQ = m\angle SOQ = \frac{1}{2}m\angle ROS$; $m\angle RQO = m\angle SQO = \frac{1}{2}m\angle RQS$ (Corr. parts of $\cong \triangle$ are $\cong$, $\angle$ Bis. Thm.)   6. $m\widehat{RVS} = 60$; $m\widehat{RUS} = 120$ (Given)   7. $m\angle ROS = 60$; $m\angle RQS = 120$ (Def. of meas. of an arc)   8. $m\angle ROQ = 30$; $m\angle RQO = 60$ (Subst. Prop.)   9. $m\angle ORQ = 180 - (m\angle ROQ + m\angle RQO) = 90$ (The sum of the meas. of the $\triangle$ of a $\triangle$ is 180; Subst. Prop.)   10. $\overline{OR} \perp \overline{RQ}$ (Def. of $\perp$ lines)   11. $\overline{OR}$ is tan. to $\odot Q$; $\overline{QR}$ is tan. to $\odot O$. (If a line in the plane of a $\odot$ is tan. to a radius at its outer endpt., then the line is tan. to the $\odot$.)

20. Either $\overline{JK} \parallel \overline{AB}$ or $\overline{JK}$ is a diam. of $\odot Z$.   Proof: Case I: ($\widehat{AJ}$ and $\widehat{BK}$ lie on the same side of $\overline{AB}$)   1. Draw $\overline{JK}$, $\overline{ZJ}$, and $\overline{ZK}$. (Through any 2 pts. there is exactly one line.)   2. $\overline{ZJ} \cong \overline{ZK}$ (All radii of a $\odot$ are $\cong$.)   3. $\angle KJZ \cong \angle JKZ$ (If 2 sides of a $\triangle$ are $\cong$, the $\triangle$ opp. those sides are $\cong$.)   4. $m\angle KJZ + m\angle KZJ + m\angle JKZ = 180$; $m\angle KJZ = \frac{1}{2}(180 - m\angle JKZ)$ (The sum of the meas. of a $\triangle$ is 180; algebra)   5. $\widehat{AJ} \cong \widehat{BK}$ (Given)   6. $\angle AZJ \cong \angle BZK$ (In the same $\odot$ 2 minor arcs are $\cong$ if and only if their central $\triangle$ are $\cong$.)   7. $m\angle JZK = 180 - 2 \cdot m\angle AZJ$ (Angle Add. Post.)   8. $m\angle KJZ = \frac{1}{2}(180 - (180 - 2 \cdot m\angle AZJ)) = m\angle AZJ$ (Subst. Prop.)   9. $\overline{JK} \parallel \overline{AB}$ (If 2 lines are cut by a trans. and alt. int. $\triangle$ are $\cong$, then the lines are $\parallel$.)   Case II: ($\widehat{AJ}$ and $\widehat{BK}$ lie on opp. sides of $\overline{AB}$.)   1. Draw $\overline{JK}$. (Through any 2 pts. there is exactly one line.)   2. $m\widehat{JK} = m\widehat{JB} + m\widehat{BK}$ (Arc Add. Post.)   3. $m\widehat{AJ} = m\widehat{BK}$ (Given)   4. $m\widehat{JK} = m\widehat{JB} + m\widehat{AJ} = m\widehat{AB} = 180$ (Arc Add. Post., Subst. Prop.)   5. $\widehat{JK}$ is a semicircle; $\overline{JK}$ is a diam. (Def. of semicircle)

Pages 309-311 · WRITTEN EXERCISES

A 1. $m\widehat{AB} = 95$; $AB = j$

2. $AC = 15$; $OC = \sqrt{17^2 - 15^2} = \sqrt{64} = 8$

3. $OD = \sqrt{8^2 + 6^2} = \sqrt{100} = 10$

4. $EG = 2\sqrt{13^2 - 5^2} = 2\sqrt{144} = 24$

5. $OH = \sqrt{9^2 - 5^2} = \sqrt{56} = 2\sqrt{14}$

6. $OJ = 7\sqrt{2}$

7. Given: $\odot O \cong \odot P$; $\widehat{RS} \cong \widehat{TU}$.   Prove: $\overline{RS} \cong \overline{TU}$.   Proof: 1. Draw $\overline{OR}$, $\overline{OS}$, $\overline{PT}$, and $\overline{PU}$. (Through any 2 pts. there is exactly one line.)   2. $\overline{OR} \cong \overline{OS} \cong \overline{PT} \cong \overline{PU}$ (All radii of $\cong$ $\circledS$ are $\cong$.)   3. $\widehat{RS} \cong \widehat{TU}$ (Given)   4. $\angle ROS \cong \angle TPU$ (In $\cong$ $\circledS$,

2 minor arcs are $\cong$ if and only if their central $\measuredangle$ are $\cong$.)   5. $\triangle$ ROS $\cong$ $\triangle$ TPU (SAS)

6. $\overline{RS} \cong \overline{TU}$ (Corr. parts of $\cong$ $\triangle$ are $\cong$.)

8. a. 1. $\overset{\frown}{JZ} \cong \overset{\frown}{KZ}$ (Given)   2. $\overline{JZ} \cong \overline{KZ}$ (In the same $\odot$, $\cong$ arcs have $\cong$ chords.)

3. $\angle J \cong \angle K$ (If 2 sides of a $\triangle$ are $\cong$, then the $\measuredangle$ opp. those sides are $\cong$.)   b. yes

B   9. 1. $\overline{RS} \cong \overline{UT}$ (Given)   2. $\overset{\frown}{RS} \cong \overset{\frown}{UT}$ (In the same $\odot$, $\cong$ chords have $\cong$ arcs.)

3. $m\overset{\frown}{RS} + m\overset{\frown}{ST} = m\overset{\frown}{UT} + m\overset{\frown}{ST}$ (Add. Prop. of =)   4. $m\overset{\frown}{RT} = m\overset{\frown}{US}$ (Arc Add.

Post.; Subst. Prop.)   5. $\overline{RT} \cong \overline{US}$ (In the same $\odot$, $\cong$ arcs have $\cong$ chords.)

10. 1. $\overset{\frown}{RS} \cong \overset{\frown}{UT}$ (Given)   2. $\overline{RS} \cong \overline{UT}$ (In the same $\odot$, $\cong$ arcs have $\cong$ chords.)

3. $\angle R \cong \angle U$ (Given)   4. $\angle RVS \cong \angle UVT$ (Vert. $\measuredangle$ are $\cong$.)   5. $\triangle RVS \cong \triangle UVT$

(AAS)   6. $\overline{VS} \cong \overline{VT}$; $\overline{RV} \cong \overline{UV}$ (Corr. parts of $\cong$ $\triangle$ are $\cong$.)

11. $\overset{\frown}{AB} \cong \overset{\frown}{BC}$ so AB = BC and 2 $\cdot$ AB = AB + BC > AC by the $\triangle$ Ineq. Thm.

12. a., b. Answers may vary.   c. $\angle A$ and $\angle C$ are supp.; $\angle B$ and $\angle D$ are supp.

d. If a quad. is inscribed in a $\odot$, opp. $\measuredangle$ of the quad. are supp.

13. Draw $\overline{OX} \perp \overline{JK}$; $m\angle XOJ = 60$; JK = 2 $\cdot$ JX = 2 $\cdot$ $6\sqrt{3}$ = $12\sqrt{3}$

14. $m\angle FOE = 30$; OF = 16; HG = 2 $\cdot$ OF = 32

15. $m\angle AOC = 90$; $\overline{OA} \cong \overline{OC}$; $\triangle AOC$ is a 45-45-90 $\triangle$ so AC = $9\sqrt{2}$; BC = $\dfrac{1}{2}$ $\cdot$ AC = $\dfrac{9\sqrt{2}}{2}$

16. $2\sqrt{j^2 - k^2}$

C   17. Answers may vary.   Example: If a chord of the outer $\odot$ of 2 concentric $\circledS$ is tan.

to the inner $\odot$, then the pt. of tangency is the midpt. of the chord.   Given: Con-

centric $\circledS$ with center O, chord $\overline{AC}$ of outer $\odot$ tan. to inner $\odot$ at B.

Prove: AB = BC.   Proof: 1. Draw $\overline{OB}$. (Through any 2 pts. there is exactly one

line.)   2. $\overline{AC}$ is tan. to inner $\odot O$ at B. (Given)   3. $\overline{OB} \perp \overline{AC}$ (If a line is tan.

to a $\odot$, then the line is $\perp$ to the radius drawn to the pt. of tangency.)   4. AB = BC

(A diam. that is $\perp$ to a chord bis. the chord.)

18. Answers may vary.   Example: If a chord of a $\odot$ is $\parallel$ to a line tan. to the $\odot$, then

the pt. of tangency is the midpt. of the arc of the chord.   Given: ℓ tan. to $\odot O$ at F;

$\overline{DE}$ a chord of $\odot O$, $\overline{DE} \parallel \ell$.   Prove: $\overset{\frown}{DF} = \overset{\frown}{FE}$.   Proof: 1. Draw $\overline{OF}$. (Through

any 2 pts. there is exactly one line.)   2. ℓ is tan. to $\odot O$ at F. (Given)   3. $\overline{OF} \perp \ell$

(If a line is tan. to a $\odot$, then the line is $\perp$ to the radius drawn to the pt. of tangency.)

4. $\overline{DE} \parallel \ell$ (Given)   5. $\overline{OF} \perp \overline{DE}$ (If a trans. is $\perp$ to one of 2 $\parallel$ lines, then it is $\perp$

to the other.)   6. $\overset{\frown}{DF} = \overset{\frown}{FE}$ (A diam. that is $\perp$ to a chord bis. the chord and its arc.)

19. Let $\overline{AB}$ and $\overline{CD}$ be chords of $\odot O$ with radius r such that AB = x and CD = 2x.

Distance from O to $\overline{AB}$ = $\sqrt{r^2 - \left(\frac{x}{2}\right)^2}$ = $\sqrt{r^2 - \frac{x^2}{4}}$ = $\sqrt{\frac{4r^2 - x^2}{4}}$ = $\frac{\sqrt{4r^2 - x^2}}{2}$;

Distance from O to $\overline{CD}$ = $\sqrt{r^2 - x^2}$.   If the ratio of the distances is 2:1, $\frac{\sqrt{4r^2 - x^2}}{2}$ =

= $2\sqrt{r^2 - x^2}$; $\sqrt{4r^2 - x^2} = 4\sqrt{r^2 - x^2}$; $4r^2 - x^2 = 16(r^2 - x^2)$; $4r^2 - x^2$ =

$16r^2 - 16x^2$; $15x^2 = 12r^2$; $x^2 = \frac{4}{5}r^2$; $x = \sqrt{\frac{4}{5}}r = \frac{2\sqrt{5}}{5}r$; AB = $\frac{2\sqrt{5}}{5}r$; CD = $\frac{4\sqrt{5}}{5}r$

20. Refer to semicircle O with diameter $\overline{AB}$.

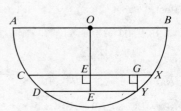

OE = $\sqrt{10^2 - 8^2}$ = $\sqrt{36}$ = 6; OF =

$\sqrt{10^2 - 6^2}$ = $\sqrt{64}$ = 8; GY = EF =

8 - 6 = 2; GX = 8 - 6 = 2; XY =

$2\sqrt{2} \approx$ 2.8 cm.

Pages 315-317 · WRITTEN EXERCISES

A 1. x = 180 - (100 + 50) = 30; y = $\frac{50}{2}$ = 25; z = $\frac{30}{2}$ = 15

2. x = 2 · 65 = 130; y = 2 · 60 = 120; z = 2 · 55 = 110

3. x = 180 - 70 = 110; y = 180 - 80 = 100; $\frac{z + 120}{2}$ = 110; z = 100

4. x = $\frac{140}{2}$ = 70; y = 2 · 55 = 110; z = 360 - (140 + 110) = 110

5. x = 50; y = 2 · 65 = 130; z = 65   6. x = y = z = 90

7. 1. $\overline{AB} \parallel \overline{CD}$ (Given)   2. Draw $\overline{BC}$. (Through any 2 pts. there is exactly one line.)

3. m∠ABC = m∠BCD (If 2 ∥ lines are cut by a trans., then alt. int. ∠s are ≅.)

4. m∠ABC = $\frac{1}{2}$m$\overarc{AC}$; m∠BCD = $\frac{1}{2}$m$\overarc{BD}$ (The meas. of an inscribed ∠ is = half

the meas. of the intercepted arc.)   5. $\frac{1}{2}$m$\overarc{AC}$ = $\frac{1}{2}$m$\overarc{BD}$ (Subst. Prop.)

6. m$\overarc{AC}$ = m$\overarc{BD}$; $\overarc{AC} \cong \overarc{BD}$ (Mult. Prop. of =)

8. 1. ∠U ≅ ∠Y; ∠X ≅ ∠V (If 2 inscribed ∠s intercept the same arc, then the ∠s are ≅.)

2. △UXZ ~ △YVZ (AA)

9. 1. If a line is tan. to a $\odot$, then the line is ⊥ to the radius drawn to the pt. of

tangency; def. of ⊥ lines.   2. Def. of semicircle   3. Mult. or Div. Prop. of =

4. Subst. Prop.

B 10. 1. Draw diam. $\overline{TZ}$. (Through any 2 pts. there is exactly one line.)   2. m∠ATZ =

$\frac{1}{2}$m$\overarc{AZ}$ (The meas. of an inscribed ∠ = half the meas. of its intercepted arc.)

3. m∠ZTP = $\frac{1}{2}$m$\overarc{ZNT}$ (Case I)   4. m∠ATP = m∠ATZ + m∠ZTP (Angle Add.

Post.)   5. $m\angle ATP = \frac{1}{2}m\overset{\frown}{AZ} + \frac{1}{2}m\overset{\frown}{ZNT} = \frac{1}{2}(m\overset{\frown}{AZ} + m\overset{\frown}{ZNT})$ (Subst. and Dist.

Props.)   6. $m\overset{\frown}{AZ} + m\overset{\frown}{ZNT} = m\overset{\frown}{ANT}$ (Arc. Add. Post.)   7. $m\angle ATP =$

$\frac{1}{2}m\overset{\frown}{ANT}$ (Subst. Prop.)

11. 1. Draw diam. $\overline{TZ}$. (Through any 2 pts. there is exactly one line.)   2. $m\angle ZTA =$

$\frac{1}{2}m\overset{\frown}{ZA}$ (The meas. of an inscribed $\angle$ = half the meas. of its intercepted arc.)

3. $m\angle ZTP = \frac{1}{2}m\overset{\frown}{ZNT}$ (Case I)   4. $m\angle ZTP = m\angle ZTA + m\angle ATP$; $m\angle ATP =$

$m\angle ZTP - m\angle ZTA$ (Angle Add. Post.)   5. $m\angle ATP = \frac{1}{2}m\overset{\frown}{ZNT} - \frac{1}{2}m\overset{\frown}{ZA} =$

$\frac{1}{2}(m\overset{\frown}{ZNT} - m\overset{\frown}{ZA})$ (Subst. and Dist. Props.)   6. $m\overset{\frown}{ZNT} = m\overset{\frown}{ZA} + m\overset{\frown}{ANT}$;

$m\overset{\frown}{ANT} = m\overset{\frown}{ZNT} - m\overset{\frown}{ZA}$ (Arc Add. Post.)   7. $m\angle ATP = \frac{1}{2}m\overset{\frown}{ANT}$ (Subst. Prop.)

12. $m\overset{\frown}{AE} = \frac{360}{15} \cdot 4 = 96$; $m\angle ABE = \frac{1}{2}(360 - 96) = 132$

13. $m\angle J = 180 - x$; $x + (x + 20) = 180$; $2x = 160$; $x = 80$; $m\angle J = 100$

14. $x^2 + 11x = 180$; $x^2 + 11x - 180 = 0$; $(x + 20)(x - 9) = 0$; $x = -20$ (reject) or

$x = 9$; $x^2 = 81$; $9x - 2 = 79$; $11x = 99$; $x^2 + 20 = 101$; $\angle J$ is the largest $\angle$;

$m\angle J = 101$.

15. a. Suppose a $\odot$ is circumscribed about the polygon.   The sides of the polygon are $\cong$

chords and so have $\cong$ arcs.   Since the meas. of each numbered $\angle$ is half the meas.

of one of the $\cong$ arcs, the $\angle$ are $\cong$.   b. yes

C 16. Assume temp. that D is not on $\odot$O.   Case I: (D is inside $\odot$O.)   Let X be the pt.

where $\overrightarrow{AD}$ int. $\odot$O and draw $\overline{CX}$.   Quad. ABCX is inscribed in $\odot$O so

$m\angle AXC + m\angle B = 180$.   But $m\angle D + m\angle B = 180$ so $m\angle AXC = m\angle D$.   Then

$\overline{CD} \parallel \overline{CX}$.   This contradicts the fact that $\overline{CX}$ and $\overline{CD}$ int. at C.   Case II: (D is

outside $\odot$O.)   Let X be the pt. where $\overrightarrow{AD}$ int. $\odot$O and draw $\overline{CX}$.   Again,

$m\angle AXC + m\angle B = 180$ and $m\angle D + m\angle B = 180$ so $m\angle AXC = m\angle D$.   Then

$\overline{CD} \parallel \overline{CX}$.   This contradicts the fact that $\overline{CX}$ and $\overline{CD}$ int. at C.   In either case,

our temp. assumption must be false.   It follows that D is on $\odot$O.

17. $\triangle PRT \sim \triangle PTS \sim \triangle SUT$ Given that $\overline{PT}$ is a tangent and $\overline{TU} \parallel \overline{PS}$, prove that

$\triangle PRT \sim \triangle PTS \sim \triangle SUT$.   Proof: $m\angle PTR = \frac{1}{2}m\overset{\frown}{TR} = m\angle TSR$; $\angle P \cong \angle P$.   Then

$\triangle PRT \sim \triangle PTS$ by the AA $\sim$ Post. $\angle U$ and $\angle TRS$ are supp. and $\angle PRT$ and $\angle TRS$

are supp. so $\angle U \cong \angle PRT$.   Since $\overline{TU} \parallel \overline{RS}$, $\angle STU \cong \angle PST$; $\angle PST \cong \angle PTR$ (Corr.

$\angle$ of $\sim$ $\triangle$ are $\cong$.)   Then $\angle STU \cong \angle PTR$ and $\triangle PRT \sim \triangle SUT$. (AA)

18. $\overline{KG} \cong \overline{KH} \cong \overline{KI}$ Given: $\odot I$ inscribed in $\triangle FGH$

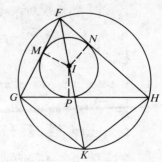

and $\odot O$ circumscribed about $\triangle FGH$.

Prove: $\overline{KG} \cong \overline{KH} \cong \overline{KI}$ Proof: 1. $\odot I$ is

inscribed in $\triangle FGH$ (Given)   2. $\overline{FG}$, $\overline{FH}$, and

$\overline{GH}$ are tan. to $\odot I$ at M, N, and P, resp.

(Def. of an inscribed $\odot$)   3. Draw $\overline{IM}$, $\overline{IN}$,

and $\overline{IP}$. (Through any 2 pts. there is exactly one

line.)   4. $\overline{IM} \cong \overline{IN} \cong \overline{IP}$ (All radii of a $\odot$ are $\cong$.)   5. $\overline{FM} \cong \overline{FN}$; $\overline{HN} \cong \overline{HP}$ (Tan.

to a $\odot$ from a pt. are $\cong$.)   6. $\overline{FI} \cong \overline{FI}$; $\overline{HI} \cong \overline{HI}$ (Refl. Prop.)   7. $\triangle FMI \cong \triangle FNI$;

$\triangle HNI \cong \triangle HPI$ (SSS)   8. $m\angle GFK = m\angle KFH$; $m\angle FHI = m\angle GHI$ (Corr. parts of $\cong$

$\triangle$ are $\cong$.)   9. $\frac{1}{2}m\angle GFK = \frac{1}{2}m\angle KFH$ (Mult. Prop. of =)   10. $\overparen{KG} \cong \overparen{KH}$ (The

meas. of an inscribed $\angle$ = half the meas. of its intercepted arc, Subst. Prop.)

10. $\overline{KG} \cong \overline{KH}$ (In the same $\odot$ $\cong$ arcs have $\cong$ chords.)   11. $m\angle GFK = m\angle GHK$

(If 2 inscribed $\angle$ intercept the same arc, then the $\angle$ are $\cong$.)   12. $m\angle KHI =$

$m\angle GHK + m\angle GHI$ (Angle Add. Post.)   13. $m\angle KHI = m\angle KFH + m\angle FHI$ (Subst.

Prop.)   14. $m\angle KIH = m\angle KFH + m\angle FHI$ (The meas. of an ext. $\angle$ of a $\triangle$ = the sum

of the meas. of the 2 remote int. $\angle$.)   15. $m\angle KHI = m\angle KIH$ (Subst. Prop.)

16. $\overline{KI} \cong \overline{KH}$ (If 2 $\angle$ of a $\triangle$ are $\cong$, then the sides opp. those $\angle$ are $\cong$.)

17. $\overline{KG} \cong \overline{KH} \cong \overline{KI}$ (Trans. Prop.)

19. Let $\overline{CD}$ be the alt. to the hyp.   The diam. of the smallest $\odot$ through C that is tan.

to $\overline{AB}$ is CD.   The center of the $\odot$ is M, the midpt. of $\overline{CD}$.   Since $m\angle JCK = 90$,

JK is a diam. of $\odot M$ and JK = CD.   To find CD in terms of a, b, and c, note that

$\triangle ABC \sim \triangle ACD$; $\frac{c}{b} = \frac{a}{CD}$; $CD = \frac{ab}{c}$; $JK = \frac{ab}{c}$.

20. Given: $\triangle ABC$ with $\overline{AB} \cong \overline{AC} \cong \overline{BC}$; $\odot O$ circumscribed

about $\triangle ABC$; P on $\odot O$.   Prove: BP = AP + PC.

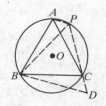

Proof: 1. $\triangle ABC$ is equilateral. (Given)   2. $m\angle ABC =$

$m\angle BCA = m\angle BAC = 60$ (Each $\angle$ of an equilateral $\triangle$ has

meas. 60.)   3. $m\angle APB = m\angle ACB = 60$; $m\angle BPC =$

$m\angle BAC = 60$ (If 2 inscribed $\angle$ intercept the same arc, the $\angle$ are $\cong$.)   4. Extend

$\overrightarrow{PC}$ to draw PD = BP. (Ruler Post.)   4. $m\angle PBD = m\angle PDB = 60$ (If 2 sides of a $\triangle$

are $\cong$, then the $\angle$ opp. those sides are $\cong$; the sum of the meas. of the $\angle$ of a $\triangle$ is

180.)   5. △PBD is equilateral. (An equiangular △ is equilateral.)   6. m∠ABP +

m∠PBC = 60 = m∠PBC + m∠CBD (Angle Add. Post.)   7. m∠ABP = m∠CBD

(Subtr. Prop. of =)   8. △ABP ≅ △CBD (ASA)   9. AP = CD (Corr. parts of ≅

▲ are ≅.)   10. BP = CD + PC (Subst. Prop., Seg. Add. Post.)   11. BP =

AP + PC (Subst. Prop.)

21. Given: Quad. ABCD inscribed in ⊙ ; diag. $\overline{AC}$, $\overline{BD}$ intersect

at M   Prove: AC · BD = AB · CD + AD · BC

Proof: 1. Draw $\overline{DX}$ such that ∠ADX ≅ ∠BDC, intersecting

$\overline{AC}$ at X. (Protractor Post.)   2. ∠ABD ≅ ∠ACD; ∠DAC ≅

∠DBC (If 2 inscribed ▲ intercept the same arc, then the ▲

are ≅.)   3. △ADX ~ △BDC (AA)   4. ∠XDB ≅ ∠XDB (Refl. Prop.)   5. ∠ADB ≅

∠XDC (Angle Add. Post., Add. Prop. of =)   6. △ADB ~ △XDC (AA)

7. $\frac{XC}{AB} = \frac{CD}{BD}$; $\frac{AX}{BC} = \frac{AD}{BD}$ (Corr. sides of ~ ▲ are in prop.)   8. XC · BD = AB · CD;

AX · BD = AD · BC (Means-extremes prop.)   9. XC · BD + AX · BD =

AB · CD + AD · BC (Add. Prop. of =)   10. (XC + AX) · BD = AB · CD +

AD · BC and AC · BD = AB · CD + AD · BC (Algebra, Seg. Add. Post.)

Pages 319-320 · WRITTEN EXERCISES

A 1. m∠1 = 90   2. m∠2 = 90

3. m∠3 = $\frac{1}{2}$(30 + 20) = 25   4. m∠4 = 90 - 25 = 65

5. m∠5 = $\frac{1}{2}$(90 + 20) = 55   6. m∠6 = $\frac{1}{2}$(220 + 30) = 125

7. m∠7 = $\frac{1}{2}$(90 - 20) = 35   8. m∠8 = $\frac{1}{2}$(90 + 30) = 60

9. m∠9 = 90   10. m∠10 = $\frac{1}{2}$ · 120 = 60

11. $\frac{1}{2}$(80 + 40) = 60   12. $\frac{1}{2}$(360 - (130 + 100)) = 65

13. 50 = $\frac{1}{2}$(70 + m$\overparen{US}$); 100 = 70 + m$\overparen{US}$; m$\overparen{US}$ = 30

14. 52 = $\frac{1}{2}$(36 + m$\overparen{RT}$); 104 = 36 + m$\overparen{RT}$; m$\overparen{RT}$ = 68

15. m∠P = $\frac{1}{2}$(250 - (360 - 250)) = $\frac{1}{2}$ · 140 = 70

16. m∠P = $\frac{1}{2}$((360 - 90) - 90) = $\frac{1}{2}$ · 180 = 90

17. $85 = \frac{1}{2}((360 - m\overset{\frown}{XY}) - m\overset{\frown}{XY})$; $170 = 360 - 2m\overset{\frown}{XY}$; $2m\overset{\frown}{XY} = 190$; $m\overset{\frown}{XY} = 95$

18. $m\angle A = \frac{1}{2}(110 - 50) = 30$

19. $40 = \frac{1}{2}(m\overset{\frown}{CT} - 40)$; $80 = m\overset{\frown}{CT} - 40$; $m\overset{\frown}{CT} = 120$

20. $35 = \frac{1}{2}(110 - m\overset{\frown}{BT})$; $70 = 110 - m\overset{\frown}{BT}$; $m\overset{\frown}{BT} = 40$

B 21. Let ABCD be the quad. with $m\angle A = 80$, $m\angle B = 90$, $m\angle C = 94$, $m\angle D = 96$, and

let W, X, Y, and Z be the pts. of tangency of $\overline{AB}$, $\overline{BC}$, $\overline{CD}$, and $\overline{AD}$, resp.

$90 = \frac{1}{2}((360 - m\overset{\frown}{WX}) - m\overset{\frown}{WX})$; $180 = 360 - 2m\overset{\frown}{WX}$; $2m\overset{\frown}{WX} = 180$; $m\overset{\frown}{WX} = 90$;

$94 = \frac{1}{2}((360 - m\overset{\frown}{XY}) - m\overset{\frown}{XY})$; $188 = 360 - 2m\overset{\frown}{XY}$; $2m\overset{\frown}{XY} = 172$; $m\overset{\frown}{XY} = 86$;

$96 = \frac{1}{2}((360 - m\overset{\frown}{YZ}) - m\overset{\frown}{YZ})$; $192 = 360 - 2m\overset{\frown}{YZ}$; $2m\overset{\frown}{YZ} = 168$; $m\overset{\frown}{YZ} = 84$;

$80 = \frac{1}{2}((360 - m\overset{\frown}{WZ}) - m\overset{\frown}{WZ})$; $160 = 360 - 2m\overset{\frown}{WZ}$; $2m\overset{\frown}{WZ} = 200$; $m\overset{\frown}{WZ} = 100$

(or $m\overset{\frown}{WZ} = 360 - (90 + 86 + 84) = 100$)

22. Given: Tangents $\overline{PA}$ and $\overline{PB}$.   Prove: $m\angle 1 =$

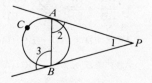

$\frac{1}{2}(m\overset{\frown}{ACB} - m\overset{\frown}{AB})$.   Proof: 1. Draw chord $\overline{AB}$.

(Through any 2 pts. there is exactly one line.)

2. $m\angle 3 = m\angle 2 + m\angle 1$; $m\angle 1 = m\angle 3 - m\angle 2$

(The meas. of an ext. $\angle$ of a $\triangle$ = the sum of the meas. of the 2 remote int. $\angle$s ; Subtr.

Prop. of =)   3. $m\angle 3 = \frac{1}{2}m\overset{\frown}{ACB}$; $m\angle 2 = \frac{1}{2}m\overset{\frown}{AB}$ (The meas. of an $\angle$ formed by a

chord and a tan. = half the meas. of the intercepted arc.)   4. $m\angle 1 = \frac{1}{2}m\overset{\frown}{ACB} -$

$\frac{1}{2}m\overset{\frown}{AB} = \frac{1}{2}(m\overset{\frown}{ACB} - m\overset{\frown}{AB})$ (Subst. and Dist. Props.)

23. Given: Secant $\overline{PA}$ and tangent $\overline{PC}$.   Prove: $m\angle 1 =$

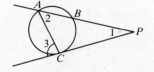

$\frac{1}{2}(m\overset{\frown}{AC} - m\overset{\frown}{BC})$ Proof: 1. Draw chord $\overline{AC}$.

(Through any 2 pts. there is exactly one line.)

2. $m\angle 3 = m\angle 2 + m\angle 1$; $m\angle 1 = m\angle 3 - m\angle 2$ (The

meas. of an ext. $\angle$ of a $\triangle$ = the sum of the meas. of the 2 remote int. $\angle$s; Subtr.

Prop. of =)   3. $m\angle 3 = \frac{1}{2}m\overset{\frown}{AC}$; $m\angle 2 = \frac{1}{2}m\overset{\frown}{BC}$ (The meas. of an $\angle$ formed by a

chord and a tan. = half the meas. of the intercepted arc.)   4. $m\angle 1 = \frac{1}{2}m\overset{\frown}{AC} -$

$\frac{1}{2}m\overset{\frown}{BC} = \frac{1}{2}(m\overset{\frown}{AC} - m\overset{\frown}{BC})$ (Subst. and Dist. Props.)

24. Let $\angle 1$ be the $\angle$ inscribed in the outer $\odot$; $m\angle 1 = \frac{1}{2}c$; $m\angle 1 = \frac{1}{2}(b - a)$;

$\frac{1}{2}c = \frac{1}{2}(b - a)$; $c = b - a$

25. $n = \frac{1}{2}(x - y)$ so $2n = x - y$; also, $2n = \frac{1}{2}(x + y)$; $x - y = \frac{1}{2}(x + y)$; $2x - 2y = x + y$; $x = 3y$; $\frac{x}{y} = 3$; $x:y = 3:1$

C 26. Let X be a pt. on the $\odot$ not on $\overset{\frown}{RST}$. $m\angle P = \frac{1}{2}(m\overset{\frown}{RXT} - m\overset{\frown}{ST})$; $m\overset{\frown}{RXT} = 360 - (m\overset{\frown}{RS} + m\overset{\frown}{ST})$; $160 < m\overset{\frown}{RS} + m\overset{\frown}{ST} < 180$; $180 < m\overset{\frown}{RXT} < 200$; $90 < m\overset{\frown}{RXT} - m\overset{\frown}{ST} < 120$; $45 < m\angle P < 60$

27. $m\overset{\frown}{CE} = 3m\overset{\frown}{BD}$.   Proof: 1. $m\angle CAO = \frac{1}{2}(m\overset{\frown}{CE} - m\overset{\frown}{BD})$ (The meas. of an $\angle$ formed by 2 secants drawn from a pt. outside a $\odot$ = half the diff. of the meas. of the intercepted arcs.)   2. $m\angle BOD = m\overset{\frown}{BD}$ (Def. of meas. of an arc)   3. $\overline{AB} \cong \overline{OB}$ (Given) 4. $m\angle CAO = m\angle BOD$ (If 2 sides of a $\triangle$ are $\cong$, then the $\angle$ opp. those sides are $\cong$.) 5. $\frac{1}{2}(m\overset{\frown}{CE} - m\overset{\frown}{BD}) = m\overset{\frown}{BD}$ (Subst. Prop.)   6. $m\overset{\frown}{CE} - m\overset{\frown}{BD} = 2m\overset{\frown}{BD}$; $m\overset{\frown}{CE} = 3m\overset{\frown}{BD}$ (By algebra)

28. $\overset{\frown}{AX} \cong \overset{\frown}{XB}$.   Given: $\overline{PT}$ a tan.; PK = PT   Prove: $\overset{\frown}{AX} \cong \overset{\frown}{XB}$

Proof: 1. PK = PT (Given)   2. $m\angle PTK = m\angle PKT$ (If 2 sides of a $\triangle$ are $\cong$, then the $\angle$ opp. those sides are $\cong$.)   3. $\overline{PT}$ is a tan. (Given)   4. $m\angle PTK = \frac{1}{2}m\overset{\frown}{TBX}$ (The meas. of an $\angle$ formed by a chord and a tan. = half the meas. of the intercepted arc.)   5. $m\overset{\frown}{TBX} = m\overset{\frown}{TB} + m\overset{\frown}{BX}$ (Arc Add. Post.) 6. $m\angle PTK = \frac{1}{2}(m\overset{\frown}{TB} + m\overset{\frown}{BX}) = \frac{1}{2}m\overset{\frown}{TB} + \frac{1}{2}m\overset{\frown}{BX}$ (Subst. and Dist. Props.) 7. $m\angle PKT = \frac{1}{2}(m\overset{\frown}{TB} + m\overset{\frown}{AX}) = \frac{1}{2}m\overset{\frown}{TB} + \frac{1}{2}m\overset{\frown}{AX}$ (The meas. of an $\angle$ formed by 2 chords that intersect inside a $\odot$ = half the sum of the meas. of the intercepted arcs; Dist. Prop.)   8. $\frac{1}{2}m\overset{\frown}{TB} + \frac{1}{2}m\overset{\frown}{AX} = \frac{1}{2}m\overset{\frown}{TB} + \frac{1}{2}m\overset{\frown}{BX}$ (Subst. Prop.) 9. $m\overset{\frown}{AX} = m\overset{\frown}{BX}$ or $\overset{\frown}{AX} \cong \overset{\frown}{BX}$ (By algebra)

Pages 323-325 · WRITTEN EXERCISES

A   1. $4x = 40$; $x = 10$ 2. $x^2 = 9 \cdot 16 = 144$; $x = 12$

3. $x^2 = 3 \cdot 7 = 21$; $x = \sqrt{21}$

4. $2x \cdot 3x = 3 \cdot 8$; $6x^2 = 24$; $x^2 = 4$; $x = 2$

5. $4(x + 4) = 5 \cdot 8$; $4x + 16 = 40$; $4x = 24$; $x = 6$

6. $x^2 = 3 \cdot 9 = 27$; $x = 3\sqrt{3}$ 7. $5x = 3 \cdot 10 = 30$; $x = 6$

8. $\frac{9}{2}x = \frac{9}{4} \cdot \frac{16}{3} = 12$; $x = \frac{24}{9} = 2\frac{2}{3}$

9. $x \cdot 4x = 10^2$; $4x^2 = 100$; $x^2 = 25$; $x = 5$

<u>10.</u> 1. Through any 2 pts. there is exactly one line.   2. The meas. of an inscribed $\angle$ = half the meas. of the intercepted arc.   3. = half the meas. of the intercepted arc. 4. Trans. Prop.   5. Refl. Prop.   6. $\triangle$ ACP $\sim$ $\triangle$ CBP (AA)   7. $\frac{s}{t} = \frac{t}{r}$ (Corr. sides of $\sim$ $\triangle$ are in prop.)   8. r $\cdot$ s = t^2 (Means-extremes Prop.)

<u>B</u> <u>11.</u> 1. $\overline{UT}$ is tan to $\odot$O and $\odot$P; $\overline{UW}$ and $\overline{UY}$ are secants. (Given)   2. UV $\cdot$ UW = (UT)^2; UX $\cdot$ UY = (UT)^2 (When a secant seg. and a tan. seg. are drawn to a $\odot$ from an outside pt., the prod. of the length of the secant seg. and the length of its ext. seg. = the square of the length of the tan. seg.)   3. UV $\cdot$ UW = UX $\cdot$ UY (Subst. Prop.)

<u>12.</u> 1. $\overline{AB}$ is tan to $\odot$Q; $\overline{AC}$ is tan to $\odot$S; $\overline{AE}$ and $\overline{AG}$ are secants. (Given)   2. (AB)^2 = AD $\cdot$ AE; (AC)^2 = AF $\cdot$ AG (When a secant seg. and a tan. seg. are drawn to a $\odot$ from an outside pt., the prod. of the length of the secant seg. and the length of its ext. seg. = the square of the length of the tan. seg.)   3. AD $\cdot$ AE = AF $\cdot$ AG (When 2 secant seg. are drawn to a $\odot$ from an outside pt., the prod. of the lengths of one secant seg. and its ext. seg. = the prod. of the lengths of the other secant seg. and its ext. seg.)   4. (AB)^2 = (AC)^2; AB = AC or $\overline{AB} \cong \overline{AC}$ (Subst. Prop.; algebra)

<u>13.</u> Let DP = x; x(16 - x) = 6 $\cdot$ 8; 16x - x^2 = 48; x^2 - 16x + 48 = 0; (x - 12)(x - 4) = 0; x = 12 or x = 4; DP = 12 or 4

<u>14.</u> Let AP = x; x(11 - x) = 6 $\cdot$ 4; 11x - x^2 = 24; x^2 - 11x + 24 = 0; (x - 8)(x - 3) = 0; x = 8 or x = 3; AP = 8 or 3

<u>15.</u> Let BP = x; x(12 - x) = 9 $\cdot$ 4; 12x - x^2 = 36; x^2 - 12x + 36 = 0; (x - 6)^2 = 0; x = 6; BP = 6

<u>16.</u> Let DP = x; x $\cdot$ 3x = 5 $\cdot$ 6; 3x^2 = 30; x^2 = 10; x = $\sqrt{10}$; DP = $\sqrt{10}$

<u>17.</u> 3(AB + 3) = 6^2; 3 $\cdot$ AB + 9 = 36; 3 $\cdot$ AB = 27; AB = 9

<u>18.</u> PC(PC - 18) = 12^2; (PC)^2 - 18 PC - 144 = 0; (PC - 24)(PC + 6) = 0; PC = -6 (reject) or PC = 24; PC = 24

<u>19.</u> PB(PB + 11) = 5 $\cdot$ 12; (PB)^2 + 11 $\cdot$ PB = 60; (PB)^2 + 11 $\cdot$ PB - 60 = 0; (PB + 15)(PB - 4) = 0; PB = -15 (reject) or PB = 4; PB = 4

<u>20.</u> (PT)^2 = 5 $\cdot$ 10 = 50; PT = $\sqrt{50}$ = 5$\sqrt{2}$; 4 $\cdot$ PC = 5 $\cdot$ 10 = 50; PC = 12.5

C 21. By prod. of segments $6x = 8 \cdot 12$,

x = 16; diameters bisect both segments

so that XQ = QZ = 10 and WQ = 2,

YP = 11 and WP = 5   a. Radius $\overline{OZ}$

has measure $\sqrt{10^2 + 5^2} = 5\sqrt{5}$

b. The distance WO is $\sqrt{5^2 + 2^2} =$

$\sqrt{29}$

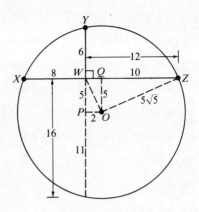

22. Extend $\overrightarrow{PN}$ to intersect $\odot O$ at R; $8(RN + 12) = 12^2$; $8 \cdot RN + 96 = 144$;

$8 \cdot RN = 48$; RN = 6; let r = radius of $\odot O$; extend $\overrightarrow{ON}$ to intersect $\odot O$ at A

and extend $\overrightarrow{NO}$ to intersect $\odot O$ at B; $BN \cdot AN = 6 \cdot 4$; $(BO + ON)NB = 24$;

$(r + 4)(r - 4) = 24$; $r^2 - 16 = 24$; $r^2 = 40$; $r = \sqrt{40} = 2\sqrt{10}$

23. $m\angle FCD = \frac{1}{2}m\widehat{BC} = \frac{1}{2}m\widehat{AC} = m\angle ABF$ and $m\angle CFD = m\angle BFA$ so $\triangle CFD \sim \triangle BFA$;

$\frac{FD}{6} = \frac{CD}{3}$; $CD = \frac{FD}{2} = \frac{FE + ED}{2} = \frac{10 + ED}{2}$; also, $ED(ED + 16) = (CD)^2 =$

$(\frac{10 + ED}{2})^2$; $(ED)^2 + 16 \cdot ED = \frac{100 + 20 \cdot ED + (ED)^2}{4}$; $4(ED)^2 + 64 \cdot ED =$

$100 + 20 \cdot ED + (ED)^2$; $3(ED)^2 + 44 \cdot ED - 100 = 0$; by the quad. formula,

$ED = -\frac{50}{3}$ (reject) or ED = 2; ED = 2

Page 326 · APPLICATION

1. $3600\sqrt{16} = 3600(4) = 14,400$; about 14 km

2. $3600\sqrt{36} = 3600(6) = 21,600$; about 22 km

3. $3600\sqrt{10000} = 3600(100) = 360,000$; about 360 km

4. $3600\sqrt{h} = 8000$; $\sqrt{h} = \frac{8000}{3600} \approx 2.2$; $h \approx 5$ m

5. The distance is the same as that from an observer at the top of Mt. Fuji to the horizon;

$3600\sqrt{3776} \approx 3600(60) = 216,000$; about 220 km

Page 328 · CALCULATOR KEY-IN

1. yes   2-5. Answers will vary depending on numbers of terms used.

Pages 329-330 · CHAPTER REVIEW

1. chord; secant   2. radius   3. diameter   4. inscribed in   5. $\perp$

6. $\sqrt{6^2 + 8^2} = \sqrt{100} = 10$ 7. $\overline{ZX} \cong \overline{ZY}$; $\triangle XYZ$ is a 45-45-90 $\triangle$; $XY = 13\sqrt{2}$

8. 42   9. $360 - (120 + 130) = 110$ 10. a. 180   b. $\cong$ 11. $\frac{1}{2} \cdot 120 = 60$

12. $m\widehat{AC} = 120$ 13. $\angle$ 14. $\sqrt{12^2 + 5^2} = \sqrt{169} = 13$ 15. $180 - 105 = 75$

16. $\frac{1}{2} \cdot 100 = 50$; $\frac{1}{2} \cdot 100 = 50$ 17. $2 \cdot 110 = 220$; $360 - 220 = 140$

18. $\frac{1}{2}(40 + 60) = 50$ 19. $55 = \frac{1}{2}(44 + m\widehat{BD})$; $110 = 44 + m\widehat{BD}$; $m\widehat{BD} = 66$

20. $\frac{1}{2}(100 - 40) = 30$ 21. $25 = \frac{1}{2}(90 - m\widehat{FH})$; $50 = 90 - m\widehat{FH}$; $m\widehat{FH} = 40$

22. $4x = 6 \cdot 8 = 48$; $x = 12$

23. $7(x + 7) = 8(14)$; $7x + 49 = 112$; $7x = 63$; $x = 9$

24. $x^2 = 5 \cdot 11 = 55$; $x = \sqrt{55}$

Pages 330-331 · CHAPTER TEST

1. true   2. true   3. false   4. false   5. true   6. false

7. false   8. true   9. true   10. false

11. $180 - \frac{1}{2} \cdot 100 = 130$ 12. $\sqrt{17^2 - 15^2} = \sqrt{64} = 8$

13. $m\angle C = m\angle A = \frac{1}{2} \cdot 80 = 40$; $m\angle ABC = 180 - 2 \cdot 40 = 100$

14. $110 = \frac{1}{2}((360 - m\widehat{BA}) - m\widehat{BA})$; $220 = 360 - 2m\widehat{BA}$; $2m\widehat{BA} = 140$; $m\widehat{BA} = 70$;

 $m\angle BCA = \frac{1}{2} \cdot 70 = 35$

15. $\frac{1}{2}(50 + 38) = 44$ 16. $15 \cdot ED = 10 \cdot 9 = 90$; $ED = 6$

17. $m\widehat{RT} = 360 - (120 + 160) = 80$; $m\angle P = \frac{1}{2}(160 - 80) = 40$

18. $18 \cdot PR = 12^2 = 144$; $PR = 8$

19. 1. Draw $\overline{OT}$ and $\overline{OQ}$. (Through any 2 pts. there is exactly one line.)   2. $\overline{OT} \cong \overline{OQ}$
(All radii of a $\odot$ are $\cong$.)   3. $\overline{OK} \cong \overline{OK}$ (Refl. Prop.)   4. $\overline{TK} \cong \overline{KQ}$ (Given)
5. $\triangle OKT \cong \triangle OKQ$ (SSS)   6. $\angle TKO \cong \angle QKO$ (Corr. parts of $\cong \triangle$ are $\cong$.)
7. $\overline{TQ} \perp \overline{OK}$ (If 2 lines form $\cong$ adj. $\angle$, then the lines are $\perp$.)

20. 1. $\overline{AD}$ is tan. to $\odot P$ (Given)   2. $m\angle BAD = 90$ (If a line is tan. to a $\odot$, then the
line is $\perp$ to the radius drawn to the pt. of tangency; def. of $\perp$ lines, rt. $\angle$)
3. $m\angle ACB = 90$ (An $\angle$ inscribed in a semicircle is a rt. $\angle$; def. of rt. $\angle$)
4. $m\angle ACD = 180 - 90 = 90$ (Angle Add. Post.)   5. $m\angle BAD = m\angle ACD$ (Subst.
Prop.)   6. $m\angle ABD = \frac{1}{2}m\widehat{AC}$ (The meas. of an inscribed $\angle$ = half the meas. of

the intercepted arc.)   7. $m\angle CAD = \frac{1}{2}m\widehat{AC}$ (The meas. of an $\angle$ formed by a chord

and a tan. = half the meas. of the intercepted arc.)   8. $m\angle ABD = m\angle CAD$ (Subst.

Prop.)   9. $\triangle BAD \sim \triangle ACD$ (AA)

Page 332 · MIXED REVIEW

1. 3; $2x + 3$

2. $\dfrac{180 - x}{90 - x} = \dfrac{5}{2}$; $360 - 2x = 450 - 5x$; $3x = 90$; $x = 30$

3. 1. $\overline{MN}$ is the median of trap. WXYZ. (Given)   2. $\overline{MN} \parallel \overline{WX} \parallel \overline{ZY}$ (The median of a

trap. is $\parallel$ to the bases.)   3. M is the midpt. of $\overline{WZ}$. (Def. of median)

4. $\overline{WM} \cong \overline{MZ}$ (Def. of midpt.)   5. $\overline{WV} \cong \overline{VY}$ (If 3 $\parallel$ lines cut off $\cong$ seg. on one

trans., then they cut off $\cong$ seg. on every trans.)   6. $\overline{MN}$ bisects $\overline{WY}$. (Def. of bis.)

4. Given: Rhombus ABCD with diag. intersecting at X.

  Prove: $\triangle AXB \cong \triangle CXB \cong \triangle CXD \cong \triangle AXD$.

  Proof: 1. ABCD is a rhombus (Given)   2. $m\angle AXB =$

$m\angle CXB = m\angle CXD = m\angle AXD = 90$ (The diag. of a rhombus are $\perp$.)   3. $\overline{AX} \cong \overline{XC}$;

$\overline{DX} \cong \overline{XB}$ (The diag. of a $\square$ bisect each other.)   4. $\triangle AXB \cong \triangle CXB \cong \triangle CXD \cong$

$\triangle AXD$ (SAS)

5. hyp. = 14; legs = 7 and $7\sqrt{3}$

6. no; check students' drawings (Example: 3 $\parallel$ edges of a cube.)

7. $\dfrac{(18 - 2)180}{18} = 160$; $\dfrac{360}{18} = 20$; meas. of each int. $\angle = 160$; meas. of each ext. $\angle = 20$

8. $AB = \dfrac{4}{\sqrt{2}} = \dfrac{4\sqrt{2}}{2} = 2\sqrt{2}$

9. $x^2 = 6^2 + 10^2 = 136$; $x = \sqrt{136} = 2\sqrt{34}$; or $x^2 + 6^2 = 10^2$; $x^2 = 100 - 36 = 64$; $x = 8$

10. No conclusion is possible.

11. 1. $\angle 1 \cong \angle 2$; $\angle 2 \cong \angle 3$ (Given)   2. $\overline{AB} \parallel \overline{DC}$ (If 2 lines are cut by a trans. and alt.

int. $\angle$ are $\cong$, then the 2 lines are $\parallel$.)   3. $\overline{AD} \parallel \overline{BC}$ (If 2 lines are cut by a trans.

and corr. $\angle$ are $\cong$, the 2 lines are $\parallel$.)   4. ABCD is a $\square$. (Def. of $\square$)

  5. $\overline{AB} \cong \overline{DC}$ (Opp. sides of a $\square$ are $\cong$.)

12. $\dfrac{18}{x} = \dfrac{x}{8}$; $x^2 = 144$; $x = 12$ 13. a. inside   b. on   c. on

14. $2(5t - 7) = 8t + 10$; $10t - 14 = 8t + 10$; $2t = 24$; $t = 12$; $m\angle BOC = m\angle AOB =$

  $5(12) - 7 = 53$

15. $9t = 15(12) = 180; \ t = 20$ 16. 0; 1

17. $RS = |3 - (-11)| = |14| = 14; \ ST = \frac{1}{2} \cdot RS = 7$

Page 333 · ALGEBRA REVIEW

1. $s^2 = (1.3)^2 = 1.69$

2. $\sqrt{a^2 + b^2} = \sqrt{(20)^2 + (21)^2} = \sqrt{400 + 441} = \sqrt{841} = 29$

3. $2(x + y) = 2(\frac{5}{3} + \frac{3}{2}) = 2(\frac{10}{6} + \frac{9}{6}) = 2(\frac{19}{6}) = \frac{19}{3}$

4. $a + b + c = 11.5 + 7.2 + 9.9 = 28.6$

5. $\ell w = (2\sqrt{6})(3\sqrt{3}) = 6\sqrt{6 \cdot 3} = 6\sqrt{18} = 18\sqrt{2}$

6. $2r + s + t = 2(\frac{4}{7}) + 1 + \frac{13}{7} = \frac{8}{7} + \frac{7}{7} + \frac{13}{7} = \frac{28}{7} = 4$

7. $\pi r^2 = \pi(30)^2 \approx 3.14(900) = 2826$

8. $\ell wh = 8(6\frac{1}{4})(3\frac{1}{2}) = 8(\frac{25}{4})(\frac{7}{2}) = 25(7) = 175$

9. $2(\ell w + wh + \ell h) = 2((4.5)(3) + 3(1) + (4.5)(1)) = 2(21) = 42$

10. $\frac{x - 3}{y + 2} = \frac{3 - 3}{-4 + 2} = \frac{0}{-2} = 0$ 11. $\frac{x + 5}{y - 2} = \frac{-2 + 5}{-4 - 2} = \frac{3}{-6} = -\frac{1}{2}$

12. $mx + b = \frac{5}{2}(-6) + (-2) = -15 + (-2) = -17$

13. $6t^2 = 6(3^2) = 6(9) = 54$ 14. $(6t)^2 = (6 \cdot 3)^2 = 18^2 = 324$

15. $\frac{1}{2}h(a + b) = \frac{1}{2} \cdot 3(3\sqrt{2} + 7\sqrt{2}) = \frac{3}{2}(10\sqrt{2}) = 15\sqrt{2}$

16. $\sqrt{(x - 5)^2 + (y - 3)^2} = \sqrt{(1 - 5)^2 + (0 - 3)^2} = \sqrt{(-4)^2 + (-3)^2} = \sqrt{16 + 9} = \sqrt{25} = 5$

17. $\frac{1}{3}x^2 h = \frac{1}{3}(4\sqrt{3})^2(6) = \frac{1}{3}(48)(6) = 96$

18. $2s^2 + 4sh = 2(\sqrt{6})^2 + 4\sqrt{6}(\frac{5}{2}\sqrt{6}) = 12 + 10 \cdot 6 = 12 + 60 = 72$

19. $c(x + y) = cd$

20. $\frac{1}{3}Bh = \frac{1}{3}(\pi r^2)h = \frac{1}{3}\pi r^2 h$

21. $\frac{1}{2}p\ell = \frac{1}{2}(2\pi r)\ell = \pi r \ell$

22. $2(\ell + w) = 2(s + s) = 2(2s) = 4s$

23. $4\pi r^2 = 4\pi(\frac{1}{2}d)^2 = 4\pi(\frac{1}{4}d^2) = \pi d^2$

24. $n(\frac{1}{2}sa) = (ns)(\frac{1}{2}a) = p(\frac{1}{2}a) = \frac{1}{2}pa$

25. $ax = c - by; \ x = \frac{c - by}{a}$

26. $d = \frac{C}{\pi}$

27. $n - 2 = \frac{S}{180}; \ n = \frac{S}{180} + 2$

28. $y^2 = r^2 - x^2; \ y = \pm\sqrt{r^2 - x^2}$

29. $h^2 = xy; \ h = \pm\sqrt{xy}$

30. $b^2 = (a\sqrt{2})^2 - a^2 = a^2; \ b = \pm a$

31. $bh = 2A; \ h = \frac{2A}{b}$

32. $y + 4 = m(x - 2); \ y = m(x - 2) - 4$

Pages 338-339 · WRITTEN EXERCISES

A 1.

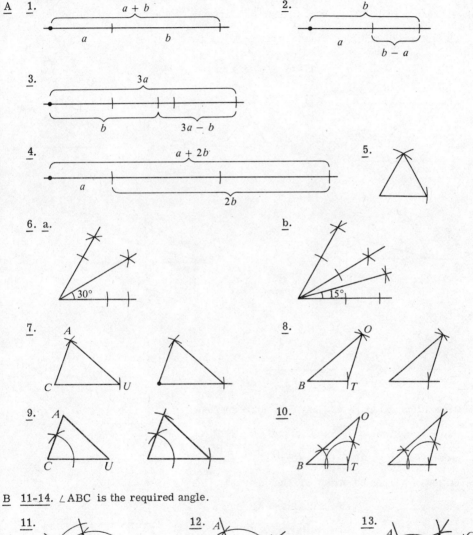

2.

3.

4.

5.

6. a.

b.

7.

8.

9.

10.

B 11-14. ∠ABC is the required angle.

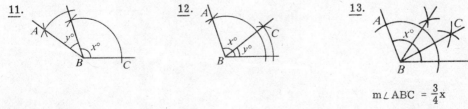

11.

12.

13.

m∠ABC = $\frac{3}{4}$x

14.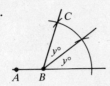

15. a. 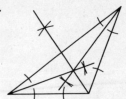   b.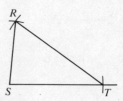

C Answers may vary. All 3 ∠ bis. of each △ intersect in one pt.; the pts. of int. of the ∠

bis. are equidistant from the sides of the △.

16.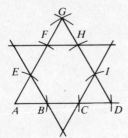

17-26. Methods may vary.

17.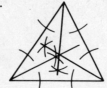

18.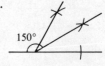

19.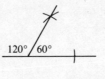

20.

21.

22. Draw a line and mark $\overline{AB}$, any convenient segment.

Using AB as radius, mark off pts. C, D, E, F, G,

and H, such that AB = BC = CD = DE = EF =

FG = GH.   Then construct $\overline{ST}$ such that ST = AG;

with ctrs. S and T and radii AE and AH, resp.,

draw arcs int. at R.   Draw $\overline{RS}$ and $\overline{RT}$.

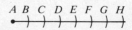

23.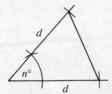

24. Construct an ∠ with meas. n at A; bisect
its supp. to construct ∠1; mark off AB = s;
at B, construct ∠2 ≅ ∠1.   Extend sides of
∠1 and ∠2 to intersect at C.

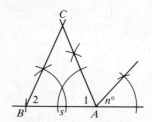

C 25. Construct ∠A with meas. n; construct $\overline{AB}$ so
that AB = s.   Construct ∠B ≅ ∠A; with ctr.
A and radius d, draw arc int. side of ∠B at C.

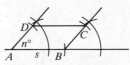

Construct $\overline{AD}$ ≅ $\overline{BC}$; draw $\overline{DC}$.   Since ∠A ≅ ∠B, $\overline{AD}$ ∥ $\overline{BC}$; since $\overline{AD}$ ≅ $\overline{BC}$ as
well, ABCD is a ▱.

26. Draw a circle ⊙ with radius r; draw any chord $\overline{AB}$;
construct ∠A ≅ ∠2, int. ⊙ at C.   Draw $\overline{BC}$.
Construct an ∠ at B ≅ ∠1, int. ⊙ at D.   Since ∠D
and ∠A int. the same arc, ∠D ≅ ∠A ≅ 2.   Then
m∠BCD = 180 - (m∠DBC + m∠D) = 180 -
(m∠1 + m∠2) = m∠3.

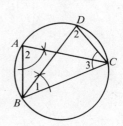

Pages 342-343 · WRITTEN EXERCISES

A 1. Construction 5   2. Construction 6   3. Construction 4   4. Construction 7

5. Construction 5   6. Construction 7   7. Construction 6

8. Use Construction 6 to construct $\overline{KP}$ ⊥ $\overline{MN}$.   △KML is a rt. △ so its acute ∡, ∠KMN
and ∠MKP are comp. ∡.   Or, use Construction 5 to construct $\overline{QM}$ ⊥ $\overline{MN}$ with
∠QMK acute; ∠QMK is a comp. of ∠KMN.

9-12. Methods may vary.

9.

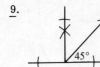

45°

10.

135°

11.

$22\frac{1}{2}$°

12.

105°

13.

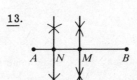

A N M B

NB

X   Y

14-16. △ JKL is the given △.

14. a. 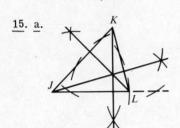   c. 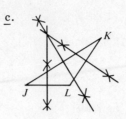   b. yes; yes

15. a. 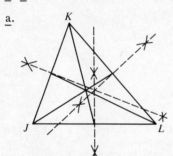   c. 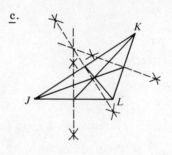   b. yes; yes

16. a, c. Locate midpts. of the sides by constructing ⊥ bis. as in Ex. 14, above.

a. 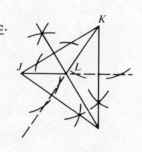   c. 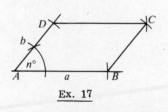   b. yes; yes

17-28. Methods may vary.

17. Draw a line and construct $\overline{AB}$ so that AB = a; construct ∠A with meas. n; construct $\overline{AD}$ so that AD = b; with ctrs. D and B and radii a and b, resp., draw arcs intersecting at C. Draw $\overline{DC}$.

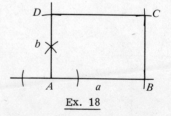

Ex. 17   Ex. 18

18. Draw a line, construct $\overline{AB}$ so that AB = a and construct a ⊥ at A; construct $\overline{AD}$ so that AD = b; with ctrs. D and B and radii a and b resp., draw arcs intersecting at C; draw $\overline{DC}$.

19. Draw a line and construct $\overline{AB}$ such that AB = a.   Construct the ⊥ bis. of $\overline{AB}$,

intersecting $\overline{AB}$ at M.   Construct a ⊥ to $\overline{AB}$ at A.   Construct $\overline{AD}$ and $\overline{MC}$ both ≅

to $\overline{AM}$.   Draw $\overline{DC}$.

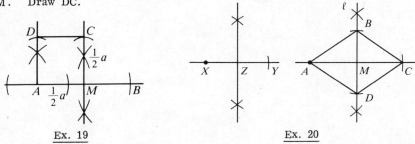

Ex. 19   Ex. 20

20. Draw 2 lines and construct $\overline{AC}$ so that AC = a and $\overline{XY}$ so that XY = b.   Construct

ℓ, the ⊥ bis. of $\overline{AC}$ intersecting $\overline{AC}$ at M and the ⊥ bis. of $\overline{XY}$, intersecting $\overline{XY}$ at

Z.   On ℓ, construct $\overline{MB}$ and $\overline{MD}$ both ≅ to $\overline{XZ}$.   Draw ABCD.

21. Draw a line and construct $\overline{AC}$ so that AC = b.   Construct the ⊥ bis. of $\overline{AC}$,

intersecting $\overline{AC}$ at M.   Construct $\overline{MB}$ and $\overline{MD}$ both ≅ to $\overline{AM}$.   Draw ABCD.

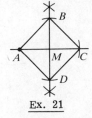
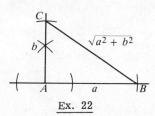

Ex. 21   Ex. 22

22. Draw a line and construct $\overline{AB}$ so that AB = a.   Construct a ⊥ to $\overline{AB}$ at A and

construct AC = b.   Draw $\overline{CB}$.

23. Draw a line and construct $\overline{AB}$ so that AB = b.   Construct a ⊥ to $\overline{AB}$ at A;

construct $\overline{AD}$ ≅ $\overline{AB}$.   With ctrs. D and B and radii both = b, draw arcs intersecting

at C.   Draw $\overline{DC}$ and $\overline{BC}$.

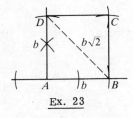
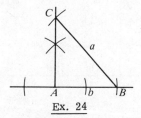

Ex. 23   Ex. 24

24. Draw a line and construct $\overline{AB}$ so that AB = b.   Construct a ⊥ to $\overline{AB}$ at A.   With

ctr. B and radius a, draw an arc intersecting the ⊥ at C.   Draw $\overline{BC}$.

138

C 25. Given AB = s, construct a ⊥ to $\overline{AB}$ at A. With ctrs. A and B and both radii = s, draw arcs intersecting at X. Extend $\overrightarrow{BX}$ to intersect the ⊥ at C. △ABC is a 30-60-90 △ and AC = $s\sqrt{3}$.

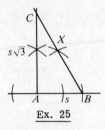

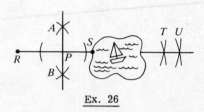

Ex. 25   Ex. 26

26. Choose a pt. P on $\overline{RS}$ and construct $\overline{AB} \perp \overline{RS}$ as shown. $\overleftrightarrow{RS}$ is the ⊥ bis. of $\overline{AB}$. With ctrs. A and B, draw a pair of arcs intersecting at T, on the other side of the lake. Using a larger radius, repeat to find a pt. U. Draw $\overleftrightarrow{TU}$. Since T and U are equidistant from A and B, T and U are on the ⊥ bis. of $\overline{AB}$; so $\overleftrightarrow{TU} = \overleftrightarrow{RS}$.

27. RT = half the length of the side with midpt. S. Construct ⊙S with radius RT, ⊙R with radius ST, and ⊙T with radius RS. R, S, and T are the midpts. of the sides of △ABC.

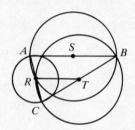

28. a. Let AB = 1. Construct $\overline{BC} \cong \overline{AB}$ and construct a ⊥ to $\overline{AB}$ at A. Construct $\overline{AD} \cong \overline{AB}$. DC = $\sqrt{1^2 + 2^2} = \sqrt{5}$.

b. Draw a line and construct $\overline{EF} \cong \overline{AB}$ and $\overline{FG} \cong \overline{DC}$. Construct the ⊥ bis. of $\overline{EG}$, int. $\overline{EG}$ at H. EH = $\dfrac{1 + \sqrt{5}}{2}$

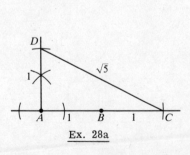

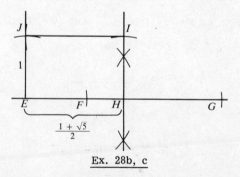

Ex. 28a   Ex. 28b, c

c. Construct $\overline{HI} \cong \overline{AB}$. With ctrs. E and I and radii AB and EH, resp., draw arcs intersecting at J. Draw $\overline{JI}$ and $\overline{JE}$.

Page 343 · CHALLENGE

Draw $\overrightarrow{AZ}$ and choose C on $\overrightarrow{AZ}$. Draw $\overline{CB}$, $\overline{CM}$, and $\overline{ZB}$,

with $\overline{ZB}$ and $\overline{CM}$ intersecting at D. Draw $\overrightarrow{AD}$, inter-

secting $\overline{CB}$ at E. Draw $\overleftrightarrow{ZE}$; $\overleftrightarrow{ZE} \parallel \overline{AB}$. By Ceva's

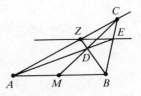

Thm., $\dfrac{AM}{MB} \cdot \dfrac{BE}{EC} \cdot \dfrac{CZ}{ZA} = 1$; $\dfrac{AM}{MB} = 1$ so $\dfrac{BE}{EC} \cdot \dfrac{CZ}{ZA} = 1$;

$\dfrac{BE}{EC} = \dfrac{ZA}{CZ}$, $\dfrac{BE + EC}{EC} = \dfrac{ZA + CZ}{CZ}$; $\dfrac{BC}{EC} = \dfrac{CA}{CZ}$; then since $\angle ACB \cong \angle ACB$,

$\triangle CZE \sim \triangle CAB$ (SAS), $\angle CZE \cong \angle CAB$ and $\overleftrightarrow{ZE} \parallel \overline{AB}$.

Pages 346-347 · WRITTEN EXERCISES

A   1. a. any acute $\triangle$ b. any obtuse $\triangle$ c. any rt. $\triangle$

    2. x = 6; y = $\dfrac{5}{2}$ 3. 2; 4   4. $\dfrac{7}{3}$; $\dfrac{14}{3}$

    5. 3.8; 5.7   6. Construction 4   7. Construction 3

B   8. The pt. equidistant from all 3 towns, the intersection of the $\perp$ bis. of $\overline{XY}$, $\overline{XZ}$, and $\overline{YZ}$

    is distant from all 3 towns.   It would be wiser to build it equidistant from X and Z,

    near Y.

    9. Let X, Y, and Z be collinear.

   10. a. GD = $\dfrac{1}{3} \cdot$ AD = $\dfrac{1}{3} \cdot$ BE = GE   b. GB   c. $\angle$GBA, $\angle$GED, $\angle$GDE

   11. $x^2 = 2 \cdot 2x$; $x^2 - 4x = 0$; $x(x - 4) = 0$; $x = 0$ (reject) or $x = 4$

   12. $y^2 + 1 = 2(y + 2)$; $y^2 + 1 = 2y + 4$; $y^2 - 2y - 3 = 0$; $(y - 3)(y + 1) = 0$;

    y = 3 or y = -1

   13. $z^2 - 15 = \dfrac{2}{3}(2z^2 - 5z - 12)$; $3z^2 - 45 = 4z^2 - 10z - 24$; $z^2 - 10z + 21 = 0$;

    $(z - 3)(z - 7) = 0$; z = 3 or z = 7; if z = 3, CP = -6 so reject z = 3; z = 7;

    CW = 51; PW = $\dfrac{1}{3} \cdot 51 = 17$

   14. 1. Draw $\overline{BD}$ intersecting $\overline{AC}$ at Y. (Through any 2 pts. there is exactly one line.)

    2. ABCD is a $\square$; M is the midpt. of $\overline{DC}$. (Given)   3. Y is the midpt. of $\overline{BD}$;

    CY = $\dfrac{1}{2} \cdot$ AC (The diag. of a $\square$ bis. each other.)   4. $\overline{BM}$ and $\overline{CY}$ are medians

    of $\triangle$ BDC. (Def. of median)   5. CX = $\dfrac{2}{3} \cdot$ CY (The medians of a $\triangle$ intersect in a

    pt. that is $\dfrac{2}{3}$ of the distance from each vertex to the opp. side.)   6. CX =

    $\dfrac{2}{3} \cdot \dfrac{1}{2} \cdot$ AC = $\dfrac{1}{3}$AC (Subst. Prop.)

C   15. a. pts. in the interior of $\angle$XPY   b. pts. in the interior of the $\angle$ vertical to $\angle$XPY.

16. Given: $\triangle ABC$; median $\overline{BN} \cong$ median $\overline{CM}$;

Prove: $\overline{AB} \cong \overline{AC}$.   Proof: 1. CM = BN (Given)

2. $\frac{1}{3} \cdot$ CM = $\frac{1}{3} \cdot$ BN (Mult. Prop. of =)

3. CM and BN are medians (Given)   4. XM =

$\frac{1}{3} \cdot$ CM; XN = $\frac{1}{3}$ BN (The medians of a $\triangle$ intersect in a pt. that is $\frac{2}{3}$ the distance from

each vertex to the opp. side.)   5. XM = XN (Subst. Prop.)   6. $\angle$ NMX $\cong \angle$ MNX

(If 2 sides of a $\triangle$ are $\cong$, then the $\angle$ opp. those sides are $\cong$.)   7. $\overline{MN} \cong \overline{MN}$ (Refl.

Prop.)   8. $\triangle$ NMB $\cong \triangle$ MNC (SAS)   9. MB = NC (Corr. parts of $\cong$ $\triangle$ are $\cong$.)

10. 2 · MB = 2 · NC (Mult. Prop. of =)   11. M and N are the midpts. of $\overline{AB}$ and

$\overline{AC}$. (Def. of median)   12. AB = 2 · MB; AC = 2 · NC (Midpt. Thm.)

13. AB = AC or $\overline{AB} \cong \overline{AC}$ (Subst. Prop.)

Page 348 · APPLICATION

1. a-c. Check students' work.

2. b. The lines drawn are the medians of the $\triangle$.   3. yes

Pages 352-353 · WRITTEN EXERCISES

A   1. Construction 8   2. Construction 9   3. Construction 10   4. Construction 10

5. Construction 10   6. Construction 11   7. Construction 11   8. Construction 11

B   9. Draw $\odot$O with radius r.   Choose pt. A on $\odot$O and with ctr. A and radius r, mark

off $\overarc{AB}$.   With ctr. B and radius r, mark off $\overarc{BC}$.   Similarly, mark off $\cong$ arcs $\overarc{CD}$,

$\overarc{DE}$ and $\overarc{EF}$.   Draw $\overline{AC}$, $\overline{EC}$, and $\overline{AE}$.

Ex. 9

Ex. 10

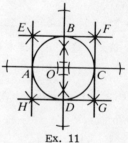

Ex. 11

10. Draw $\odot$O and diam. $\overline{AC}$.   Construct the $\perp$ bis. of $\overline{AC}$, intersecting $\odot$O at B and D.

Draw $\overline{AB}$, $\overline{BC}$, $\overline{CD}$, and $\overline{AD}$.

11. Draw $\odot$O and diam. $\overline{AC}$.   Construct the $\perp$ bis. of $\overline{AC}$, intersecting $\odot$O at B and D.

Construct tans. to $\odot$O at A, B, C, and D intersecting at E, F, G, and H as shown.

<u>12.</u> Draw the diag. of the square, intersecting at O.   Draw the ⊙ with ctr. O and radius

OA.

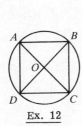

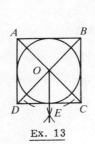

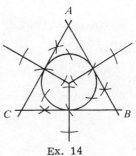

Ex. 12   Ex. 13   Ex. 14

<u>13.</u> Draw the diag. of the square, intersecting at O.   Construct a ⊥ to $\overline{DC}$ from O,

intersecting $\overline{DC}$ at E.   Draw the ⊙ with ctr. O, radius OE.

<u>14.</u> Divide the ⊙ into 6 ≅ arcs as described in Ex. 9 above, determining 6 pts. on the ⊙.

At every other pt., construct a tan to the ⊙.

<u>15.</u> Construct a ⊥ to ℓ through O, intersecting ⊙O at P.   Construct a tan. to ⊙O at P.

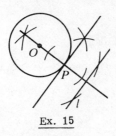

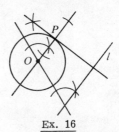

Ex. 15   Ex. 16

<u>16.</u> Construct a ∥ to ℓ through O, int. ⊙O at P.   Construct a tan to ⊙O at P.

<u>C</u> <u>17.</u> Construct equilateral △ ABC. (Draw $\overline{AB}$. With ctrs. A and B and radius AB, draw

arcs intersecting at C.   Draw $\overline{CA}$ and $\overline{CB}$.)   Construct the ⊥ bis. of AB intersect-

ing $\overline{AB}$ at D.   Draw ⊚A, B, and C with radius AD.   Construct $\overline{AG} \perp \overline{AC}$,

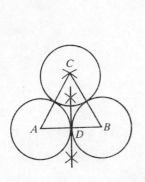

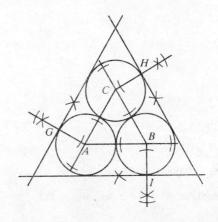

$\overline{CH} \perp \overline{CB}$, and $\overline{BI} \perp \overline{AB}$. Construct a tan. to $\odot A$ at G, a tan. to $\odot C$ at H, and a tan. to $\odot B$ at I.   The pts. where the tans. intersect are the vertices of an equilateral $\triangle$.

18. Draw $\overleftrightarrow{PQ}$ intersecting $\odot P$ at X and $\odot Q$ at Y, as shown.   Let R be the ctr. of the required $\odot$.   PR = PQ + p = XQ and QR = PQ + q = PY.   With ctrs. P and Q and radii XQ and PY, resp., draw arcs intersecting at a pt.; label it R.   Draw $\odot R$ with radius PQ.

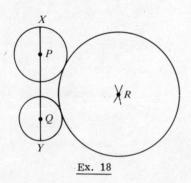

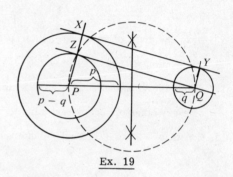

Ex. 18   Ex. 19

19. XY = ZQ; XZ = p - (p - q) = q = QY so XYQZ is a $\square$.   Since $\angle XZQ$ is a rt. $\angle$, XYQZ is a rect.   Then $\overleftrightarrow{XY}$ is $\perp$ to radii $\overline{PX}$ and $\overline{QY}$ and $\overleftrightarrow{XY}$ is a common tan. of $\odot P$ and Q.

20. Draw a $\odot$ with ctr. P and radius p + q.   Construct a tan. to this $\odot$ from Q.   Let Z be the pt. of tangency.   Draw $\overline{PZ}$, intersecting the inner $\odot P$ at X.   With ctr. X and radius ZQ, draw an arc intersecting $\odot Q$ at Y.   Draw $\overleftrightarrow{XY}$.

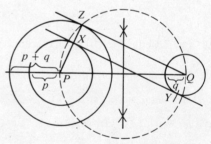

XY = ZQ and XZ = p + q - p = q = YQ so XYQZ is a $\square$.   Since $\angle PZQ$ is a rt. $\angle$, XYQZ is a rect.   Then $\overleftrightarrow{XY}$ is $\perp$ to radii $\overline{PX}$ and $\overline{QY}$ and $\overleftrightarrow{XY}$ is a common tan. of $\odot P$ and Q.

21. Draw an acute $\angle RST$ with meas. n.   Construct $\angle TSV$, the supp. of $\angle RST$, by extending $\overline{RS}$ past the vertex.   Bisect $\angle TSV$ so that $m\angle TSU = \frac{1}{2}(180 - n) = m\angle USV$. Let $\frac{1}{2}(180 - n) = x$.   Draw a line containing a seg. $\overline{PQ}$ and construct the $\perp$ bis. of $\overline{PQ}$.   Using P and Q as centers, construct $\odot P$ and $\odot Q$, each with radius $\frac{1}{2}PQ$. Construct $\overline{PA} \perp \overline{PQ}$ and $\overline{PB} \perp \overline{PQ}$.   Draw $\overleftrightarrow{AB}$.   Choose C and D on $\overleftrightarrow{AB}$.

Construct $\angle$ ECA and $\angle$ FDB, each with meas. x.   Construct a $\perp$ to $\overline{CE}$ from P,

intersecting $\odot$P at G, and a $\perp$ to $\overline{DF}$ from Q, intersecting $\odot$Q at H.   Construct a

tan. to $\odot$P at G and a tan. to $\odot$Q at H.   Extend the tangents to intersect $\overleftrightarrow{AB}$ at X

and Y, and each other at Z.   Since $\overline{PG} \perp \overline{CE}$ and $\overline{PG} \perp \overline{XY}$, $\overline{CE} \parallel \overline{XY}$ and

$m\angle$ GXA = $m\angle$ ECA = x.   Similarly, $m\angle$ HYB = x.   Then $\triangle$XYZ is an isos. $\triangle$; $\overline{XY}$

(the base of $\triangle$XYZ) is tan. to $\odot$P and $\odot$Q; $\overline{XZ}$ is tan. to $\odot$P and $\overline{YZ}$ is tan. to

$\odot$Q; $m\angle$Z = 180 - ($m\angle$X + $m\angle$Y) = n.

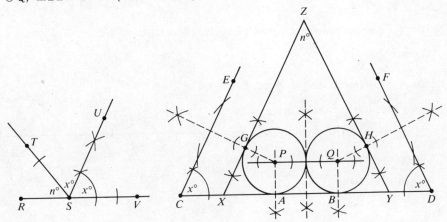

Page 356 · WRITTEN EXERCISES

A   1. Use Construction 12.   2. a. Use Construction 12   b. Use Construction 4

   3. a. Use Construction 12 to divide $\overline{AB}$ into 5 $\cong$ parts, $\overline{AW}$, $\overline{WX}$, $\overline{XY}$, $\overline{YZ}$, and $\overline{ZB}$.

      b. no   c. AX:XB = 2:3

   4. Use Construction 12 to divide $\overline{AB}$ into 7 $\cong$ parts, $\overline{AU}$, $\overline{UV}$, $\overline{VW}$, $\overline{WX}$, $\overline{XY}$, $\overline{YZ}$, and

      $\overline{ZB}$.   AW:WB = 3:4.

   5. Use Construction 13.   6. Use Construction 14.   7. Use Construction 14.

   8. Use Construction 1 to construct a seg. $\overline{XY}$ with length w + 2y.   Use Construction 12

      to divide $\overline{XY}$ into 3 $\cong$ parts with length x.

   9. zx = wy; $z = \dfrac{wy}{x}$; $\dfrac{z}{w} = \dfrac{y}{x}$ or $\dfrac{z}{y} = \dfrac{w}{x}$; use Construction 13.

10-13. Methods may vary.

   10. $x = \dfrac{yp}{z}$; $\dfrac{x}{y} = \dfrac{p}{z}$; $\dfrac{z}{p} = \dfrac{y}{x}$; use Construction 13.

   11. Use Construction 14 to construct $\overline{XY}$ with length $\sqrt{yp}$; use Construction 12 to divide

      $\overline{XY}$ into 3 $\cong$ parts with length x.

12. Use Construction 1 to construct a seg. with length 3x (or 3z); use Construction 14.

13. Use Construction 1 to construct 2 segs., the prod. of whose lengths is 6yz (for example, 2y and 3z or 6y and z); use Construction 14.

14. Draw $\overrightarrow{AX}$ and construct $\overline{AR}$ and $\overline{RS}$ on $\overrightarrow{AX}$

so that AR = w and RS = y. Draw $\overline{SB}$.

Construct a ∥ to $\overline{SB}$ through R, intersecting

$\overline{AB}$ at T. AT : TB = w : y

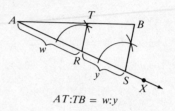

$AT:TB = w:y$

15. Draw a line and construct $\overline{AB}$ so that AB = 3 and $\overline{BC}$ so that BC = 5. Use Construction 14.

C 16. Draw a ray from A and mark off 7 ≅

segs. as shown. Construct ∠s ≅ to

∠CZD at X and Y. With radius AB

and ctrs. B and D, draw arcs intersect-

ing at E. Draw $\overline{BE}$ and $\overline{DE}$.

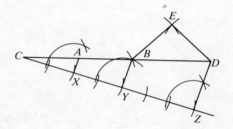

17. $\overline{GA} \cong \overline{GB}$ so ∠B ≅ ∠A and $\overline{BY} \cong \overline{AX}$ so △GBY ≅ △GAX. Then $\overline{GY} \cong \overline{GX}$ so m∠GYA = m∠GXY. Consider △GYA and △GXA. m∠YGA > m∠1 so m∠GYA < m∠GXA. Then m∠GXY < m∠GXA. Consider △GXA and △GXY. By the SAS Ineq. Thm., GA > GY. Assume temp. that m∠1 = m∠2. Then $\overrightarrow{GX}$ bis. ∠YGA and $\frac{YX}{XA} = \frac{GY}{GA}$; $\frac{YX}{XA} = 1 = \frac{GY}{GA}$ and GY = GA. This contradicts the fact that GA > GY. Our temp. assumption must be false. It follows that m∠1 ≠ m∠2 and ∠G is not trisected.

Pages 360-362 · WRITTEN EXERCISES

A 1. the ⊥ bis. of $\overline{AB}$

2. a line ∥ to j and k, halfway between them   3. a ⊙ with ctr. O, radius 2 cm

4. a pair of lines on either side of h, both ∥ to h and 2 cm from it

5. the seg. joining the midpts. of $\overline{BC}$ and $\overline{DA}$ 6. diagonal $\overline{AC}$

7. diagonal $\overline{BD}$ 8. the int. of $\overline{AC}$ and $\overline{BD}$

9. a plane ∥ to both planes, halfway between them

10. a pair of planes on either side of the given plane, both ∥ to it and 5 cm from it

<u>11</u>. a sphere with ctr. E, radius 3 cm

<u>12</u>. a plane that bis. $\overline{CD}$ and is $\perp$ to $\overline{CD}$

B <u>13</u>. a. Bisect $\angle$ HEX; use Construction 3.

  b. Bisect all 4 $\angle$ formed by j and k; use Construction 3.

<u>14</u>. Construct a pair of lines on either side of n, both $\parallel$ to n and at a distance DE from n.

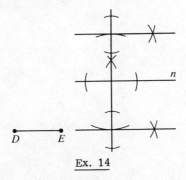

Ex. 14

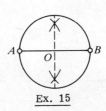

Ex. 15

<u>15</u>. Construct the circle (excluding pts. A and B) with ctr. the midpt. of $\overline{AB}$ and radius $\frac{1}{2}$AB.

<u>16</u>. Construct the $\perp$ bis. (excluding the midpt. of $\overline{CD}$) of $\overline{CD}$.

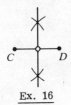

Ex. 16

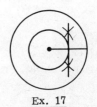

Ex. 17

<u>17</u>. Construct a $\odot$ concentric to the given $\odot$ with radius half as great.

<u>18</u>. a sphere with the same ctr. as the given sphere and radius half as great.

<u>19</u>. a line $\perp$ to the plane of the square at the int. of the diag.

<u>20</u>. a line $\perp$ to the plane of the $\triangle$ at the int. of the $\perp$ bis. of the sides.

C <u>21</u>. Let P be the pt. where the corner of the house meets the ground. The locus is a 90° arc of $\odot$P with radius AM.

<u>22</u>. a sphere (excluding pts. C and D) with ctr. the midpt. of $\overline{CD}$ and radius $\frac{1}{2}$CD.

<u>23</u>. The region is determined by 5 circles as shown in the diagram on the next page: $\odot$A with rad. 5 m, $\odot$B and $\odot$E with rad. 4 m, and $\odot$C and $\odot$D with rad. 2 m.

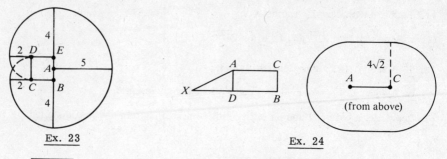

Ex. 23   Ex. 24

24. DX = $\sqrt{6^2 - 2^2}$ = $\sqrt{32}$ = $4\sqrt{2}$; the region over which the dog can roam is made up of

semicircles A and C, each with radius $4\sqrt{2}$ m, and a rectangle with length $8\sqrt{2}$ m and

width AC = 5 m.

Pages 364-366 · WRITTEN EXERCISES

<u>A</u> 1. a. 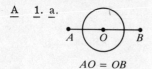   b.   c.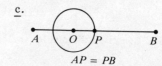

AO = OB   AP = PB

2. a.    b.   c.

3. a. a circle with ctrs. D, radius 1 cm   b. a circle with ctr. E, radius 2 cm

c.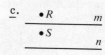

DE > 3 cm   DE = 3 cm   DE < 3 cm

d. The locus is 0, 1, or 2 pts. depending on the int. of ⊙C with radius 1 cm and ⊙D,

with radius 2 cm.

4. a. a circle with ctr. A, radius 3 cm

b. a pair of lines on either side of k, both ‖ to k and 1 cm from k

c.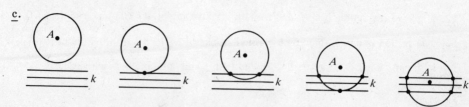

d. The locus is 0, 1, 2, 3, or 4 pts. depending on the int. of ⊙A, with radius 3 cm,

and 2 lines ‖ to k, 1 cm from k.

5. The locus is the int. of ⊙P, with radius 3 cm, and ℓ (2 pts.)

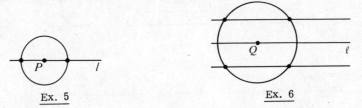

Ex. 5   Ex. 6

6. The locus is the int. of ⊙Q, with rad. 5 cm, and 2 lines ‖ to ℓ and 3 cm from ℓ.

(4 pts.)

7. The locus is the int. of ⊙A and ⊙B, each with radius 2 cm. (2 pts.)

Ex. 7   Ex. 8

8. The locus is the int. of ⊙P, with rad. 2 cm, and the ∠ bis. of the ⦠ formed by

j and k. (4 pts.)

9. The locus is the int. of ⊙A, with radius 2 cm, and the bis. of ∠A. (1 pt.)

Ex. 9   Ex. 10

10. The locus is the int. of the bis. of ∠R and the ⊥ bis. of $\overline{RS}$. (1 pt.)

B 11.

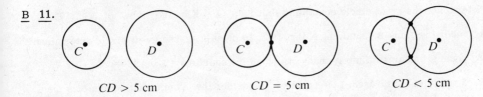

CD > 5 cm   CD = 5 cm   CD < 5 cm

<u>12.</u> Let d be the distance from E to k.

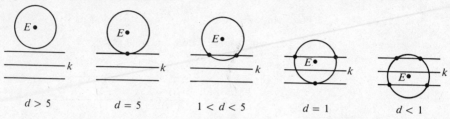

$d > 5$ $d = 5$ $1 < d < 5$ $d = 1$ $d < 1$

<u>13.</u> Figures may vary.   Example:

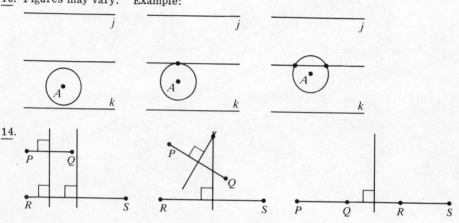

<u>14.</u>

<u>15.</u> 0 pts., 1 pt., or a ⊙   <u>16.</u> 2 Ⓢ

<u>17.</u> a line ⊥ to the plane of the square at the pt. where the diag. intersect

<u>18.</u> 0 pts. (d > 5); 2 pts. (d = 5); 2 Ⓢ (d < 5)

<u>19.</u> <u>a.</u> a plane that bisects $\overline{RS}$ and is ⊥ to $\overline{RS}$ <u>b.</u> a plane that bis. $\overline{RT}$ and is ⊥ to $\overline{RT}$

<u>c.</u> line; line   <u>d.</u> a plane that bis. $\overline{RW}$ and is ⊥ to $\overline{RW}$ <u>e.</u> point; point

<u>20.</u> <u>a.</u> yes; R, S, T, and W not coplanar; no 3 collinear   <u>b.</u> yes; R, S, T and W the

vertices of a rect., for example   <u>c.</u> no   <u>d.</u> yes; any 3 collinear

<u>21.</u> <u>a.</u> Infinitely many; let H represent Houston and T Toronto. Consider the plane A that

determines the great circle containing H and T. Let X be the midpt. of $\overparen{HT}$. Then

consider the plane B containing X that is ⊥ to plane A. The great circle determined

by plane B contains infinitely many pts. that are equidistant from H and T.

<u>b.</u> 2 pts.; let L represent Los Angeles. Consider the plane C that determines the

great circle containing L and H. Let Y be the midpt. of $\overparen{LH}$. Then consider the

plane D containing Y that is ⊥ to plane C. The great circle determined by plane D

contains the pts. that are equidistant from L and H.   Pts. P and Q which lie on

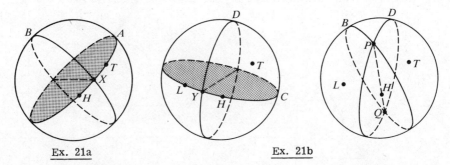

Ex. 21a   Ex. 21b

the line of intersection of planes B and D, and on the surface of the sphere, are

equidistant from H, T, and L.   c. none

22. a. Inside the region bounded by $\overset{\frown}{AB}$,

$\overset{\frown}{AC}$, and $\overset{\frown}{BC}$

b. on $\overset{\frown}{AC}$

c. at A or G

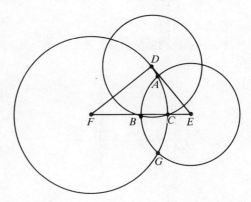

Pages 368-369 · WRITTEN EXERCISES

A   1. The locus is j and k

2. a. The locus is p, excluding D.

b. The locus is ⊙M with radius $\frac{1}{2}$CD, excluding C and D.

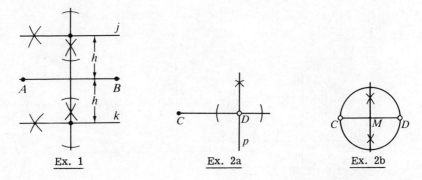

Ex. 1   Ex. 2a   Ex. 2b

<u>3</u>. The ⊙, of radius a, has ctr. W, the int. of the bis. of ∠XYZ and a ∥ to $\overrightarrow{YZ}$, a

units from $\overrightarrow{YZ}$.

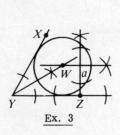

Ex. 3

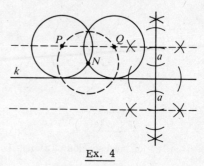

Ex. 4

<u>4</u>. The ⊙, of radius a, has ctr. at P or Q, the int. of ⊙N with radius a and a line ∥

to k, a units from k.

<u>5</u>. The locus is lines j and k, both ∥ to $\overline{AB}$ and r units from $\overline{AB}$.

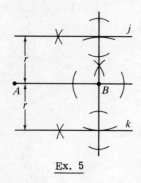

Ex. 5

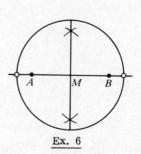

Ex. 6

<u>6</u>. The locus is the ⊙ with ctr. M, the midpt. of $\overline{AB}$, and radius s, excluding the pts.

where $\overleftrightarrow{AB}$ intersects ⊙M.

<u>B</u>.   <u>7-19</u>. Constructions may vary.

<u>7</u>. Construct line j ⊥ k. Mark off MA = s, then construct $\overline{AB}$ and $\overline{AC}$ such that

AB = t = AC.

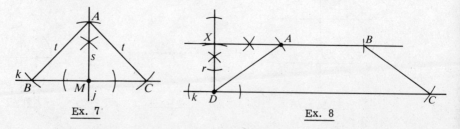

Ex. 7   Ex. 8

<u>8</u>. Draw a line k; choose D on k and construct a ⊥ to k at D. Construct $\overline{DX}$ so that

DX = r.   Construct a ∥ to k through X.   With ctr. D and radius t, draw an arc intersecting the ∥ at A.   Draw $\overline{AD}$ and construct $\overline{AB} \cong \overline{AD}$.   With ctr. B and radius

t, draw an arc intersecting k at C.   Draw $\overline{BC}$.

9. Construct $\overline{AB}$ so that AB = t.   Construct the ⊥ bis. of $\overline{AB}$, intersecting $\overline{AB}$ at M.

Draw a semicircle with ctr. M and radius r.   With ctr. A and radius s, draw an arc

intersecting the semicircle at C.   Draw $\overline{CA}$ and $\overline{CB}$.

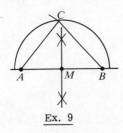

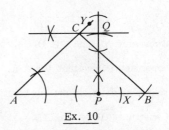

Ex. 9	Ex. 10

10. Construct ∠XAY with meas. n.   Choose P on $\overrightarrow{AX}$ and construct a ⊥ to $\overrightarrow{AX}$ at P.

Construct $\overline{PQ}$ so that PQ = s.   Construct a ∥ to $\overrightarrow{AX}$ through Q, intersecting $\overrightarrow{AY}$ at

C.   With ctr. C and radius AC, draw an arc intersecting $\overrightarrow{AX}$ at B.   Draw $\overline{CB}$.

11. Construct ∠XAY with meas. n.   Choose P on $\overrightarrow{AX}$ and construct $\overline{PQ}$ so that PQ = s.

Construct a ∥ to $\overrightarrow{AX}$ through Q, intersecting $\overrightarrow{AY}$ at C.   Construct a ⊥ to $\overrightarrow{AY}$ at C,

intersecting $\overrightarrow{AX}$ at B.

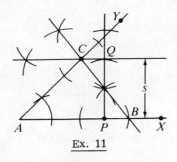

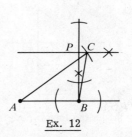

Ex. 11	Ex. 12

12. Construct $\overline{AB}$ so that AB = s.   Construct a ⊥ to $\overline{AB}$ at B.   Construct $\overline{BP}$ so that

BP = r and construct a ∥ to $\overline{AB}$ through P.   With ctr. A and radius t, draw an arc

intersecting the ∥ at C.   Draw $\overline{CA}$ and $\overline{CB}$.

13. Construct $\overline{AB}$ so that AB = t.   Construct the ⊥ bis. of $\overline{AB}$, intersecting $\overline{AB}$ at M

and construct $\overline{MP}$ so that MP = r.   Construct a ∥ to $\overline{AB}$ through P.   With ctr. A

and radius s, draw an arc intersecting the ∥ at C.   Draw $\overline{CA}$ and $\overline{CB}$.   See diagram,

top of next page.

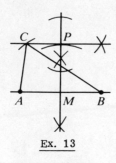

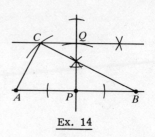

Ex. 13   Ex. 14

14. Construct $\overline{AP}$ and $\overline{PB}$ so that AP = PB = s. Construct a ⊥ to $\overline{AB}$ at P and construct $\overline{PQ}$ so that PQ = r. Construct a ∥ to $\overline{AB}$ through Q. With ctr. P and radius s, draw an arc intersecting the ∥ at C. Draw $\overline{CA}$ and $\overline{CB}$.

15. Construct $\overline{AB}$ so that AB = r. Construct a ⊥ to $\overline{AB}$ at B. With ctr. A and radius s, draw an arc intersecting the ⊥ at C. Draw $\overline{AC}$. Construct $\overline{CE}$ and $\overline{CD}$ ≅ to $\overline{AC}$. △ ACD and △ ACE are the required ⧍. Draw the alt. $\overline{DF}$ to $\overline{AC}$ in △ ACD. △ DFC ≅ △ ABC by AAS so DF = AB = r. Justifying that △ ACE is the required obtuse △ is done in a similar manner.

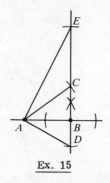

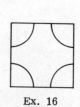

Ex. 15   Ex. 16

C 16. To construct the locus, note that when the seg. is not lying on a side of the square, it forms a rt. △ with the sides of the square. Then the midpt. of the seg. is equidistant from the vert. of the △; it lies on a ⊙ with ctr. the vertex of the square and radius $\frac{3s}{2}$. The locus is the 4 90° arcs shown and the segments joining them.

17. Construct $\overline{AB}$ and $\overline{BC}$ so that AB = r and BC = s. Construct the ⊥ bis. of $\overline{AC}$, intersecting $\overline{AC}$ at M. Draw ⊙M with radius $\frac{1}{2}$AB, intersecting the ⊥ bis. of $\overline{AC}$ at D. Draw $\overrightarrow{DB}$, intersecting ⊙M at E. Draw $\overline{EA}$ and $\overline{EC}$. Since m∠ AEB = $\frac{1}{2}$m$\overset{\frown}{AD}$ = $\frac{1}{2}$m$\overset{\frown}{DC}$ = m∠ DEC, $\overrightarrow{ED}$ is the bis. of ∠ AEC. See diagram, top of next page.

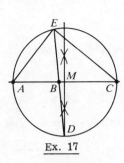

Ex. 17

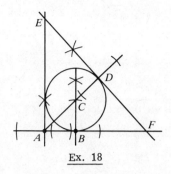

Ex. 18

18. Construct rt. ∠A and $\overline{AB}$ so that AB = r.   Construct a ⊥ to $\overline{AB}$ at B and construct

$\overline{BC}$ so that BC = r.   Draw ⊙C with radius r.   Draw $\overrightarrow{AC}$, intersecting ⊙C at D.

Construct a tan to ⊙C at D, intersecting the sides of ∠A at E and F.   △ABC is an

isos. rt. △ so m∠EAD = m∠FAD = 45.   Then △EAD ≅ △FAD and $\overline{AE}$ ≅ $\overline{AF}$.

19. Draw a line and construct $\overrightarrow{AB}$ so that AB = t.   Construct ∠DBC on $\overleftrightarrow{AB}$ so that

m∠DBC = n.   Bisect ∠ABD (the supp. of ∠DBC)

to construct ∠ABE and ∠EBD, each with meas.

$x = \frac{1}{2}(180 - n)$.   Construct the ⊥ bisector of $\overline{AB}$

and locate P at the pt. where the ⊥ bisector of $\overline{AB}$

intersects $\overrightarrow{BE}$.   Use Construction 10 to circum-

scribe a ⊙ about △APB.   The locus is $\overparen{APB}$,

excluding pts. A and B.

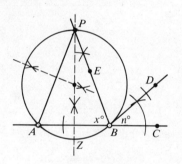

Page 369 · CHALLENGE

Since △DAE and △CDA are isos. △, ∠DEA ≅

∠DAE ≅ ∠ADC.   Then △DAE ~ △CDA by the

AA ~ Post. $\frac{AE}{DA} = \frac{CD}{AD}$; $\frac{AE}{AB} = \frac{2 \cdot AB}{AB}$;

$AE = \frac{1}{2}AB$ and E is the midpt. of $\overline{AB}$.

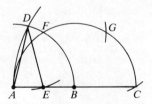

Pages 370-371 · EXTRA

1-2. Check students' constructions.   Figures may vary.

3. Some of the pts. are the same: L and R, M and S, N and T

4. 3; if C is a rt. ∠ the legs are alt. and S = T = Z = C

5. 1. NM ∥ AB; XY ∥ AB; NM = $\frac{1}{2}$AB; XY = $\frac{1}{2}$AB (The seg. that joins the midpts. of

2 sides of a △ is ∥ to the third side and has length = half the length of the third side.)

2. $\overline{NM} \parallel \overline{XY}$; NM = XY (Trans. Prop.; Subst. Prop.)   3. XYMN is a $\square$. (If one pair of opp. sides of a quad. are both $\cong$ and $\parallel$, then the quad. is a $\square$.)   4. $\overline{CR} \perp \overline{AB}$ (Def. of alt.)   5. $\overline{CR} \perp \overline{NM}$ (If a trans. is $\perp$ to one of 2 $\parallel$ lines, then it is $\perp$ to the other one also.)   6. $\overline{NX} \parallel \overline{CH}$ (The seg. that joins the midpts. of 2 sides of a $\triangle$ is $\parallel$ to the third side), and so $\overline{NX} \parallel \overline{CR}$.   7. $\overline{NM} \perp \overline{NX}$ (If a trans. is $\perp$ to one of 2 $\parallel$ lines, then it is $\perp$ to the other one also.)   8. $\angle MNX$ is a rt. $\angle$ (Def. of rt. $\angle$)
9. XYMN is a rect. (If an $\angle$ of a $\square$ is a rt. $\angle$, then the $\square$ is a rect.)

6. If the students' figures are carefully drawn, the ratio of the radius of the nine-point circle to the radius of the circumscribed circle will appear to be $1:2$. The proof is rather difficult and lengthy.

Pages 372-373 · CHAPTER REVIEW

1.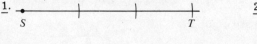

2. $m\angle X + m\angle Z$

3. Use Construction 3.   4. Use Construction 4.   5. Use Construction 5.

6. Use Construction 6.   7. Use Construction 7.   8.   bisectors of the sides

9. $\angle$ bisectors   10. $12 = \frac{2}{3} \cdot MP$; MP = 18   11. $1:2$

12. Use Construction 8.   13. Use Construction 9.

14. Construct the bisectors of 2 of the $\angle$. Their int. is the ctr. of the inscribed circle.

15. Use Construction 10.   16. Use Construction 14.   17. Use Construction 13.

18. Use Construction 1 twice to construct a seg. with length a + b; then use Construction 12 to divide the seg. into thirds.

19. a line $\parallel$ to both lines, halfway between them

20. a plane $\perp$ to $\overline{AB}$ that bisects $\overline{AB}$

21. a plane $\parallel$ to both planes, halfway between them

22. a line $\perp$ to the plane of $\triangle HJK$ at the int. of the medians (altitudes or $\angle$ bisectors)

23. the int. of the $\perp$ bis. of $\overline{PQ}$ and $\odot P$ with radius 8 cm (2 pts.)

24. the int. of the sphere R, of radius 8 cm, and the cylinder of radius 8 cm formed by lines $\parallel$ to ℓ (a circle)

Ex. 23

25. 0 pts., 1 pt., a circle, a circle and a pt., or 2 circles, depending on the int. of 2

    planes, ∥ to Q and 1 m from Q and a sphere with ctr. Z and radius 2 m.

26. Draw a line; choose pt. C and construct a ⊥ to the line at C. Bisect ∠ C and mark

    off $\overline{CX}$ such that CX = $\frac{1}{2}$a. Construct a ⊥ to $\overline{CX}$ at X, intersecting the sides of ∠ C

    at A and B. Since △ ACX, △ BCX and △ ABC are all 45°-45°-90° &, the hyp. of

    rt. △ ABC = a.

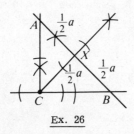
Ex. 26

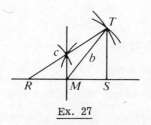
Ex. 27

27. Construct $\overline{RS}$ so that RS = a. Construct the ⊥ bis. of $\overline{RS}$, intersecting $\overline{RS}$ at M.

    Draw an arc with ctr. M and radius b. With ctr. R and radius c, draw another arc

    intersecting the first arc at T. Draw $\overline{TR}$ and $\overline{TS}$.

Page 374 · CHAPTER TEST

1-7. Methods may vary.

1. Construct ∠ A ≅ ∠ 1. With A as ctr. and radius z, draw arcs intersecting sides of

   ∠ A at B and C. Draw $\overline{BC}$.

2. Draw a line and choose pt. P. Construct $\overline{PQ}$ such that PQ = y. Construct a ⊥ at P.

   With radius y, and ctrs. P and Q, draw arcs intersecting at X. Draw $\overrightarrow{QX}$ intersecting

   ⊥ at R. △ RPQ is a 30°-60°-90° △.

3. Use Construction 14.   4. Use Construction 1 and Construction 12.

5. Use Construction 13.

6. Use Construction 9 to construct $\overline{KA}$ and $\overline{KB}$ tangent to ⊙O at A and B. Draw $\overrightarrow{KO}$,

   intersecting ⊙O at C. At C, construct p ⊥ $\overline{KC}$. Draw $\overrightarrow{KA}$ to intersect p at L;

   draw $\overrightarrow{KB}$ intersecting p at M. △ KLM is circumscribed about ⊙O.

7. Use Construction 11.

8. a. ⊥ bis.   b. ∠ bis., medians   c. vertex   9. a. 3   b. 2; 1

10. a. the ⊥ bis. of $\overline{RS}$ b. the plane that bisects $\overline{RS}$ and is ⊥ to $\overline{RS}$

11. a ⊙ that is the int. of sphere T, with radius 6, and sphere u, with radius 4

12. the int. of ⊙A, with radius y, and 2 lines ∥ ℓ and z units from ℓ (4 pts.)

Page 375 · PREPARING FOR COLLEGE ENTRANCE EXAMS

1. B   2. C   3. E   4. A   5. B   6. C   7. A

8. C   9. E

Pages 376-377 · CUMULATIVE REVIEW: CHAPTERS 1-8

A   1. sometimes   2. never   3. sometimes; always   4. never   5. never

6. sometimes   7. always   8. never   9. sometimes   10. sometimes

11. always   12. sometimes   13. sometimes   14. always   15. always

16. sometimes   17. never   18. always   19. always   20. always

21. sometimes   22. 107   23. 9   24. 15   25. 39

26. Methods may vary.   Example: Construct $\overline{XY} \cong \overline{RS}$, $\angle X \cong \angle R$, and $\angle Y \cong \angle S$; extend

the sides of $\angle X$ and $\angle Y$ to intersect at Z.

B   27. The locus is no pts., 1 pt., 2 pts., a pt. and a ⊙ or 2 Ⓢ, depending on the int. of a

sphere with ctr. J and radius 8 cm and 2 planes ∥ to X and 4 cm away from X, on

either side of X.

28. x < 4 + 7, 4 < x + 7, and 7 < x + 4; 3 < x < 11; x = 4, 5, 6, 7, 8, 9, or 10.

29. a. DF = $\sqrt{6^2 + 8^2}$ = 10; $\dfrac{DF}{DE} = \dfrac{DE}{DX}$; DX = $\dfrac{(DE)^2}{DF} = \dfrac{36}{10}$ = 3.6

b. $\dfrac{DY}{10 - DY} = \dfrac{6}{8} = \dfrac{3}{4}$; 4 · DY = 30 - 3 · DY; 7 · DY = 30; DY = $4\dfrac{2}{7}$

30. 60

31. $\dfrac{(n - 2)180}{n}$ = 160; 180n - 360 = 160n; 20n = 360; n = 18

32. Given: Rhombus PQRS   Prove: $\triangle$ PQM $\cong$ $\triangle$ RQM

Proof: 1. PQRS is a rhombus. (Given)

2. $\overline{PM} \cong \overline{MR}$ (The diag. of a ▱ bisect each other.)

3. m∠ PMQ = m∠ RMQ = 90 (The diag. of a rhombus

are ⊥.)   4. $\overline{MQ} \cong \overline{MQ}$ (Refl. Prop. of $\cong$)   5. $\triangle$ PQM $\cong$ $\triangle$ RQM (SAS)

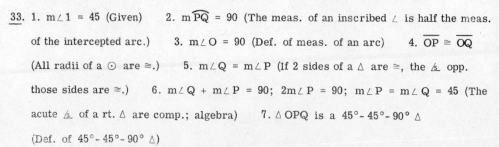

33. 1. m∠ 1 = 45 (Given)   2. m$\overset{\frown}{PQ}$ = 90 (The meas. of an inscribed $\angle$ is half the meas.

of the intercepted arc.)   3. m∠ O = 90 (Def. of meas. of an arc)   4. $\overline{OP} \cong \overline{OQ}$

(All radii of a ⊙ are $\cong$.)   5. m∠ Q = m∠ P (If 2 sides of a $\triangle$ are $\cong$, the ⓐ opp.

those sides are $\cong$.)   6. m∠ Q + m∠ P = 90; 2m∠ P = 90; m∠ P = m∠ Q = 45 (The

acute ⓐ of a rt. $\triangle$ are comp.; algebra)   7. $\triangle$ OPQ is a 45°- 45°- 90° $\triangle$

(Def. of 45°- 45°- 90° $\triangle$)

<u>34.</u> 1. $\angle X \cong \angle Y$; $\angle W \cong \angle Z$ (If 2 inscribed $\angle$ intercept the same arc, the $\angle$ are $\cong$.)

2. $\triangle VXW \sim \triangle VYZ$ (AA)   3. $\dfrac{WX}{ZY} = \dfrac{XV}{YV}$ (Corr. sides of $\sim \triangle$ are in prop.)

4. $WX \cdot YV = ZY \cdot XV$ (Means-extremes Prop.)

<u>35.</u> $6x + 4 + 2x^2 = 180$; $2x^2 + 6x - 176 = 0$; $x^2 + 3x - 88 = 0$; $(x + 11)(x - 8) = 0$;

$x = -11$ (reject) or $x = 8$; $x = 8$

<u>36.</u> $m\angle BCA = \dfrac{1}{2}(180 - 66) = \dfrac{1}{2}(114) = 57$; $x = 180 - 57 = 123$

<u>37.</u> $x^2 = 2(4\sqrt{3})^2 = 2(48) = 96$; $x = \sqrt{96} = 4\sqrt{6}$

<u>38-39.</u> Methods may vary.

<u>38.</u> Draw $\odot$ and a diam., $\overline{AE}$. Construct the $\perp$ bis. of $\overline{AE}$, int. $\odot O$ at C and G.

Construct the bis. of $\angle AOC$, int. $\odot O$ at B and F, and the bis. of $\angle COE$, int. $\odot O$

at D and H. Draw ABCDEFGH.

<u>39.</u> Construct the $\perp$ bis. of $\overline{XY}$ to locate M, the midpt. of $\overline{XY}$. Construct $\odot M$ with

radius $\overline{MX}$. Choose P on $\odot M$ and draw $\overrightarrow{PM}$, int. $\odot M$ at Q. Draw XPYQ.

CHAPTER 9 · Areas of Plane Figures

Pages 382-384 · WRITTEN EXERCISES

A 1. 60 cm²   2. 32.8 cm²   3. 5 cm   4. 15 m   5. 24   6. $2\sqrt{3}$

7. $2x^2 - 6x$ 8. $4k^2 + 7k - 2$ 9. 36 cm²; 26 cm   10. 5 cm; 50 cm²

11. 5 cm; 80 cm²   12. $x^2 + 5x$; $4x + 10$ 13. $a^2 - 9$; $4a$

14. $k + 3$; $k^2 + 10k + 21$ 15. $x - 3$; $4x - 6$ 16. $y + 7$; $4y + 14$

B 17. $5(14) + 2(5)(6) = 130$ 18. $10(2)(2.8) = 56$

19. $h = \sqrt{10^2 - 8^2} = 6$; $A = 8(6) = 48$

20. $h = \frac{18}{2} = 9$; $b = 9\sqrt{3}$; $A = 9(9\sqrt{3}) = 81\sqrt{3}$

21. $S = \frac{7}{\sqrt{2}} = \frac{7\sqrt{2}}{2}$; $A = (\frac{7\sqrt{2}}{2})^2 = \frac{49}{2} = 24\frac{1}{2}$

22. $\sin 26° = \frac{h}{10}$; $0.4384 = \frac{h}{10}$; $h \approx 4.384$; $\cos 26° = \frac{b}{10}$; $0.8988 = \frac{b}{10}$; $b \approx 8.988$; $A \approx 39.4$

23. $2(8y)(2x) + 2y(4x) = 32xy + 8xy = 40xy$

24. $2y(y) + 8y(3y) + 4y(2y) = 2y^2 + 24y^2 + 8y^2 = 34y^2$

25. $A = 4(12) + 9(6) = 102$; $4(102) = 408$; \$408

26. $[(45 + 2(2.5)) \times (25 + 2(2.5))] - (45 \times 25) = 375$; 375 m²

27. $S = \frac{6\sqrt{2}}{2} = 6$; $A = 6^2 = 36$

28. $S = \frac{8}{\sqrt{2}} = \frac{8\sqrt{2}}{2}$ cm; $A = (\frac{8\sqrt{2}}{2})^2 = 32$ cm²

29. $h = 6$ cm; $b = 6\sqrt{3}$ cm; $A = 36\sqrt{3}$ cm²

30. $s^2 + (s + 1)^2 + (s + 2)^2 = 365$; $s^2 + s^2 + 2s + 1 + s^2 + 4s + 4 = 365$; $3s^2 + 6s - 360 = 0$; $s^2 + 2s - 120 = 0$; $(s + 12)(s - 10) = 0$; $s = -12$ (reject) or $s = 10$; $s = 10$

31. $\ell = 3w$; $3w^2 = 432$; $w^2 = 144$; $w = 12$ cm; $\ell = 36$ cm

32. a. Say $\ell = x$; $p = 2\ell + 2w$ so $w = \frac{1}{2}(p - 2\ell) = \frac{1}{2}(40 - 2x) = 20 - x$.   b. $20x - x^2$

c. 36; 64; 96; 100; 96; 64; 36; 0

d. 10 m by 10 m

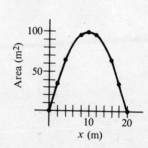

<u>C</u> <u>33.</u> Since $\triangle ABC$ is a 30-60-90 $\triangle$, $AB = \sqrt{3}\,(BC)$.   Area of $ABCD = AB(BC) = 64\sqrt{3}$;

$\sqrt{3}\,(BC)^2 = 64\sqrt{3}$; $(BC)^2 = 64$; $BC = 8 =$ width, $AB = 8\sqrt{3} =$ length

<u>34.</u> $3x^2 + 3x - 18 > 0$; $x^2 + x - 6 > 0$; $(x + 3)(x - 2) > 0$; $x + 3 > 0$ and $x - 2 > 0$

or $x + 3 < 0$ and $x - 2 < 0$; $x > -3$ and $x > 2$ or $x < -3$ and $x < 2$;

$x > 2$ or $x < -3$.

<u>35.</u> <u>a.</u> $\ell = 100 - 2x$; $A = x(100 - 2x)$ <u>b.</u>

<u>c.</u> width = 25 m, length = 50 m

<u>36.</u> Let ℓ and w be the dimensions of the

rectangle.   Use Construction 14 to construct

$\overline{AB}$ with length $\sqrt{\ell w}$.   At A and B use

Construction 5 to construct $\underline{\!\!\perp\!\!s}$ to AB and

mark off AD and BC so that AD = BC = AB.   Draw $\overline{DC}$.   ABCD is a square

with area ℓw.

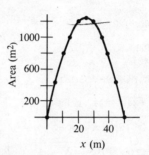

Area (m²) axis with values 200, 600, 1000; x (m) axis with values 20, 40.

Page 385 · COMPUTER KEY-IN

<u>1.</u> 10   FOR X =0.001 TO 1.0 STEP 0.001
    30   LET A =A+Y∗0.001

<u>2-3.</u> Programs may vary.   Sample BASIC programs are given.   Results may vary,

due to round-off.

<u>2.</u> 10   FOR X =.2 TO 2 STEP 0.2
   20   LET Y =X↑3
   30   LET A =A+Y∗0.2
   40   NEXT X
   50   PRINT "AREA IS APPROXIMATELY "; A
   60   END

Area ≈ 3.24

<u>3.</u> 10   FOR X =.2 TO 2 STEP 0.2
   20   LET Y =4-X↑2
   30   LET A =A+Y∗0.2
   40   NEXT X
   50   PRINT "AREA IS APPROXIMATELY "; A
   60   END

Area ≈ 4.92

Pages 387-390 · WRITTEN EXERCISES

<u>A</u> <u>1.</u> 28 cm²   <u>2.</u> 29.9 m²   <u>3.</u> 12   <u>4.</u> 8   <u>5.</u> 6   <u>6.</u> $27\sqrt{2}$ <u>7.</u> 6y

<u>8.</u> 16   <u>9.</u> $h = \sqrt{10^2 - 8^2} = 6$; $A = \frac{1}{2}(16)(6) = 48$

<u>10.</u> $h = 4\sqrt{3}$; $A = \frac{1}{2}(8)(4\sqrt{3}) = 16\sqrt{3}$

<u>11.</u> $d_1 = 6$; $d_2 = 2(3\sqrt{3}) = 6\sqrt{3}$; $A = \frac{1}{2}(6)(6\sqrt{3}) = 18\sqrt{3}$ (or $h = \frac{1}{2}(6)(\sqrt{3}) = 3\sqrt{3}$;

$A = 6(3\sqrt{3}) = 18\sqrt{3}$)

<u>12.</u> $h = 8$; $A = 5(8) = 40$　　　　　<u>13.</u> $A = 4(8) + \frac{1}{2}(8)(3) = 44$

<u>14.</u> length of horizontal leg $= \sqrt{13^2 - 5^2} = 12$; height of upper $\triangle = \sqrt{15^2 - 12^2} = 9$;

$A = \frac{1}{2}(12)(9) + \frac{1}{2}(12)(5) = 84$

<u>15.</u> $A = bh = 20 \cdot 6 =$

$12 \cdot RN$; $RN = 10$ cm.

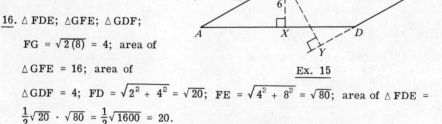

<u>16.</u> $\triangle FDE$; $\triangle GFE$; $\triangle GDF$;

FG $= \sqrt{2(8)} = 4$; area of

$\triangle GFE = 16$; area of

Ex. 15

$\triangle GDF = 4$; FD $= \sqrt{2^2 + 4^2} = \sqrt{20}$; FE $= \sqrt{4^2 + 8^2} = \sqrt{80}$; area of $\triangle FDE =$

$\frac{1}{2}\sqrt{20} \cdot \sqrt{80} = \frac{1}{2}\sqrt{1600} = 20$.

<u>B</u> <u>17.</u> <u>a.</u> Area of $\triangle ABC = \frac{1}{2}(16)(5) = 40$; area of $\triangle ABM = \frac{1}{2}(8)(5) = 20$　　<u>b.</u> Area of

$\triangle ABM = \frac{1}{2} \cdot BM \cdot h = \frac{1}{2} \cdot \frac{1}{2} \cdot BC \cdot h = \frac{1}{2} \cdot$ Area of $\triangle ABC$

<u>18.</u> Let $\angle A$ be the vertex $\angle$ and $\angle B$ and $\angle C$ the base $\angle\!\!\!\angle$ and let $\overline{AM}$, $\overline{BN}$, and $\overline{CP}$ be the

altitudes.　　<u>a.</u> AM $= \sqrt{5^2 - 4^2} = 3$; area of $\triangle ABC = \frac{1}{2}(8)(3) = 12$ cm²

<u>b.</u> AM $= 3$ cm (from part (a) above); $\frac{1}{2}(AC)(BN) = 12$ so BN $= \frac{2}{5}(12) = 4.8$ cm;

similarly, CP $= 4.8$ cm.

<u>19.</u> Let h = height of PQRS = height of $\triangle$ TRS.　Area of $\triangle TRS = \frac{1}{2}(RS)(h) =$

$\frac{1}{2}$(area of PQRS) $= 18$

<u>20.</u> Let h = height of $\triangle$ ABD = height of $\triangle$ ADC; area of $\triangle ABD = \frac{1}{2}(12)(h) = 6h$; area of

$\triangle ADC = \frac{1}{2}(18)(h) = 9h$; ratio of areas = $6h : 9h = 2 : 3$

<u>21.</u> Let $\overline{CF}$ be the alt. from C to $\overleftrightarrow{AB}$.　Area of $\triangle ABC = \frac{1}{2}(AB)(CF) = 240$;

CF $= \frac{240}{12} = 20$

<u>22.</u> Perimeter = 40, so s = 10; $d_1 = 12$; $\frac{d_1}{2} = 6$; $\frac{1}{2}d_2 = \sqrt{10^2 - 6^2} = 8$; $d_2 = 16$;

area $= \frac{1}{2}(12)(16) = 96$

<u>23.</u> Length of legs = 4 and $4\sqrt{3}$; area $= \frac{1}{2}(4)(4\sqrt{3}) = 8\sqrt{3}$

<u>24.</u> Length of legs $= \frac{x}{\sqrt{2}} = \frac{x\sqrt{2}}{2}$; area $= \frac{1}{2}(\frac{x\sqrt{2}}{2})^2 = \frac{x^2}{4}$

<u>25.</u> $s = 2(\frac{12}{\sqrt{3}}) = 8\sqrt{3}$; area $= \frac{1}{2}(8\sqrt{3})(12) = 48\sqrt{3}$

26. The diag. divide the hexagon into 6 $\cong$ equilateral $\triangle$ with sides of length 10; h = $\sqrt{10^2 - 5^2}$ = $5\sqrt{3}$; area of $\triangle$ = $\frac{1}{2}(10)(5\sqrt{3})$ = $25\sqrt{3}$; area of hexagon = $6(25\sqrt{3})$ = $150\sqrt{3}$

27. Let ABCD be the rectangle with AB = DC = 24; $\overline{AC}$ and $\overline{DB}$ are diameters of the circle so AC = DB = 26; BC = $\sqrt{26^2 - 24^2}$ = 10; area of ABCD = 240

28. a. 30(16) = 480   b. $\frac{1}{2}(30)(16)$ = 240   c. area of $\triangle$OSR = $\frac{1}{2}$ area of $\triangle$PSR = 120
    d. 120   e. 120; $\triangle$POQ $\cong$ $\triangle$ROS; 120 because $\triangle$OQR $\cong$ $\triangle$OPS   f. The diag. of a $\square$ divide the $\square$ into 4 $\triangle$ with = area.

29. $\overline{DX}$ $\perp$ $\overline{AC}$ and $\triangle$ABC $\cong$ $\triangle$ADC. Area of ABCD = 2 (area of $\triangle$ABC) = $2 \cdot (\frac{1}{2}d_1 \cdot \frac{1}{2}d_2)$ = $\frac{1}{2}d_1 d_2$

30. (Let $\overline{XW}$ be the alt. to $\overline{YZ}$.)   1. $\overline{XW}$ $\perp$ $\overline{YZ}$ (Def. of alt.)   2. m$\angle$YWX = 90 (Def. of $\perp$ lines, rt. $\angle$)   3. $\triangle$XYW is a 30-60-90 $\triangle$. The sum of the meas. of the $\angle$ of a $\triangle$ is 180; Def. of 30-60-90 $\triangle$)   4. XW = $\frac{s}{2}(\sqrt{3})$ (30-60-90 Thm.)   5. A = $\frac{1}{2}(s)(\frac{s}{2}\sqrt{3})$ (A = $\frac{1}{2}$bh)   6. A = $\frac{s^2\sqrt{3}}{4}$ (By algebra)

31. a. h = $\frac{10}{2}$ = 5; A = 20 $\cdot$ 5 = 100   b. h = $\frac{10}{\sqrt{2}}$ = $5\sqrt{2}$; A = $20(5\sqrt{2})$ = $100\sqrt{2}$ c. h = $5\sqrt{3}$; A = $20(5\sqrt{3})$ = $100\sqrt{3}$ d. h = 10; A = 20(10) = 200   e. h = $5\sqrt{3}$; A = $20(5\sqrt{3})$ = $100\sqrt{3}$ f. (b) A $\approx$ 140; (c) 170; (e) 170; see graph.

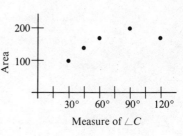

32. A = $\frac{1}{2}$bh = $\frac{1}{2}(h + 1)h$; $\frac{1}{2}(h^2 + h)$ = 210; $h^2 + h$ = 420; $h^2 + h - 420$ = 0; (h + 21)(h - 20) = 0; h = -21 (reject) or h = 20; 20 cm

C 33. Suppose ABCD is a $\square$ with AC = 82 and BD = 30. $\angle$A and $\angle$C must be the acute $\angle$. Let $\overline{AX}$ and $\overline{BY}$ be altitudes from $\overline{AB}$ to $\overleftrightarrow{DC}$ and suppose AX = BY = 18. Either $\overline{AX}$ and $\overline{BY}$ both intersect $\overleftrightarrow{DC}$ outside of $\overline{DC}$ or $\overline{AX}$ intersects $\overleftrightarrow{DC}$ outside of $\overline{DC}$ and Y is on $\overline{DC}$. (If X and Y

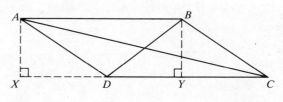

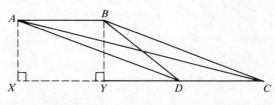

are both on $\overline{DC}$, then $\triangle AXD \simeq \triangle BXC$, $\angle D \simeq \angle C$ and ABCD is a rect.   This contradicts the given fact that the diag. are not $\simeq$.)   If Y is on $\overline{DC}$ and X is not, then XC = $\sqrt{82^2 - 18^2} = 80$; DY = $\sqrt{30^2 - 18^2} = 24$.   Since $\triangle AXD \simeq \triangle BYC$, XD = YC; YC = $\frac{1}{2}(80 - 24) = 28$; DC = 24 + 28 = 52; A = 18 · 52 = 936 cm^2.   If $\overline{AX}$ and $\overline{BY}$ both intersect $\overleftrightarrow{DC}$ outside of $\overline{DC}$, again XC = 80; also DY = 24.   But XY = AB = DC, so DC = $\frac{1}{2}$(XC - YD) = 28 and A = 28(18) = 504 cm^2.   The same results are obtained by considering the altitudes from $\overline{AD}$ to $\overleftrightarrow{BC}$.   Then the 2 poss. values are 936 cm^2 and 504 cm^2.

34. Given scalene $\triangle ABC$, use Const. 6 to construct $\overline{AX} \perp \overline{BC}$.   Area of $\triangle ABC$ = $\frac{1}{2}$(BC)(AX).   Use Const. 1 to construct $\overline{EF} \simeq \overline{BC}$ and use Const. 4 to construct the $\perp$ bis. of $\overline{EF}$, intersecting $\overline{EF}$ at Y.   Mark off a seg. $\overline{DY}$ on the $\perp$ bis. such that DY = AX.   Draw $\overline{DE}$ and $\overline{DF}$. $\triangle DEF$ is isos. and area of $\triangle DEF$ = $\frac{1}{2}$(EF)(DY) = $\frac{1}{2}$(BC)(AX) = area of $\triangle ABC$.

35. Given $\triangle ABC$, use Const. 6 to construct $\overline{AX} \perp \overline{BC}$.   Use Const. 14 to construct $\overline{EF}$ such that EF is the geom. mean of AX and BC.   Construct a $\perp$ to $\overline{EF}$ through E using Const. 5 and mark off $\overline{DE}$ such that DE = EF.   Draw $\overline{DF}$. $\triangle DEF$ is an isos. rt. $\triangle$ and area of $\triangle DEF$ = $\frac{1}{2}$(EF)(DE) = $\frac{1}{2}(\sqrt{AX \cdot BC})(\sqrt{AX \cdot BC})$ = $\frac{1}{2}$(AX)(BC) = area of $\triangle ABC$.

36. Given scalene $\triangle ABC$, use Const. 6 to construct $\overline{AX} \perp \overline{BC}$.   Construct $\overline{DE} \simeq \overline{AX}$ using Const. 1, then extend $\overline{DE}$ through E and on $\overrightarrow{DE}$ mark off EF and FG = DE, so that DG = 3DE.   Use Const. 14 to construct $\overline{HI}$ so that HI is the geom. mean between DE and DG.   (HI = $\sqrt{3}$ DE = $\sqrt{3}$ AX).   Use Const. 1 again to construct $\overline{JK} \simeq \overline{BC}$ and use Const. 12 to divide $\overline{JK}$ into 3 $\simeq$ seg., $\overline{JL}$, $\overline{LM}$, and $\overline{MK}$.   Now construct $\overline{NP}$ so that NP is the geom. mean between HI and JM, i. e. NP = $\sqrt{AX\sqrt{3} \cdot \frac{2}{3}BC}$.   With ctrs. at N and P and radius NP, draw arcs intersecting at Q. $\triangle QNP$ is an equilateral $\triangle$ with height = $\frac{NP\sqrt{3}}{2}$ and area = $\frac{\sqrt{3}}{4}$(NP)^2 = $\frac{\sqrt{3}}{4}$(AX · BC · $\frac{2}{3}$ · $\sqrt{3}$) = $\frac{1}{2}$(AX)(BC) = area of $\triangle ABC$.

37. a. x + y + z = height of the $\triangle$.   b. x + y + z = height of the $\triangle$.   Draw the seg. from the chosen pt. to each vertex.   Let each base of $\triangle$ = b.   Area of $\triangle$ = $\frac{1}{2}$bx + $\frac{1}{2}$by + $\frac{1}{2}$zy = $\frac{1}{2}$b(x + y + z).   If h is the height of $\triangle$, area = $\frac{1}{2}$bh = $\frac{1}{2}$b(x + y + z), so h = x + y + z.

<u>38.</u> Draw $\overline{AX} \perp \overline{BC}$ and $\overline{AY} \perp \overleftrightarrow{DC}$. $\angle BAX$ and $\angle DAY$

are $\simeq$ since both are comp. of $\angle XAD$.   Then

$\triangle BAX \cong \triangle DAY$ by ASA and their areas are =.   So

area of ABCD = area of $\triangle BAX$ + area of AXCD =

area of $\triangle DAY$ + area of AXCD = area of AXCY =

$6 \cdot 6 = 36$;   36 cm^2

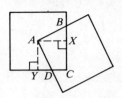

Page 390 · CALCULATOR KEY-IN

<u>1.</u> <u>a</u>. $s = \dfrac{3 + 13 + 14}{2} = 15$; $K = \sqrt{15(15 - 3)(15 - 13)(15 - 14)} = \sqrt{360} = 6\sqrt{10}$

   <u>b</u>. $6\sqrt{10} = \dfrac{1}{2} \cdot 3h$; $h = \dfrac{2}{3} \cdot 6\sqrt{10} = 4\sqrt{10}$ <u>c</u>. $6\sqrt{10} = \dfrac{1}{2} \cdot 13h$; $h = \dfrac{2}{13} \cdot 6\sqrt{10} =$

   $\dfrac{12\sqrt{10}}{13}$ <u>d</u>. $6\sqrt{10} = \dfrac{1}{2} \cdot 14h$; $h = \dfrac{6\sqrt{10}}{7}$

<u>2.</u> $s = \dfrac{11 + 13 + 15}{2} = 19.5$; $K = \sqrt{19.5(8.5)(6.5)(4.5)} \approx 69.629$; $69.629 \approx \dfrac{1}{2} \cdot 11h_1$;

   $h_1 \approx \dfrac{69.629}{5.5} \approx 12.660$; $69.629 \approx \dfrac{1}{2} \cdot 13h_2$; $h_2 \approx \dfrac{69.629}{6.5} \approx 10.712$; $69.629 \approx \dfrac{1}{2} \cdot 15h_3$;

   $h_3 \approx \dfrac{69.629}{7.5} \approx 9.284$

<u>3.</u> $s = \dfrac{8 + 8 + 10}{2} = 13$; $K = \sqrt{13(5)(5)(3)} = \sqrt{975} \approx 31.225$; $31.225 = \dfrac{1}{2} \cdot 8h_1 = \dfrac{1}{2} \cdot 8h_2$;

   $h_2 = h_1 \approx \dfrac{31.225}{4} \approx 7.806$; $31.225 \approx \dfrac{1}{2} \cdot 10h_3$; $h_3 \approx \dfrac{31.225}{5} \approx 6.245$

<u>4.</u> $s = \dfrac{12 + 18 + 27}{2} = 28.5$; $K = \sqrt{28.5(16.5)(10.5)(1.5)} = \sqrt{7406.4375} \approx 86.061$;

   $86.061 \approx \dfrac{1}{2} \cdot 12h_1$; $h_1 \approx \dfrac{86.061}{6} \approx 14.344$; $86.061 \approx \dfrac{1}{2} \cdot 18h_2$; $h_2 \approx \dfrac{86.061}{9} \approx 9.562$;

   $86.061 \approx \dfrac{1}{2} \cdot 27h_3$; $h_3 \approx \dfrac{86.061}{13.5} \approx 6.375$

<u>5.</u> $s = \dfrac{6.3 + 7.2 + 10.1}{2} = 11.8$; $K = \sqrt{11.8(5.5)(4.6)(1.7)} = \sqrt{507.518} \approx 22.528$;

   $22.528 \approx \dfrac{1}{2}(6.3h_1)$; $h_1 \approx \dfrac{22.528}{3.15} \approx 7.152$; $22.528 \approx \dfrac{1}{2}(7.2h_2)$; $h_2 \approx \dfrac{22.528}{3.6} \approx 6.258$;

   $22.528 \approx \dfrac{1}{2}(10.1h_3)$; $h_3 \approx \dfrac{22.528}{5.05} \approx 4.461$

<u>6.</u> $s = \dfrac{68 + 77 + 105}{2} = 125$; $K = \sqrt{125(57)(48)(20)} = \sqrt{6840000} \approx 2615.339$; $2615.339 \approx$

   $\dfrac{1}{2} \cdot 68h_1$; $h_1 \approx \dfrac{2615.339}{34} \approx 76.922$; $2615.339 \approx \dfrac{1}{2} \cdot 77h_2$; $h_2 \approx \dfrac{2615.339}{38.5} \approx 67.931$;

   $2615.339 \approx \dfrac{1}{2} \cdot 105h_3$; $h_3 \approx \dfrac{2615.339}{52.5} \approx 49.816$

7. $s = \dfrac{5.5 + 6.5 + 10}{2} = 11$; $K = \sqrt{11(5.5)(4.5)(1)} = \sqrt{272.25} = 16.5$; $16.5 = \frac{1}{2}(5.5h_1)$;

$h_1 = \dfrac{16.5}{2.75} = 6$; $16.5 = \frac{1}{2}(6.5h_2)$; $h_2 = \dfrac{16.5}{3.25} \approx 5.077$; $16.5 = \frac{1}{2}(10h_3)$; $h_3 = \dfrac{16.5}{5} = 3.3$

Pages 392-393 · WRITTEN EXERCISES

__A__ __1.__ 70   __2.__ 30.5   __3.__ 6   __4.__ 10   __5.__ 5   __6.__ 5   __7.__ 1   __8.__ 15k

__9.__ (1) $\frac{1}{2}(12 + 8) = 10$ (2) $\frac{1}{2}(6.8 + 3.2) = 5$ (3) $\frac{1}{2}(3\frac{1}{6} + 4\frac{1}{3}) = 3\frac{3}{4}$

__10.__ $\frac{1}{2}h(b_1 + b_2) = 54$; $b_1 + b_2 = 18$; length of median = 9

__11.__ $h = \sqrt{13^2 - 5^2} = 12$; $A = \frac{1}{2}(12)(10 + 20) = 180$

__12.__ $h = \frac{8}{2} = 4$; $A = \frac{1}{2}(4)(2 + 10) = 24$

__13.__ $b_1 = 5 + \sqrt{10^2 - 8^2} = 11$; $A = \frac{1}{2}(8)(11 + 5) = 64$

__14.__ $h = \frac{6}{2}\sqrt{3} = 3\sqrt{3}$; $b_1 = 10 - 2(3) = 4$; $A = \frac{1}{2}(3\sqrt{3})(4 + 10) = 21\sqrt{3}$

__15.__ $h = \frac{3\sqrt{3}}{2}$; $b_1 = 3 + 2 \cdot \frac{3}{2} = 6$; $A = \frac{1}{2}(\frac{3\sqrt{3}}{2})(3 + 6) = \frac{27}{4}\sqrt{3}$

__16.__ $b_2 = 6 + \frac{9\sqrt{2}}{\sqrt{2}} = 15$; $h = \frac{9\sqrt{2}}{\sqrt{2}} = 9$; $A = \frac{1}{2}(9)(6 + 15) = 94\frac{1}{2}$

__17.__ $h = \frac{1}{2}(20 - 8) = 6$; $A = \frac{1}{2}(6)(8 + 20) = 84$

__B__ __18.__ __a.__ $h = \sqrt{10^2 - (\frac{1}{2}(21 - 9))^2} = 8$; $A = \frac{1}{2}(8)(9 + 21) = 120$ cm²

__b.__ length of each diag. = $\sqrt{15^2 + 8^2} = 17$ cm

__19.__ __a.__ $300 = \frac{1}{2}h(12 + 28)$; $h = 15$ __b.__ length of leg = $\sqrt{15^2 + (\frac{1}{2}(28 - 12))^2} = 17$;

perimeter = $2 \cdot 17 + 12 + 28 = 74$

__20.__ $\sin 37° = \frac{h}{4}$; $h \approx 4(0.6018) \approx 2.4072$; $A \approx \frac{1}{2}(2.4072)(5 + 11) \approx 19.3$

__21.__ Area of $\triangle DMC$ = Area of ABCD - (Area of $\triangle AMD$ + Area of $\triangle MBC$ =

$\frac{1}{2}(16)(12 + 8) - (\frac{1}{2}(8)(12) + \frac{1}{2}(8)(8)) = 160 - (48 + 32) = 80$

__22.__ __a.__ 1:1 (Area of $\triangle ABD = 6h$ = area of $\triangle ABC$)   __b.__ 1:1 (Area of $\triangle ACD = 2h$ =

area of $\triangle BDC$; area of $\triangle AOD$ = area of $\triangle ACD$ - area of $\triangle DOC$ = area of $\triangle BDC$ -

area of $\triangle DOC$ = area of $\triangle BOC$.)   __c.__ 3:1 (Area of $\triangle ABD = 6h$;

area of $\triangle ADC = 2h$)

__23.__ $\triangle ABC$ is an isos. $\triangle$ with base $\angle$ of 30°.   Height = 6 and base = $12\sqrt{3}$; area of

$\triangle ABC = \frac{1}{2}(6)(12\sqrt{3}) = 36\sqrt{3}$. $\triangle ACD$ is a rt. $\triangle$ with legs 12 and $12\sqrt{3}$ so area of

$\triangle ACD = \frac{1}{2}(12)(12\sqrt{3}) = 72\sqrt{3}$.   Area of AFED = area of $\triangle ABC$ + area of $\triangle ACD$ =

$108\sqrt{3}$. (Alternatively, find AD = 24; AFED is an isos. trap. with bases 12 and 24

and base $\angle$ of 60°, so h = $\frac{12}{2}\sqrt{3}$ = $6\sqrt{3}$ and area = $\frac{1}{2}(6\sqrt{3})(12 + 24) = 108\sqrt{3}$.)

24. Let AB = 12 and DC = 16 with AB and DC the bases of trap. ABCD and let O be the

ctr. of the circle. Draw $\overline{OA}$, $\overline{OB}$, $\overline{OD}$, and $\overline{OC}$. △ODC is an isos. △ with legs 10

and base 16 so its height = $\sqrt{10^2 - 8^2}$ = 6.   △OAB is an isos. △ with legs 10 and

base 12 so its height = $\sqrt{10^2 - 6^2}$ = 8.   The height of ABCD is the sum of the heights

of △ODC and △OAB. Area of ABCD = $\frac{1}{2}(6 + 8)(12 + 16)$ = 196.

C 25. Given a non-isos. trap. ABCD with bases $\overline{AB}$ and $\overline{DC}$, use Const. 6 to construct a ⊥

from A to $\overline{DC}$ intersecting $\overline{DC}$ at E. Construct $\overline{FG} \cong \overline{DC}$, using Const. 1. Use

Const. 4 to construct the ⊥ bis. of $\overline{FG}$, intersecting $\overline{FG}$ at H. Mark off a seg. $\overline{HI}$

on the ⊥ bis. so that HI = AE. Use Const. 7 to construct a ∥ to $\overline{FG}$ through I.

Locate the midpt., M, of $\overline{AB}$ by using Const. 4 to construct the ⊥ bis. of $\overline{AB}$.

Mark off $\overline{JI}$ and $\overline{IK}$ on the ∥ through I so that JI = IK = AM. Draw $\overline{JF}$ and $\overline{KG}$.

JKGF is an isos. trap. with the same area as trap. ABCD.

26. Let $\overline{ZA}$ and $\overline{YB}$ be ⊥s to $\overline{WX}$. ZA = $\frac{10}{2}$ = 5 and WA = $5\sqrt{3}$; YB = ZA = 5 so

BX = 5. Then ZY = AB = 20 - $(5\sqrt{3} + 5)$ = 15 - $5\sqrt{3}$ and A =

$\frac{1}{2}(5)(20 + 15 - 5\sqrt{3})$ = 87.5 - $12.5\sqrt{3}$.

27. Let $\overline{SA}$ and $\overline{RB}$ be ⊥ to $\overline{PQ}$. AB = 10 so PA + BQ = 14. Let PA = x and

BQ = 14 - x. SA = RB so $\sqrt{13^2 - x^2}$ = $\sqrt{15^2 - (14 - x)^2}$; $13^2 - x^2$ =

$15^2 - (14 - x)^2$; $169 - x^2 = 225 - 196 + 28x - x^2$; 28x = 140; x = 5.

SA = $\sqrt{13^2 - 5^2}$ = 12; A = $\frac{1}{2}(12)(10 + 24)$ = 204

28. Let s = length of a side of ABCD. △CHB $\cong$ △DEA (AAS) so HB = EA. But HB =

HE + EB and EA = EB + BA so HE = BA = s. ∠GCD $\cong$ ∠H so △GCD $\cong$ △FHE.

Area of EFGD = area of △GCD + area of CFED = area of △FHE + CFED = area of

$\square$CHED = HE · CB = s · s = s^2 = area of ABCD.

29. First note that area of MNOP = area of MNSR + area of NOVS - area of MPTR -

area of POVT. Draw a ∥ to $\overline{RV}$ through M intersecting $\overline{NS}$ at A and a ∥ to $\overline{RV}$

through P intersecting $\overline{OV}$ at B. By extending $\overline{PO}$ in both directions to intersect $\overleftrightarrow{MA}$

and $\overleftrightarrow{RV}$, you can show that ∠NMA $\cong$ ∠OPB and so △NMA $\cong$ △OPB (AAS). MA =

RS = 8 so PB = TV = 8.   NA = 16 - 10 = 6 so OB = 6 and BV = PT = 3.   Then

area of MNOP = $\frac{1}{2}(8)(26) + \frac{1}{2}(11)(25) - \frac{1}{2}(11)(13) - \frac{1}{2}(8)(12) = 122$.

Page 394 · CALCULATOR KEY-IN

Area of plot = area of rect. ABYF +

area of trap. EYCD.   DX = XC = EY =

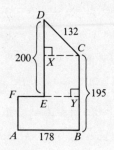

$\frac{132}{\sqrt{2}} \approx 93.338$; CY = XE $\approx$ 200 - 93.338 = 106.662;

FA = YB $\approx$ 195 - 106.662 = 88.338; area of

plot $\approx$ 15724.2 + 14311.6 = 30035.8;

30036 m^2

Page 395 · COMPUTER KEY-IN

1-3. Programs and results may vary.

<u>1.</u> 10   FOR X = 1 TO 1.999 STEP 0.001
     30   LET B2 = (X + 0.001)↑2
     40   LET A = A + 0.5 * 0.001 * (B1 + B2)

Area $\approx$ 2.32933578

<u>2.</u> 10   FOR X = 0 TO 0.9 STEP 0.1
     30   LET B2 = (X + 0.1)↑2
     40   LET A = A + 0.5 * 0.1 * (B1 + B2)

Area $\approx$ .2445

<u>3.</u> 10   FOR X = 0 TO 1.8 STEP 0.2
     20   LET B1 = 4 - X↑2
     30   LET B2 = 4 - (X + 0.2)↑2
     40   LET A = A + 0.5 * 0.2 * (B1 + B2)

Area $\approx$ 5.244

Pages 398-399 · WRITTEN EXERCISES

<u>A</u> <u>1.</u> a = 8; A = 256   <u>2.</u> r = $5\sqrt{2}$; A = 100

<u>3.</u> r = $\frac{7\sqrt{2}}{2}$; a = $\frac{7}{2}$ <u>4.</u> r = $2\sqrt{3}$; A = 24

<u>5.</u> a = 3; p = $18\sqrt{3}$; A = $27\sqrt{3}$ <u>6.</u> r = 8; p = $24\sqrt{3}$; A = $48\sqrt{3}$

<u>7.</u> r = $\frac{4\sqrt{3}}{3}$; a = $\frac{2\sqrt{3}}{3}$; A = $4\sqrt{3}$ <u>8.</u> r = 3; a = $\frac{3}{2}$; A = $\frac{27\sqrt{3}}{4}$

<u>9.</u> a = $2\sqrt{3}$; p = 24; A = $24\sqrt{3}$ <u>10.</u> r = 10; p = 60; A = $150\sqrt{3}$

<u>11.</u> r = $4\sqrt{3}$; p = $24\sqrt{3}$; A = $72\sqrt{3}$ <u>12.</u> r = $2\sqrt{3}$; a = 3; A = $18\sqrt{3}$

<u>13.</u> a = $2\sqrt{3}$; s = 12; p = 36; A = $36\sqrt{3}$

<u>14.</u> a = $\frac{8}{\sqrt{2}}$k = $4\sqrt{2}$ k; s = $8\sqrt{2}$ k; p = $32\sqrt{2}$ k; A = 128k^2

15. s = 12; a = $6\sqrt{3}$; A = $216\sqrt{3}$ 16. s = $\frac{8\sqrt{3}}{3}$; p = $16\sqrt{3}$; A = $32\sqrt{3}$

17. a = $\frac{1}{2}$; s = $\sqrt{3}$; p = $3\sqrt{3} \approx 5.19$; A = $\frac{3\sqrt{3}}{4} \approx 1.30$

18. a = $\frac{1}{\sqrt{2}} = \frac{\sqrt{2}}{2} \approx .705$; s = $\sqrt{2}$; p = $4\sqrt{2} \approx 5.64$; A = 2

19. s = 1; p = 6; a = $\frac{\sqrt{3}}{2} \approx 0.865$; A = $\frac{3\sqrt{3}}{2} \approx 2.595$

20. a. s = $r\sqrt{2}$; p = $4r\sqrt{2}$ b. p $\approx$ 5.656r

21. a. m∠AOX = $\frac{1}{2}$m∠AOB = $\frac{1}{2}(\frac{1}{10}(360)) = \frac{1}{2}(36)$ = 18   b. 0.3090; 0.9511

   c. 6.18   d. 0.2939   e. 2.939

22. m∠AOX = 15;   AX $\approx$ 0.2588; OX $\approx$ 0.9659; perimeter of dodecagon $\approx$ 6.2112;

   area of dodecagon $\approx$ 3

23. a. m∠AOX = $\frac{1}{2}$m∠AOB = $\frac{1}{2}(\frac{360}{n}) = \frac{180}{n}$ b. $\frac{AX}{1} = \sin(\frac{180}{n})°$; AX = $\sin(\frac{180}{n})°$

   c. $\frac{OX}{1} = \cos(\frac{180}{n})°$; OX = $\cos(\frac{180}{n})°$ d. AB = 2 · AX = 2 $\sin(\frac{180}{n})°$;

   p = n · AB = n · 2 · AX = n(2 $\sin(\frac{180}{n})°$) = 2n · $\sin(\frac{180}{n})°$ e. A = $\frac{1}{2}$ap =

   $\frac{1}{2}$ · $\cos(\frac{180}{n})°$ · 2n · $\sin(\frac{180}{n})°$ = n · $\sin(\frac{180}{n})°$ · $\cos(\frac{180}{n})°$

Page 400 · COMPUTER KEY-IN

2. Results may vary, due to round-off.

Number of sides	Perimeter	Area
18	6.25132918	3.0781788
180	6.28286101	3.14095205
1800	6.28317681	3.14158362
18000	6.28317989	3.1415899

3. p $\approx$ 6.28318; A $\approx$ 3.14159 (p $\approx$ 2π; A $\approx$ π)

Pages 404-406 · WRITTEN EXERCISES

A 1. C = 14π; A = 49π 2. C = 240π; A = 14400π

   3. C = 5π; A = $\frac{25\pi}{4}$ 4. C = $12\sqrt{2}\pi$; A $\approx$ 72π

   5. r = 10; A = 100π 6. r = 6; A = 36π

   7. r = 5; C = 10π 8. r = $5\sqrt{2}$; C = $10\sqrt{2}\pi$

   9. C = $84(\frac{22}{7})$ = 264; A = 42 · 42 · $\frac{22}{7}$ = 5544

<u>10.</u> $C = \frac{22}{7} \cdot \frac{7}{2} = 11$; $A = \frac{49}{16} \cdot \frac{22}{7} = \frac{77}{8} = 9\frac{5}{8}$

<u>11.</u> $C = \frac{22}{7} \cdot \frac{28}{11} = 8$; $A = \frac{22}{7} \cdot \frac{28}{22} \cdot \frac{28}{22} = \frac{56}{11} = 5\frac{1}{11}$

<u>12.</u> $C = 2 \cdot \frac{22}{7} \cdot 7k = 44k$; $A = \frac{22}{7} \cdot 49k^2 = 154k^2$

<u>13.</u> $C = (6.28)(10) = 62.8$; $A = (3.14)(100) = 314.0$

<u>14.</u> $C = (3.14)(3) \approx 9.4$; $A = (3.14)(2.25) \approx 7.1$

<u>15.</u> $C = (3.14)(0.5) \approx 1.6$; $A = (3.14)(0.0625) \approx 0.2$

<u>16.</u> $C = (6.28)(1.1) \approx 6.9$; $A = (3.14)(1.21) \approx 3.8$

<u>17.</u> The larger pizza costs about 4¢ per square inch; the smaller pizza costs about 5.1¢ per square inch. The larger pizza is the better buy.

B <u>18.</u> area of bull's-eye = π; area of second ring = $4\pi - \pi = 3\pi$; area of third ring = $9\pi - 4\pi = 5\pi$; area of fourth ring = $16\pi - 9\pi = 7\pi$. Area of n-th ring = $n^2\pi - (n - 1)^2\pi = n^2\pi - (n^2\pi - 2n\pi + \pi) = n^2\pi - n^2\pi + 2n\pi - \pi = (2n - 1)\pi$

<u>19.</u> hyp. = $\sqrt{6^2 + 8^2} = 10$; area I = $\frac{9\pi}{2}$; area II = 8π; area III = $\frac{25\pi}{2}$

<u>20.</u> area I = $\pi(\frac{a}{2})^2 = \frac{a^2\pi}{4}$; area II = $\pi(\frac{b}{2})^2 = \frac{b^2\pi}{4}$; area III = $\pi(\frac{c}{2})^2 = \frac{c^2\pi}{4}$; since $a^2 + b^2 = c^2$, $\frac{a^2\pi}{4} + \frac{b^2\pi}{4} = \frac{c^2\pi}{4}$; area I + area II = area III.

<u>21.</u> $A = 2r(2r) + \pi r^2 = 4r^2 + \pi r^2 = (\pi + 4)r^2$

<u>22.</u> $A = 2r(4r) - 2\pi r^2 = 8r^2 - 2\pi r^2 = r^2(8 - 2\pi)$ <u>23.</u> $A = \frac{1}{2}\pi(2r)^2 = 2\pi r^2$

<u>24.</u> $A = 2(r \cdot 2r) + \frac{1}{2}\pi(2r)^2 - \frac{1}{2}\pi r^2 = 4r^2 + 2\pi r^2 - \frac{1}{2}\pi r^2 = r^2(4 + \frac{3}{2}\pi)$

<u>25.</u> distance = $10(\pi d) = 700(\frac{22}{7}) = 2200$ cm or 22 m

<u>26.</u> 22 km = 2,200,000 cm; let n = number of revolutions; distance = $n\pi d$; $n = \dfrac{2,200,000}{\frac{22}{7} \cdot 70} = 10,000$

<u>27.</u> radius of inscribed circle = 3; area = 9π; radius of circumscribed circle = $3\sqrt{2}$; area = 18π

<u>28.</u> radius of inscribed circle = $\sqrt{3}$; area = 3π; radius of circumscribed circle = $2\sqrt{3}$; area = 12π

<u>29.</u> radius of inscribed circle = $3\sqrt{3}$; area = 27π; radius of circumscribed circle = 6; area = 36π

<u>30.</u> Let A and B be consecutive vertices of the dodecagon and X the midpt. of $\overline{AB}$.

If O is the center of the circle, $m\angle AOX = 15$; $\sin 15° = \dfrac{AX}{6}$; $AX \approx 1.5528$;

$\cos 15° = \dfrac{OX}{6}$; $OX \approx 5.7954$; area of $\triangle AOB \approx 8.999 \approx 9$; area of dodecagon ≈ 108;

area of circle $= 36\pi$; area of enclosed region $\approx 36\pi - 108$

31. a. r   b. $A = \pi r^2$, the area of a $\odot$

32. Let ABCD be the rhombus and O the center of the inscribed circle and draw $\overline{XY}$, a

diam. of $\odot O$ that is $\perp$ to $\overline{AB}$ and $\overline{CD}$. $\triangle AOB$ is a rt. $\triangle$ with legs 6 and 8, so

$AB = \sqrt{6^2 + 8^2} = 10$.   Area of ABCD $= 4 \cdot$ area of $\triangle AOB = 4(\dfrac{1}{2} \cdot 6 \cdot 8) = 96$.

Area of ABCD $= AB \cdot XY$ so $XY = \dfrac{96}{10} = 9.6$.   Then $C = 9.6\pi$ cm.

33. $C = 2\pi r$; $\;r = \dfrac{C}{2\pi}$; $\;A = \pi r^2 = \pi(\dfrac{C}{2\pi})^2 = \dfrac{C^2}{4\pi}$

34. Let ABC be a rt. $\triangle$ with $AB = 10$, $BC = 6$, and $AC = 8$ and let O be the center of the

inscribed circle.   Area of $\triangle AOB = 5r$; area of $\triangle BOC = 3r$, and area of $\triangle AOC = 4r$.

Area of $\triangle ABC = \dfrac{1}{2}(6 \cdot 8) = 24$ so $5r + 3r + 4r = 24$; $12r = 24$; $r = 2$; Area

of $\odot O = \pi(2^2) = 4\pi$

35. Let r be the radius of $\odot O$ and s the radius of $\odot P$.   Construct a segment $\overline{BC} \cong$ to a

radius of $\odot O$.   At C, construct a $\perp$ to $\overline{BC}$ and mark off $CA = s$.   Draw AB.

$\triangle ABC$ is a rt. $\triangle$ so $AB = \sqrt{(BC)^2 + (CA)^2} = \sqrt{r^2 + s^2}$.   Draw a circle with radius AB.

Area of circle $= \pi(\sqrt{r^2 + s^2})^2 = \pi(r^2 + s^2) = \pi r^2 + \pi s^2 =$ area of $\odot O +$ area of $\odot P$.

Pages 408-409 · WRITTEN EXERCISES

A 1. length of $\overparen{AB} = \dfrac{90}{360} \cdot 2\pi \cdot 10 = 5\pi$; area of sector AOB $= \dfrac{90}{360} \cdot \pi(10^2) = 25\pi$

2. length of $\overparen{AB} = \dfrac{60}{360} \cdot 2\pi \cdot 12 = 4\pi$; area of sector AOB $= \dfrac{60}{360} \cdot \pi \cdot 12^2 = 24\pi$

3. length of $\overparen{AB} = \dfrac{30}{360} \cdot 2\pi \cdot 12 = 2\pi$; area of sector AOB $= \dfrac{30}{360} \cdot \pi \cdot 12^2 = 12\pi$

4. length of $\overparen{AB} = \dfrac{45}{360} \cdot 2\pi \cdot 4 = \pi$; area of sector AOB $= \dfrac{45}{360} \cdot \pi \cdot 4^2 = 2\pi$

5. length of $\overparen{AB} = \dfrac{120}{360} \cdot 2\pi \cdot 3 = 2\pi$; area of sector AOB $= \dfrac{120}{360} \cdot \pi \cdot 3^2 = 3\pi$

6. length of $\overparen{AB} = \dfrac{240}{360} \cdot 2\pi \cdot 3 = 4\pi$; area of sector AOB $= \dfrac{240}{360} \cdot \pi \cdot 3^2 = 6\pi$

7. length of $\overparen{AB} = \dfrac{180}{360} \cdot 2\pi \cdot 5 = 5\pi$; area of sector AOB $= \dfrac{180}{360} \cdot \pi \cdot 5^2 = \dfrac{25\pi}{2}$

8. length of $\overparen{AB} = \dfrac{270}{360} \cdot 2\pi \cdot 8 = 12\pi$; area of sector AOB $= \dfrac{270}{360} \cdot \pi \cdot 8^2 = 48\pi$

9. length of $\overparen{AB} = \dfrac{40}{360} \cdot 2\pi \cdot 6 = \dfrac{4\pi}{3}$; area of sector AOB $= \dfrac{40}{360} \cdot \pi \cdot 6^2 = 4\pi$

10. length of $\overparen{AB} = \dfrac{320}{360} \cdot 2\pi \cdot 6 = \dfrac{32\pi}{3}$; area of sector AOB $= \dfrac{320}{360} \cdot \pi \cdot 6^2 = 32\pi$

11. length of $\overset{\frown}{AB}$ = $\dfrac{108}{360}$ · 2π · 25 = 15π; area of sector AOB = $\dfrac{108}{360}$ · π · 25^2 = $\dfrac{375\pi}{2}$

12. length of $\overset{\frown}{AB}$ = $\dfrac{200}{360}$ · 2π · 3 = $\dfrac{10\pi}{3}$; area of sector AOB = $\dfrac{200}{360}$ · π · 3^2 = 5π

13. $\dfrac{100}{360}$ · πr^2 = 10π; r^2 = 10 · $\dfrac{360}{100}$ = 36; r = 6

14. $\dfrac{315}{360}$ · πr^2 = $\dfrac{7\pi}{2}$; r^2 = $\dfrac{7}{2}$ · $\dfrac{360}{315}$ = 4; r = 2

B 15. Area of sector = $\dfrac{90}{360}$ · π · 4^2 = 4π; area of shaded region = 4π - $\dfrac{1}{2}$(4 · 4) = 4π - 8

16. Area of sector = $\dfrac{60}{360}$ · π · 3^2 = $\dfrac{3\pi}{2}$; area of shaded region = $\dfrac{3\pi}{2}$ - $\dfrac{3^2\sqrt{3}}{4}$ = $\dfrac{3\pi}{2}$ - $\dfrac{9\sqrt{3}}{4}$

17. Area of shaded region = $\dfrac{1}{2}$ · area of circle = $\dfrac{25\pi}{8}$

18. Draw the sector determined by the radii intersecting endpts. of the chord.   Area of

   sector = $\dfrac{90}{360}$ · π · 4^2 = 4π; area of unshaded region = 4π - $\dfrac{1}{2}$(4 · 4) = 4π - 8;

   area of $\odot$ = 16π; area of shaded region = 16π - (4π - 8) = 12π + 8

19. Area of semicircle = $\dfrac{1}{2}\pi$ · 6^2 = 18π; area of shaded region = 18π - $\dfrac{1}{2}$ · 6 · $6\sqrt{3}$ =

   18π - $18\sqrt{3}$

20. Draw diag. seg. from endpts. of chords.   2 isos. $\triangle$ and 2 sectors are formed.

   Radius of circle = length of legs of isos. $\triangle$ = 2; area of sector = $\dfrac{60}{360}$ · π · 2^2 = $\dfrac{2\pi}{3}$;

   area of isos. $\triangle$ = $\dfrac{1}{2}$ · $\sqrt{3}$ · 2 = $\sqrt{3}$; area of shaded region = $2(\dfrac{2\pi}{3})$ + $2(\sqrt{3})$ = $\dfrac{4\pi}{3}$ + $\sqrt{3}$

21. Radius of $\odot$ = $\dfrac{1}{2}$ length of a diag. = $\dfrac{1}{2}\sqrt{12^2 + 16^2}$ = $\dfrac{1}{2}$ · 20 = 10; area of region inside

   of $\odot$ but outside of rect. = π · 10^2 - 12 · 16 = 100π - 192.

22. $\overline{PA}$ $\cong$ $\overline{PB}$ (tan. to a $\odot$ from a pt. are $\cong$) and $\angle$ A and $\angle$ B are rt. $\angle$ (if a line is tan.

   to a $\odot$, then it is $\perp$ to the radius drawn to the pt. of tangency) so $\triangle OAP$ and $\triangle OBP$

   are $\cong$ 30-60-90 $\triangle$ with short leg 6.   Area of AOBP = $2(\dfrac{1}{2}$ · 6 · $6\sqrt{3})$ = $36\sqrt{3}$; area

   of each sector = $\dfrac{60}{360}$ · π · 6^2 = 6π; area of region outside $\odot$ but inside quad. =

   $36\sqrt{3}$ - 12π.

23. Let O be the center of the $\odot$ and draw a $\perp$ from O to $\overline{AB}$ int. $\overline{AB}$ at X.   m$\angle$ AOX = 36;

   sin 36° = $\dfrac{AX}{10}$; AX $\approx$ 10(0.5878) = 5.878; cos 36° = $\dfrac{OX}{10}$; OX $\approx$ 10(0.8090) = 8.090;

   area of $\triangle$ AOB = $\dfrac{1}{2}$ · AB · XO = AX · XO $\approx$ 47.6.   Area of sector AOB =

   $\dfrac{72}{360}$ · π · 10^2 = 20π; area of region bounded by $\overline{AB}$ and $\overset{\frown}{AB}$ $\approx$ 20π - 47.6 $\approx$ 15.2.

<u>24.</u> Area of sector BAD = $\frac{90}{360} \cdot \pi \cdot 8^2 = 16\pi$;

area of $\triangle$ BAD = $\frac{1}{2} \cdot 8 \cdot 8 = 32$; area of

region in $\odot$A bounded by $\overparen{BD}$ and $\overline{BD}$ =

16π - 32. Sim., area of region in $\odot$C

bounded by $\overparen{BD}$ and $\overline{BD}$ = 16π - 32 and

area of region inside both Ⓢ = 32π - 64.

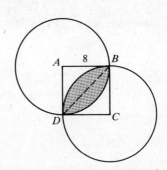

<u>25.</u> <u>a.</u> Use Construction 4 to locate the midpts. of the sides of the square.   At each of

these pts. draw a semicircle inside the square with diam. = s, the length of a side of

the square.   <u>b.</u> The region consists of 4 $\cong$ figures.   We shall find the area of one.

Radius of $\odot$X = radius of $\odot$Y = $\frac{2}{\sqrt{2}} = \sqrt{2}$; area of sector AYO = $\frac{90}{360} \cdot \pi \cdot (\sqrt{2})^2$ =

$\frac{\pi}{2}$; area of $\triangle$AYO = $\frac{1}{2}\sqrt{2} \cdot \sqrt{2} = 1$; area of region in $\odot$Y bounded by $\overparen{AO}$ and $\overline{AO}$ =

$\frac{\pi}{2}$ - 1; area of shaded region inside AYOX = π - 2; area of shaded region = 4π - 8.

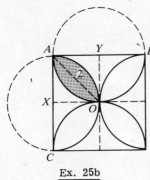

Ex. 25b

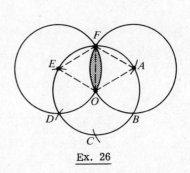

Ex. 26

<u>C</u> <u>26.</u> <u>a.</u> Draw $\odot$O with radius r.   Choose a pt. A on the $\odot$; with radius r draw an arc

intersecting the $\odot$ at B and F.   With B as ctr. and radius r, draw an arc intersecting

the $\odot$ at A and C.   Continue drawing $\cong$ arcs $\overparen{BD}$, $\overparen{CE}$, $\overparen{DF}$, and $\overparen{EF}$, completing the

figure.   <u>b.</u> The shaded region consists of 6 $\cong$ fig.   We shall find the area of one.

$\triangle$ FAO and $\triangle$ FEO are equilateral $\triangle$ with area $\frac{1}{2} \cdot 6 \cdot \frac{6\sqrt{3}}{2} = 9\sqrt{3}$.   Area of sector

FAO = $\frac{60}{360} \cdot \pi \cdot 6^2 = 6\pi$; area in $\odot$A bounded by $\overparen{FO}$ and $\overline{FO}$ = 6π - $9\sqrt{3}$; area of

shaded region inside $\odot$A and $\odot$E = 12π - $18\sqrt{3}$; area of shaded region =

72π - $108\sqrt{3}$.

<u>27.</u> Area of shaded region = area of equilateral

$\triangle$ ABC - 3 (area of sector XAY) =

$\frac{1}{2} \cdot 12 \cdot 6\sqrt{3}$ - (3 $\cdot \frac{60}{360} \cdot \pi \cdot 6^2$) = $36\sqrt{3}$ - 18π

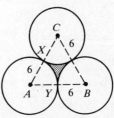

28. Since $\overline{AB}$ is tan. to $\odot X$ and $\odot Y$, AXYB is a trap. (If a line is tan. to a $\odot$, the line is $\perp$ to the radius drawn to the pt. of tangency; in a plane, 2 lines $\perp$ to the same line are $\parallel$.)   Draw a $\parallel$ to $\overline{AB}$ through Y, int. $\overline{AX}$ at P.   PX = 4, XY = 8, and m$\angle$XPY = 90; $\triangle$XPY is a 30-60-90 $\triangle$; PY = AB = $4\sqrt{3}$.   Area of AXYB = $\frac{1}{2}(4\sqrt{3})(6 + 2) = 16\sqrt{3}$.   Let Q be the pt. of tangency of $\odot X$ and $\odot Y$.   Area of sector AXQ = $\frac{60}{360} \cdot \pi \cdot 6^2 = 6\pi$; area of sector BYQ = $\frac{120}{360} \cdot \pi \cdot 2^2 = \frac{4\pi}{3}$; area of shaded region = $16\sqrt{3} - (6\pi + \frac{4\pi}{3}) = 16\sqrt{3} - \frac{22\pi}{3}$.

29. $\angle$PTS and $\angle$RST are rt. $\angle\hspace{-0.6em}\angle$; $\triangle$PRQ is a 30-60-90 $\triangle$ so TS = PR = $20\sqrt{3}$.   TS and UV are not $\parallel$ so they intersect at some pt. W.   Then WT = WU and WS = WV so TS = UV = $20\sqrt{3}$.   m$\angle$WPT = m$\angle$WPU = 180 - m$\angle$TPQ = 60; m$\angle$TPU = 120; length of $\overarc{TU} = \frac{120}{360} \cdot 2\pi \cdot 5 = \frac{10\pi}{3}$.   Let X be a pt. on the major arc with endpts. S and V; length of $\overarc{SXV} = \frac{240}{360} \cdot 2\pi \cdot 25 = \frac{100\pi}{3}$; length of belt = $\frac{10\pi}{3} + 2(20\sqrt{3}) + \frac{100\pi}{3} = 40\sqrt{3} + \frac{110\pi}{3}$.

30. a. Let D be the midpt. of $\overline{AB}$ and AD = r; AC = CB = $r\sqrt{2}$; area of $\triangle$ABC = $\frac{1}{2} \cdot 2r \cdot r = r^2$; area of region bounded by $\overarc{AC}$ and $\overline{AC} = \frac{90}{360} \cdot \pi \cdot r^2 - \frac{r^2}{2} = \frac{\pi r^2}{4} - \frac{r^2}{2}$; area of semicircle with diam. $\overline{AC} = \frac{1}{2} \cdot \pi(\frac{r\sqrt{2}}{2})^2 = \frac{\pi r^2}{4}$; area I = $\frac{\pi r^2}{4} - (\frac{\pi r^2}{4} - \frac{r^2}{2}) = \frac{r^2}{2}$.   Sim. area II = $\frac{r^2}{2}$ and area I + area II = area of $\triangle$ABC.

b. Yes. $\triangle$ABC is a rt. $\triangle$ so $(AB)^2 = (AC)^2 + (CB)^2$.   Let D, E, and F be the midpts. of $\overline{AB}$, $\overline{AC}$, and $\overline{CB}$, resp.   Notice that area I + area II = $\frac{1}{2}$ area $\odot$E + $\frac{1}{2}$ area $\odot$F + area $\triangle$ABC - $\frac{1}{2}$ area $\odot$D = $\frac{\pi(AC)^2}{4} + \frac{\pi(CB)^2}{4}$ + area $\triangle$ABC - $\frac{\pi(AB)^2}{4}$ = $\frac{\pi}{4}((AC)^2 + (CB)^2 - (AB)^2)$ + area $\triangle$ABC = area of $\triangle$ABC.

Page 409 · CHALLENGE

No matter how many segments are used, the sum of the arc lengths is $\frac{\pi}{2}$(XY).   Let n = number of seg.; length of each arc = $\pi r = \pi(\frac{XY}{2n})$; sum of arc lengths = $n(\pi)(\frac{XY}{2n}) = \frac{\pi}{2}$(XY).

Page 410 · CALCULATOR KEY-IN

Answers may vary, due to rounding.

1. a. sin $\angle$AOX = $\frac{9}{12}$ = 0.75; m$\angle$AOX $\approx$ 49; m$\angle$AOB $\approx$ 98

b. area of sector AOB $\approx \dfrac{97.181}{360} \cdot \pi \cdot 12^2 \approx 122.121$; OX = $\sqrt{12^2 - 9^2} = \sqrt{63} \approx$

7.93725; area of $\triangle$ AOB $\approx 9 \cdot$ OX ≈ 71.435; area of shaded region ≈ 50.69 cm^2.

<u>2</u>. Area = $\dfrac{1}{4}\pi\,(5^2) + \dfrac{225}{360}\pi\,(25^2) + \dfrac{1}{2} \cdot 10 \cdot 10 +$

$\dfrac{45}{360}\pi\,(25 - 10\sqrt{2})^2 \approx 1343$ m^2

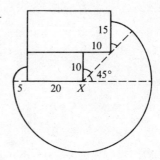

Pages 412-414 · WRITTEN EXERCISES

<u>A</u>

	1.	2.	3.	4.	5.	6.	7.	8.
Scale factor	1:4	3:2	6:7	9:5	3:13	5:1	3:8	$\sqrt{2}:1$
Ratio of perimeters	1:4	3:2	6:7	9:5	3:13	5:1	3:8	$\sqrt{2}:1$
Ratio of areas	1:16	9:4	36:49	81:25	9:169	25:1	9:64	2:1

<u>9</u>. $49\pi : 121\pi = 49 : 121$

<u>10</u>. radii = 6 and 8; $2\pi(6) : 2\pi(8) = 12 : 16 = 3 : 4$

<u>11</u>. scale factor = 1:2, ratio of perimeters = 1:2; ratio of areas = 1:4

<u>12</u>. scale factor = 6:10 or 3:5; ratio of perimeters = 3:5; ratio of areas = 9:25

<u>13</u>. scale factor = $x^2 : xy = x : y$; ratio of areas = $x^2 : y^2$

<u>14</u>. a. scale factor = 6:9 or 2:3; ratio of areas = 4:9

b. scale factor = 6:15 = 2:5; ratio of areas = 4:25

<u>15</u>. Answers may vary. $\triangle$EFD, $\triangle$EBC; scale factor = 4:10 or 2:5; ratio of areas =

4:25; $\triangle$DEF, $\triangle$ABF; scale factor = 4:6 or 2:3; ratio of areas = 4:9; $\triangle$CEG,

$\triangle$ABG; scale factor = 10:6 or 5:3; ratio of areas = 25:9; $\triangle$AFG, $\triangle$CBG, scale

factor = 3:5; ratio of areas = 9:25

<u>16</u>. a. scale factor = 8:18 or 4:9; ratio of areas = 16:81   b. Draw an alt. of $\triangle$I

(and $\triangle$II) from the upper left vert. of the trap.   From part (a), if base of $\triangle$I = 4x,

base of $\triangle$II = 9x; ratio of areas = $\dfrac{4xh}{2} : \dfrac{9xh}{2} = 4:9$ c. Draw an alt. of $\triangle$I (and

$\triangle$IV) from upper rt. vert. of the trap.   As in part (b), ratio of areas = $\dfrac{4xh}{2} : \dfrac{9xh}{2} =$

4:9   d. From parts (b) and (c), ratio of areas = 1:1.

17. <u>a</u>. scale factor = 1 : 2; ratio of areas = 1 : 4   <u>b</u>. In $\triangle$I, draw an alt. from lower left corner and note that it is also an alt. for $\triangle$II; ratio of bases is 1 : 2, so ratio of areas is also 1 : 2.   <u>c</u>. $\triangle$ formed by I and IV has same area as $\triangle$ formed by I and II (same base, same alt.), so $\triangle$II has same area as $\triangle$IV. 1 : 2   <u>d</u>. 1 : 2

18. <u>a</u>. no   <u>b</u>. $\triangle$ADE, $\triangle$ABC   <u>c</u>. scale factor = 2 : 5; ratio of areas = 4 : 25

   <u>d</u>. Area I : (area I + area II) = 4 : 25; 25 · area I = 4 · area I + 4 · area II;

   21 · area I = 4 · area II; ratio of areas = 4 : 21

19. Area I : (area I + area II) = $4^2 : 9^2$ = 16 : 81; 81 · area I = 16 · area I + 16 · area II;

   65 · area I = 16 · area II; ratio of areas = 16 : 65

20. area I : (area I + area II) = 9 : 49; 49 · area I = 9 · area I + 9 · area II;

   40 · area I = 9 · area II; ratio of areas = 9 : 40

21. Let x = shorter leg of area II; shorter leg of I = $\dfrac{x\sqrt{3}}{3}$; ratio of sides = $\dfrac{x\sqrt{3}}{3}$: x = 1 : $\sqrt{3}$; ratio of areas = 1 : 3

22. <u>a</u>. area of $\triangle$ABE = $\frac{1}{2}$ · AB · height of $\triangle$ABC = $\frac{1}{2}$ · AB · height of ABCD = $\frac{1}{2}$ · area of ABCD = 24 cm²   <u>b</u>. area of $\triangle$BEC = $\frac{1}{2}$ · EC · height of $\triangle$BEC = $\frac{1}{2}$ · $\frac{1}{3}$ · DC · height of ABCD = $\frac{1}{6}$ · area of ABCD = 8 cm²   <u>c</u>. area of $\triangle$ADE = $\frac{1}{2}$ · DE · height of $\triangle$ADE = $\frac{1}{2}$ · $\frac{2}{3}$ · DE · height of ABCD = $\frac{1}{3}$ · area of ABCD = 16 cm²   <u>d</u>. $\triangle$CEF ~ $\triangle$DEA; scale factor = 1 : 2; ratio of areas = 1 : 4; area of $\triangle$CEF = 4 cm²   <u>e</u>. $\triangle$DEF and $\triangle$ECF have the same alt. from F to $\overline{DC}$; ratio of areas = 2 : 1; area of $\triangle$DEF = 8 cm²

C 23. Each small $\triangle$ has area = $\frac{1}{6}$ area of original $\triangle$. We shall show that area of $\triangle$MBE = area of $\triangle$MEC = $\frac{1}{6}$ area of $\triangle$ABC. The other relationships can be demonstrated similarly. Draw ‖s to $\overline{BC}$ through A and M and a $\perp$ to $\overline{BC}$

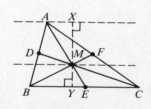

through M. Since the medians of a $\triangle$ int. in a pt. $\frac{2}{3}$ of the dist. from each vert. to the opp. side, ME = $\frac{1}{3}$ · AE. If 3 ‖ lines int. 2 trans., then they divide the trans. prop. so MY = $\frac{1}{3}$ · XY. Then area of $\triangle$MBE = $\frac{1}{2}$ · BE · MY = $\frac{1}{4}$ · BC · $\frac{1}{3}$ · XY = $\frac{1}{6}$ · $\frac{1}{2}$BC · XY = $\frac{1}{6}$ · area of $\triangle$ABC and area of $\triangle$MEC = $\frac{1}{2}$ · EC · MY = $\frac{1}{4}$ · BC · $\frac{1}{3}$XY = $\frac{1}{6}$ · area of $\triangle$ABC.

<u>24.</u> Let X be the int. of $\overline{PD}$ and $\overline{GQ}$ and Y the int. of $\overline{FR}$ and $\overline{GQ}$. $\triangle PXQ \sim \triangle FYQ$ and $FQ = \frac{1}{2}PQ$ so $QY = \frac{1}{2}XQ$.   But $\triangle PQX \cong \triangle QRY$ ($\angle PQX$ and $\angle QRY$ are both comp. of $\angle YQR$; AAS) so $PX = QY = \frac{1}{2}XQ = XY$. $(PX)^2 + (XQ)^2 = (PQ)^2$; $(XY)^2 + (2XY)^2 = (PQ)^2$; $5(XY)^2 = (PQ)^2$; $(XY)^2 = \frac{1}{5}(PQ)^2$; area of shaded region $= \frac{1}{5}$ area of PQRS.

Page 414 · CHALLENGE

Let r_1 and C_1 be the radius and circumference of the earth and r_2 and C_2 the radius and circumference of the circle formed by the stretched band. $C_2 = C_1 + 1$; $2\pi r_2 = 2\pi r_1 + 1$; $2\pi r_2 - 2\pi r_1 = 1$; $2\pi(r_2 - r_1) = 1$; $r_2 - r_1 = \frac{1}{2\pi}$.   The space between the band and the earth is $\frac{1}{2\pi}$ m ≈ 0.16 m or 16 cm.   All but the large dog could crawl under the band.

Page 417 · APPLICATION

<u>1.</u> If $\odot O$ is tan. to $\overleftrightarrow{MA}$, say at X, locate Y on $\overleftrightarrow{MB}$ such that MY = MX. $\triangle OMX \cong \triangle OMY$ (SAS) so $\angle X \cong \angle Y$.   But $\angle X$ is a rt. $\angle$ (if a line is tan. to a $\odot$, then the line is $\perp$ to the radius drawn to the pt. of tangency.) so $\angle Y$ is a rt. $\angle$ and $\odot O$ is tan. to $\overleftrightarrow{MB}$ at Y. (If a line in the plane of a $\odot$ is $\perp$ to a radius at its outer endpt., then the line is tan. to the $\odot$.)

<u>2.</u> $m\angle AOB = 60$ and length of $\overparen{AB} = \frac{60}{360} \cdot 2\pi \cdot 20000 \approx 20944$ ft   <u>3.</u> near P

<u>4.</u> <u>a.</u> Let the vertex be h units below the surface of the Earth.   Since $\triangle AEF \sim$ $\triangle ACH$, $\frac{AE}{AC} = \frac{EF}{CH}$; $\frac{30,000 + h}{12,000 + h} = \frac{20,000}{14,000} = \frac{10}{7}$; $120,000 + 10h = 210,000 + 7h$; $3h = 90,000$; h = 30,000 ft.   <u>b.</u> Let DG be the radius of the cone at 15,000 ft above the surface of the Earth. $\triangle ADG \sim \triangle ACH$;

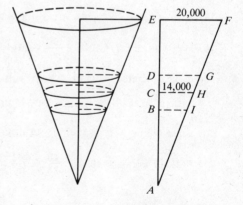

$\frac{15,000 + 30,000}{12,000 + 30,000} = \frac{DG}{14,000}$; $DG = \frac{15}{14} \cdot (14,000) = 15,000$ ft.   <u>c.</u> Let x be the height when the radius is 12,000 ft. $\frac{AC}{AB} = \frac{CH}{BI}$; $\frac{42,000}{AB} = \frac{7}{6}$; $AB = \frac{6 \cdot 42,000}{7} = 36,000$. x = AB - 30,000 = 6,000 ft.

Page 418 · CHAPTER REVIEW

1. $A = (\frac{32}{4})^2 = 64$ 2. $A = 4(\sqrt{6^2 - 4^2}) = 8\sqrt{5}$

3. $(3\sqrt{2})^2 = 18$; 18 cm²

4. length of shorter diag. = $2\sqrt{17^2 - 15^2} = 16$; $A = \frac{1}{2} \cdot 16 \cdot 30 = 240$

5. Let h = length of other altitude; Area = $6 \cdot 12 = 72 = 8 \cdot h$; h = 9

6. hyp. = 16; leg = $8\sqrt{3}$; p = $24 + 8\sqrt{3}$; $A = \frac{1}{2} \cdot 8 \cdot 8\sqrt{3} = 32\sqrt{3}$

7. sum of bases = 24; $\frac{1}{2} \cdot h \cdot 24 = 84$; h = 7

8. $h = \sqrt{5^2 - 4^2} = 3$; $A = \frac{1}{2} \cdot 3 \cdot 16 = 24$

9. Note 45-45-90 △ with legs 4 and hyp. $4\sqrt{2}$; p = $4 + 11 + 4\sqrt{2} + 15 = 30 + 4\sqrt{2}$;

   $A = \frac{1}{2} \cdot 4 \cdot 26 = 52$

10. s = 6; A = 36 m²

11. $a = \sqrt{3}$; $s = 2 \cdot 3 = 6$; p = 18; $A = \frac{1}{2} \cdot \sqrt{3} \cdot 18 = 9\sqrt{3}$

12. s = 2; $a = \sqrt{3}$; $A = \frac{1}{2} \cdot \sqrt{3} \cdot 12 = 6\sqrt{3}$ cm²

13. $C \approx 2(3.14)(30) = 188.4$; $A \approx 3.14(30^2) = 2826$

14. $\pi(\frac{d}{2})^2 = 121\pi$; $(\frac{d}{2})^2 = 121$; $\frac{d}{2} = 11$; d = 22; 22 cm

15. radius of ⊙ = radius of square = $4\sqrt{2}$; circumference = $2\pi(4\sqrt{2}) = 8\pi\sqrt{2}$

16. length = $\frac{135}{360} \cdot 2\pi \cdot 24 = 18\pi$

17. $A = \frac{240}{360} \cdot \pi \cdot 6^2 + \frac{1}{2} \cdot 6\sqrt{3} \cdot 3 = 24\pi + 9\sqrt{3}$

18. $\pi(\frac{13}{2})^2 - \frac{1}{2} \cdot 5 \cdot 12 = \frac{169\pi}{4} - 30 = 42.25\pi - 30$

19. a. scale factor = 9:12 = 3:4; ratio of areas = 9:16   b. Draw alt. from D to $\overline{AC}$.

    ratio of areas = $\frac{1}{2} \cdot AE \cdot h : \frac{1}{2} \cdot EC \cdot h$ = AE:EC = 3:4

20. Scale factor = 16:32 = 1:2; ratio of areas = 1:4

21. Ratio of areas = 49:25; $\frac{49}{25} = \frac{147}{A}$; 49A = 3675; A = 75

Page 419 · CHAPTER TEST

1. $A = \pi(\frac{10}{2})^2 = 25\pi$ 2. $s = \frac{4}{\sqrt{2}} = 2\sqrt{2}$; $A = (2\sqrt{2})^2 = 8$; 8 cm²

3. length of legs = $\frac{6\sqrt{2}}{\sqrt{2}} = 6$; $A = \frac{1}{2} \cdot 6 \cdot 6 = 18$

4. $30\pi = 2\pi r$; r = 15; $A = \pi \cdot 15^2 = 225\pi$; 225π m²   5. $A = \frac{1}{2} \cdot 5 \cdot 4 = 10$

6. $h = \sqrt{10^2 - 8^2} = 6$; $A = \frac{1}{2}(6)(6 + 22) = 84$

7. $h = \frac{6}{2} = 3$; $A = 10 \cdot 3 = 30$

8. $s = \frac{2 \cdot 2\sqrt{3}}{\sqrt{3}} = 4$; $p = 24$; $A = \frac{1}{2} \cdot 2\sqrt{3} \cdot 24 = 24\sqrt{3}$; $24\sqrt{3}$ cm

9. $A = \frac{45}{360} \cdot \pi \cdot 4^2 = 2\pi$

10. length of diag. $= 2r = 15$; width $= \sqrt{15^2 - 12^2} = 9$; $A = 9 \cdot 12 = 108$

11. $10\pi = \frac{n}{360} \cdot 2\pi \cdot 12$; $n = 150$; $A = \frac{150}{360} \cdot \pi \cdot 12^2 = 60\pi$

12. $s = 2 \cdot \frac{9}{\sqrt{2}} = 9\sqrt{2}$; $A = (9\sqrt{2})^2 = 162$

13. $A = \frac{1}{2} \cdot 8 \cdot 4\sqrt{3} + \frac{1}{2} \cdot 8 \cdot 24 = 16\sqrt{3} + 96$

14. Let b = length of base; $\frac{6}{9} = \frac{8}{b}$; $6b = 72$; $b = 12$; $h = \sqrt{3^2 - 2^2} = \sqrt{5}$;

    $A = \frac{1}{2} \cdot \sqrt{5} \cdot 20 = 10\sqrt{5}$

15. $A = \frac{90}{360} \cdot \pi \cdot 8^2 - \frac{1}{2} \cdot 8 \cdot 8 = 16\pi - 32$

16. ratio of radii $= \sqrt{100} : \sqrt{36} = 10:6 = 5:3$; ratio of circumferences $= 5:3$

17. scale factor $= 14:3.5 = 4:1$; ratio of areas $= 16:1$

18. m$\overarc{AC}$ = 360 - m$\overarc{ABC}$ = 360 - 288 = 72; length of $\overarc{AC}$ = $\frac{72}{360} \cdot 2\pi \cdot 10 = 4\pi$

Page 420 · MIXED REVIEW

1. 1. $\overline{AB} \perp \overline{BC}$; $\overline{DC} \perp \overline{BC}$ (Given)   2. $m\angle ABC = m\angle DCB = 90$ (Def. of $\perp$ lines)

   3. $\triangle ABC$ and $\triangle DCB$ are rt. $\triangle$. (Def. of rt. $\triangle$)   4. $\overline{BC} \cong \overline{BC}$ (Refl. Prop.)

   5. $\overline{AC} \cong \overline{BD}$ (Given)   6. $\triangle ABC \cong \triangle DCB$ (HL)   7. $\angle 1 \cong \angle 2$ (Corr. parts of

   $\cong \triangle$ are $\cong$.)   8. $\overline{EC} \cong \overline{EB}$ (If 2 $\angle$ of a $\triangle$ are $\cong$, then the sides opp. those $\angle$ are $\cong$.)

   9. $\triangle BCE$ is isos. (Def. of isos. $\triangle$)

2. length of alt. $= \frac{1}{2}$ length of hyp. $= \frac{1}{2}(5\sqrt{2})(\sqrt{2}) = 5$ 3. a. $\overline{EB}$ b. $\overline{EV}$

4. $\frac{x}{7 - x} = \frac{9}{5}$; $63 - 9x = 5x$; $14x = 63$; $x = 4.5$

5. $s = \frac{12}{3} = 4$; $h = 2\sqrt{3}$; $A = \frac{1}{2} \cdot 4 \cdot 2\sqrt{3} = 4\sqrt{3}$

6. length of hyp. $= \sqrt{8^2 + 4^2} = \sqrt{80} = 4\sqrt{5}$; length of median to hyp. $= 2\sqrt{5}$ (The midpt.

   of the hyp. of a rt. $\triangle$ is equidistant from the three vertices.)

7. PQ = PR; $m\angle PQR = \frac{1}{2}(180 - m\angle P) = \frac{1}{2}(180 - m\angle 1) = \frac{1}{2}(180 - 58) = 61$;

   m$\overarc{QR}$ = 2 · 66 = 122; $m\angle 2 = \frac{1}{2} \cdot 122 = 61$

8. Draw a line and construct $\overline{AB}$ and $\overline{BC}$ so that AB = BC = x. Then AC = 2x. Use Construction 13 with a = y, b = 2x, and c = x to find a seg. with length t; $\frac{y}{2x} = \frac{x}{t}$; ty = 2x^2; t = $\frac{2x^2}{y}$.

9. 1. $\overline{EF} \cong \overline{HG}$; $\overline{EF} \parallel \overline{HG}$ (Given)   2. EFGH is a $\square$. (If one pair of opp. sides of a quad. are both $\cong$ and $\parallel$, the quad. is a $\square$.)   3. $\angle$ EHF $\cong$ $\angle$ GFH (If 2 $\parallel$ lines are cut by a trans., then alt. int. $\angle$ are $\cong$.)

10. a. AA ~ Post.   b. If $\triangle$ JKL ~ $\triangle$ XYZ, then $\angle$ J $\cong$ $\angle$ X and $\angle$ K $\cong$ $\angle$ Y; true

11. a. $\frac{200}{360} \cdot 2\pi \cdot 12 = \frac{40\pi}{3}$ b. $\frac{200}{360} \cdot \pi(12^2) = \frac{200 \cdot 144}{360} \cdot \pi = 80\pi$

12. ratio of perimeters = $6\sqrt{3}:9 = 2\sqrt{3}:3$; ratio of areas = 12:9 = 4:3

13. (10 - 2)180 = 8(180) = 1440   14. skew; parallel

15. a sphere with ctr. P and radius 4 cm, along with its interior

16. 11 = $\frac{1}{2}$(x + 3 + 3x - 1); 22 = 4x + 2; 4x = 20; x = 5

17. tan A = $\frac{5}{8}$ = 0.625; m$\angle$A $\approx$ 32   18. -45

Page 421 · ALGEBRA REVIEW

1. $2\pi(\frac{9}{2}) = 9\pi$

2. $\pi(2 \cdot 2\sqrt{3}) = 4\sqrt{3}\pi$

3. $\pi(5\sqrt{3})^2 = 75\pi$

4. $\pi(\frac{2}{3}\sqrt{3})^2 = \frac{12\pi}{9} = \frac{4}{3}\pi$

5. $4\pi(\frac{10}{3})^2 = \frac{400}{9}\pi$

6. $\pi(4\frac{1}{5})(15) = 63\pi$

7. $2\pi(1\frac{3}{4})(1\frac{3}{4}) = 2\pi(\frac{7}{4})^2 = \frac{49}{8}\pi$

8. $\frac{270}{360} \cdot 2\pi \cdot 2 = 3\pi$

9. $\frac{180}{360} \cdot \pi(6\sqrt{2})^2 = \frac{1}{2} \cdot 36 \cdot 2\pi = 36\pi$

10. $\pi(\frac{1}{4})^2(4) = \frac{1}{4}\pi$

11. $\frac{1}{3}\pi(2\sqrt{6})^2(4) = 32\pi$

12. $\frac{4}{3}\pi(6^3) = \frac{864\pi}{3} = 288\pi$

13. $\pi(\sqrt{5})(\sqrt{5+5}) = \pi\sqrt{5}(\sqrt{10}) = \pi\sqrt{50} = 5\sqrt{2}\pi$

14. $2\pi(10^2) + 2\pi(10)(6) = 200\pi + 120\pi = 320\pi$

15. $\pi(2^2) + \pi(2)(\sqrt{4+12}) = 4\pi + 8\pi = 12\pi$ 16. $\pi(6^2 - (3\sqrt{2})^2) = \pi(36 - 18) = 18\pi$

17. $(3.14)(20^2) = (3.14)(400) = 1256$ 18. $\frac{22}{7}(21) = 66$

19. $\frac{4}{3}(\frac{22}{7})(27) = \frac{792}{7} = 113\frac{1}{7}$

20. 4(3.1416)(6) = 75.3984

<u>21</u>. $x^2 = \dfrac{121\pi}{\pi}$; $x^2 = 121$; $x = 11$

<u>22</u>. $x^3 = \dfrac{3}{4\pi} \cdot \dfrac{32\pi}{3} = 8$; $x = 2$

<u>23</u>. $h = \dfrac{A}{2\pi r}$

<u>24</u>. $h = \dfrac{3V}{\pi r^2}$

<u>25</u>. $r^2 = \dfrac{3 \cdot 3000\pi}{10\pi} = 900$; $r = 30$

<u>26</u>. $x = \dfrac{360}{20\pi} \cdot \dfrac{\pi}{9} = 2$

CHAPTER 10 · Areas and Volumes of Solids

<u>A</u> 1. L.A. = (2 · 6 + 2 · 4)2 = 40; T.A. = 40 + 2 · 6 · 4 = 88; V = 6 · 4 · 2 = 48

2. L.A. = (2 · 50 + 2 · 30)15 = 2400; T.A. = 2400 + 2 · 50 · 30 = 5400;

V = 50 · 30 · 15 = 22,500

3. h = $\frac{54}{6 \cdot 3}$ = 3; L.A. = (2 · 6 + 2 · 3)3 = 54; T.A. = 54 + 2 · 6 · 3 = 90

4. ℓ = $\frac{360}{8 \cdot 5}$ = 9; L.A. = (2 · 9 + 2 · 8)5 = 170; T.A. = 170 + 2 · 9 · 8 = 314

5. (2 · 9 + 2w)2 = 60; w = 6; T.A. = 60 + 2 · 9 · 6 = 168; V = 9 · 6 · 2 = 108

6. L.A. = (2 · 5x + 2 · 4x)3x = $54x^2$; T.A. = $54x^2$ + 2 · 5x · 4x = $94x^2$;

V = 5x · 4x · 3x = $60x^3$

7. T.A. = 54; V = 27   8. T.A. = 216; V = 216

9. e = $\sqrt[3]{1000}$ = 10; T.A. = 600   10. e = $\sqrt[3]{64}$ = 4; T.A. = 96

11. e = $\sqrt{\frac{150}{6}}$ = 5; V = 125   12. T.A. = $24x^2$; V = $8x^3$

13. 4; 8   14. L.A. = (3.2 + 5.8 + 6.9 + 4.7 + 9.4)13 = 390

15. L.A. = 3 · 8 · 10 = 240; T.A. = 240 + 2 · $16\sqrt{3}$ = 240 + $32\sqrt{3}$;

V = $16\sqrt{3}$ · 10 = $160\sqrt{3}$

16. L.A. = (9 + 12 + 15)10 = 360; T.A. = 360 + 2 · $\frac{9 \cdot 12}{2}$ = 468; V = $\frac{9 \cdot 12}{2}$ · 10 = 540

<u>B</u> 17. L.A. = (13 + 13 + 10)7 = 252; height of base = $\sqrt{13^2 - 5^2}$ = 12;

T.A. = 252 + 2($\frac{1}{2}$ · 10 · 12) = 372; V = $\frac{1}{2}$ · 10 · 12 · 7 = 420

18. L.A. = (10 + 5 + 4 + 5)20 = 480; height of base = $\sqrt{5^2 - 3^2}$ = 4;

T.A. = 480 + 2($\frac{1}{2}$ · 4 · 14) = 536; V = ($\frac{1}{2}$ · 4 · 14)20 = 560

19. L.A. = 6 · 8 · 12 = 576; apothem of base = $4\sqrt{3}$;

T.A. = 576 + 2 · $\frac{1}{2}$ · $4\sqrt{3}$ · 48 = 576 + $192\sqrt{3}$; V = $96\sqrt{3}$ · 12 = $1152\sqrt{3}$

20. s = $\sqrt{3^2 + 4^2}$ = 5; L.A. = 4 · 5 · 9 = 180; T.A. = 180 + 2 · $\frac{1}{2}$ · 6 · 8 = 228;

V = 24 · 9 = 216

21. Let h = original depth of water and V = volume of rock; 30 · 45 · h + V =

30 · 45(h + 2); 1350h + V = 1350h + 2700; V = 2700; 2700 cm³.

22. V = 30 · 5 · (0.03) = 4.5; 4.5 · (42) = 189; $189

23. $V_1 = 20 \cdot 10 \cdot 5 = 1000$; $V_2 = 25 \cdot 15 \cdot 4 = 1500$; $\frac{1.2}{1000} = \frac{x}{1500}$; $1000x = 1800$;

    $x = 1.8$; 1.8 kg

24. height of base $= \sqrt{0.5^2 - 0.3^2} = 0.4$; $B = \frac{1}{2}(0.4)(1.4) = 0.28$;

    $V = 0.28(2) = 0.56$; 0.56 t

25. $V = 40 \cdot 20 \cdot 20 - 2 \cdot 12 \cdot 10 \cdot 20 = 11,200$; $11,200 \text{ cm}^3 = 0.0112 \text{ m}^3$;

    weight $= (0.0112) \cdot 1700 \approx 19$ kg

26. $V = 2(0.3)(10)(0.05) + (0.05)(10)(0.2) = 0.4$; $0.4(7860) = 3144$; 3144 kg

27. $V = 4x \cdot 3x \cdot 5x - x \cdot 2x \cdot 5x = 50x^3$; T.A. $= 14x \cdot 5x + 2(4x \cdot 3x - x \cdot 2x) +$

    $6x \cdot 5x = 70x^2 + 20x^2 + 30x^2 = 120x^2$

28. $V = 6x \cdot 3y \cdot 4x + 2 \cdot 4x \cdot 3y \cdot x = 72x^2y + 24x^2y = 96x^2y$; T.A. $= 4 \cdot 4x \cdot 3y +$

    $8 \cdot x \cdot 3y + 2(4x)^2 + 8 \cdot 4x^2 = 48xy + 24xy + 32x^2 + 32x^2 = 72xy + 64x^2$

29. $\ell = 2w$; $h = 3w$; $2w \cdot w \cdot 3w = 162$; $6w^3 = 162$; $w^3 = 27$; $w = 3$; length: 6 cm;

    width: 3 cm; height: 9 cm

30. diag. of base $= \sqrt{8^2 + 6^2} = 10$; $\tan 35° = \frac{h}{10}$; $h \approx 10(0.7002) \approx 7$; $V \approx 7 \cdot 8 \cdot 6 = 336$

C 31. a. Vol. of trap. with base AYXE $= \frac{1}{2} \cdot 6 \cdot 8 \cdot 8 = 192$; vol. of trap. with base BYXF

    $= \frac{1}{2} \cdot 6 \cdot 12 \cdot 8 = 288$ (or $480 - 192 = 288$)   b. Draw $\overline{YV} \perp \overline{EF}$; YX $=$

    $\sqrt{(YV)^2 + (VX)^2} = \sqrt{6^2 + 4^2} = 2\sqrt{13}$; T.A. $= 4 \cdot 8 + 8 \cdot 8 + 6 \cdot 8 + 2 \cdot \frac{1}{2} \cdot 6 \cdot 12 +$

    $8 \cdot 2\sqrt{13} = 216 + 16\sqrt{13}$

32. The fig. shows the base of the beam and the bases of the

    resulting prisms. BE $= KH = \sqrt{8^2 + 6^2} = 10$; ID $=$

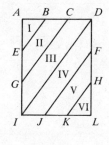

    $\sqrt{24^2 + 18^2} = 30$; GC $= JF = \frac{1}{2}(10 + 30) = 20$;

    vol. I $=$ vol. VI $= \frac{1}{2} \cdot 6 \cdot 8 \cdot 300 = 7200 \text{ cm}^3 = .0072 \text{ m}^3$;

    ratio of area of bases of I to II $= 1:3$; area of base of

    II $=$ area of base of V $= 3 \cdot 24 = 72$; vol. II $=$ vol. V $=$

    $72 \cdot 300 = 21,600 \text{ cm}^3 = .0216 \text{ m}^3$; ratio of area of bases of (I + II) to III $= 4:5$;

    area of base of III $=$ area of base of IV $= \frac{5}{4}(24 + 72) = 120$; vol. III $=$ vol. IV $=$

    $120 \cdot 300 = 36,000 \text{ cm}^3 = .036 \text{ m}^3$

33. The diag. is the hyp. of a $\triangle$ with one leg an edge of the cube and one leg a diag. of a

    face. If $s =$ length of an edge, $(4\sqrt{3})^2 = s^2 + (s\sqrt{2})^2$; $48 = s^2 + 2s^2$; $s^2 = 16$;

    $s = 4$; $V = 4^3 = 64 \text{ cm}^3$.

<u>34.</u> Let s = length of an edge; bases are equilateral $\triangle$ with height = $\dfrac{s\sqrt{3}}{2}$;

$B = \dfrac{1}{2} \cdot s \cdot \dfrac{s\sqrt{3}}{2} = \dfrac{s^2\sqrt{3}}{4}$ and $V = \dfrac{s^2\sqrt{3}}{4} \cdot s = \dfrac{s^3\sqrt{3}}{4} = 54\sqrt{3}$; $\dfrac{s^3}{4} = 54$; $s^3 = 216$;

$s = 6$; 6 cm

<u>35.</u> apothem of base = $\dfrac{s\sqrt{3}}{2}$; perimeter of base = 6s; $B = \dfrac{1}{2} \cdot \dfrac{s\sqrt{3}}{2} \cdot 6s = \dfrac{3s^2\sqrt{3}}{2}$;

$V = B \cdot h = \dfrac{3}{2}\sqrt{3}\, s^2 h$

Page 429 · COMPUTER KEY-IN

<u>1.</u> 1.6 and 1.8

<u>2.</u> 20   FOR X = 1.6 TO 1.8 STEP 0.01

$x \approx 1.7$; 12 - 2x = 8.6; 9 - 2x = 5.6.   length = 8.6 in; width = 5.6 in;

height = 1.7 in.

<u>3.</u> <u>a.</u> V = (15 - 2x) · (8 - 2x) · x   <u>b.</u> V $\approx$ 90.7 in^3

<u>c.</u> length $\approx$ 11.6 in; width $\approx$ 4.66 in; height $\approx$ 1.67 in

Page 429 · CHALLENGE

<u>a.</u> 8   <u>b.</u> 24   <u>c.</u> 24   <u>d.</u> 8

For any n: <u>a.</u> 8   <u>b.</u> 12(n - 2)   <u>c.</u> 6(n - 2)^2 <u>d.</u> (n - 2)^3

Pages 432-434 · WRITTEN EXERCISES

<u>A</u>   <u>1.</u> $\dfrac{1}{2}(4)(1.5)(9) = 27$ <u>2.</u> $\dfrac{1}{2} \cdot 3 \cdot 4 \cdot 6 = 36$

<u>3.</u> $\ell = \sqrt{10^2 - 6^2} = 8$; L.A. $= \dfrac{1}{2} \cdot 4 \cdot 12 \cdot 8 = 192$

<u>4.</u> $\ell = \sqrt{13^2 - 5^2} = 12$; L.A. $= \dfrac{1}{2} \cdot 6 \cdot 10 \cdot 12 = 360$

	5.	6.	7.	8.	9.	10.
height	4	12	24	$3\sqrt{7}$	3	15
slant height	5	13	25	12	5	$\sqrt{257}$
base edge	6	10	14	18	8	$8\sqrt{2}$
lateral edge	$\sqrt{34}$	$\sqrt{194}$	$\sqrt{674}$	15	$\sqrt{41}$	17

<u>11.</u> $\ell = \sqrt{3^2 + 4^2} = 5$; L.A. $= \dfrac{1}{2} \cdot 4 \cdot 6 \cdot 5 = 60$; T.A. = 60 + 36 = 96;

$V = \dfrac{1}{3} \cdot 36 \cdot 4 = 48$

<u>12.</u> L.A. $= \dfrac{1}{2} \cdot 4 \cdot 16 \cdot 10 = 320$; T.A. = 320 + 256 = 576; $h = \sqrt{10^2 - 8^2} = 6$;

$V = \dfrac{1}{3} \cdot 256 \cdot 6 = 512$

13. $\ell = \sqrt{17^2 - 8^2} = 15$; L.A. $= \frac{1}{2} \cdot 4 \cdot 16 \cdot 15 = 480$; T.A. $= 480 + 256 = 736$;

$h = \sqrt{15^2 - 8^2} = \sqrt{161}$; V $= \frac{1}{3} \cdot 256 \cdot \sqrt{161} = \frac{256\sqrt{161}}{3}$

14. base edge $= 2\sqrt{13^2 - 12^2} = 10$; L.A. $= \frac{1}{2} \cdot 4 \cdot 10 \cdot 13 = 260$;

T.A. $= 260 + 100 = 360$; V $= \frac{1}{3} \cdot 100 \cdot 12 = 400$

B 15. a. VX $= \sqrt{12^2 + 9^2} = 15$ cm; VY $= \sqrt{12^2 + 5^2} = 13$ cm

b. $2 \cdot \frac{1}{2} \cdot 18 \cdot 13 + 2 \cdot \frac{1}{2} \cdot 10 \cdot 15 = 234 + 150 = 384$ cm^2;

The pyramid is not regular so the faces are not $\cong \triangle$.

16. area of pyramid : area of prism $= \frac{1}{3}$Bh : Bh $= \frac{1}{3}$: 1 or 1 : 3

17. base area of pyramid $= \frac{1}{2}$ base area of the rect. solid; if Bh = volume of rect. solid,

vol. of pyramid $= \frac{1}{3}(\frac{1}{2}B)h = \frac{1}{6}$Bh $= \frac{1}{6}$ volume of rect. solid.

18. $h = \sqrt{10^2 - 6^2} = 8$; apothem of base $= 3\sqrt{3}$; B $= \frac{1}{2} \cdot 3\sqrt{3} \cdot 36 = 54\sqrt{3}$;

V $= \frac{1}{3} \cdot 54\sqrt{3} \cdot 8 = 144\sqrt{3}$

19. AO $= \frac{2}{3} \cdot$ AM $= 6$; $h = \sqrt{10^2 - 6^2} = 8$; OM $= \frac{1}{3}$AM $= 3$; $\ell = \sqrt{8^2 + 3^2} = \sqrt{73}$

20. a. AM $= \frac{6}{2}\sqrt{3} = 3\sqrt{3}$; AO $= \frac{2}{3} \cdot$ AM $= 2\sqrt{3}$

b. $h = \sqrt{4^2 - (2\sqrt{3})^2} = 2$; $\ell = \sqrt{2^2 + \sqrt{3}^2} = \sqrt{7}$

21. a. OM $= \sqrt{5^2 - 4^2} = 3$; OA $= 2 \cdot$ OM $= 6$; AM $= 9$; BC $= 2(\frac{9}{\sqrt{3}}) = 6\sqrt{3}$

b. L.A. $= \frac{1}{2} \cdot 3 \cdot 6\sqrt{3} \cdot 5 = 45\sqrt{3}$; V $= \frac{1}{3} \cdot \frac{1}{2} \cdot 6\sqrt{3} \cdot 9 \cdot 4 = 36\sqrt{3}$

22. AO $= \sqrt{5^2 - 3^2} = 4$; OM $= 2$; $\ell = \sqrt{3^2 + 2^2} = \sqrt{13}$; BC $= 2\sqrt{5^2 - (\sqrt{13})^2} = 4\sqrt{3}$;

L.A. $= \frac{1}{2} \cdot 3 \cdot 4\sqrt{3} \cdot \sqrt{13} = 6\sqrt{39}$; V $= \frac{1}{3} \cdot \frac{1}{2} \cdot 4\sqrt{3} \cdot 6 \cdot 3 = 12\sqrt{3}$

23. $\ell = \sqrt{10^2 - 6^2} = 8$; L.A. $= \frac{1}{2} \cdot 3 \cdot 12 \cdot 8 = 144$; AM $= 6\sqrt{3}$; AO $= \frac{2}{3} \cdot 6\sqrt{3} = 4\sqrt{3}$;

$h = \sqrt{10^2 - (4\sqrt{3})^2} = 2\sqrt{13}$; V $= \frac{1}{3} \cdot \frac{1}{2} \cdot 12 \cdot 6\sqrt{3} \cdot 2\sqrt{13} = 24\sqrt{39}$

24. a. AM $= 3\sqrt{3}$; AO $= \frac{2}{3} \cdot 3\sqrt{3} = 2\sqrt{3}$; $h = \sqrt{6^2 - (2\sqrt{3})^2} = \sqrt{24} = 2\sqrt{6}$

b. $\ell = \sqrt{(2\sqrt{6})^2 + (\sqrt{3})^2} = 3\sqrt{3}$; T.A. $= 4 \cdot \frac{1}{2} \cdot 6 \cdot 3\sqrt{3} = 36\sqrt{3}$;

V $= \frac{1}{3} \cdot \frac{1}{2} \cdot 6 \cdot 3\sqrt{3} \cdot 2\sqrt{6} = 6\sqrt{18} = 18\sqrt{2}$

C 25. AM $= \frac{e\sqrt{3}}{2}$; AO $= \frac{2}{3} \cdot \frac{e\sqrt{3}}{2} = \frac{e\sqrt{3}}{3}$; $h = \sqrt{e^2 - (\frac{e\sqrt{3}}{3})^2} = \frac{e\sqrt{6}}{3}$;

V $= \frac{1}{3} \cdot \frac{1}{2} \cdot e \cdot \frac{e\sqrt{3}}{2} \cdot \frac{e\sqrt{6}}{3} = \frac{e^3\sqrt{2}}{12}$

<u>26.</u> apothem of base $= \frac{x\sqrt{3}}{2}$; B $= 6 \cdot \frac{1}{2} \cdot x \cdot \frac{x\sqrt{3}}{2} = \frac{3x^2\sqrt{3}}{2}$; $\ell = \sqrt{(2x)^2 - (\frac{x}{2})^2} = \frac{x\sqrt{15}}{2}$;

h $= \sqrt{(\frac{x\sqrt{15}}{2})^2 - (\frac{x\sqrt{3}}{2})^2} = x\sqrt{3}$; V $= \frac{1}{3} \cdot \frac{3x^2\sqrt{3}}{2} \cdot x\sqrt{3} = \frac{3x^3}{2}$

<u>27.</u> Let h_1 = height of smaller pyramid, h_2 = height of other pyramid; since bases have =

area, ratio of volumes $= h_1 : h_2$; $\tan 40° = \frac{h_1}{5\sqrt{2}}$; $h_1 = 5\sqrt{2} \tan 40°$; $\tan 80° = \frac{h_2}{5\sqrt{2}}$;

$h_2 = 5\sqrt{2} \tan 80°$; $\frac{h_1}{h_2} = \frac{\tan 40°}{\tan 80°}$

<u>28.</u> <u>a.</u> Since the pyramids have $\cong$ bases and $\cong$ alt., the volumes are =.

<u>b.</u> F-ABCD; T.A. of F-ABCD = area of $\triangle$ FAB + area of $\triangle$ FBC + area of $\triangle$ FCD +

area of $\triangle$ FDA + area of ABCD $= \frac{1}{2} + \frac{1}{2} + \frac{\sqrt{2}}{2} + \frac{\sqrt{2}}{2} + 1 = 2 + \sqrt{2} \approx 3.414$; MF $=$

$\frac{\sqrt{2}}{2}$; FB = 1; MB $= \frac{\sqrt{6}}{2}$ and $\ell = \sqrt{(\frac{\sqrt{6}}{2})^2 - (\frac{1}{2})^2} = \frac{\sqrt{5}}{2}$; T.A. of M-ABCD =

$\frac{1}{2} \cdot 4 \cdot \frac{\sqrt{5}}{2} + 1 = \sqrt{5} + 1 \approx 3.236$

Page 436 · COMPUTER KEY-IN

<u>2.</u> <u>b.</u> Answers may vary, due to round-off error.

Number of steps	Volume
10	385
100	338.35
1000	333.8335
5000	333.433339
10,000	333.383335
15,000	333.366665

<u>c.</u> 333.33   <u>d.</u> 333.$\overline{33}$ <u>e.</u> The more steps in the pyramid, the closer it

approximates a regular square pyramid.

Page 436 · CALCULATOR KEY-IN

s $= \frac{7 + 8 + 9}{2} = 12$; B $= \sqrt{12(12 - 7)(12 - 8)(12 - 9)} = \sqrt{720} \approx 26.83$; V ≈ 98.38 cm^3

Page 436 · CHALLENGE

First note that any line that intersects the ctr. of a rect. divides it into 2 $\cong$ regions.

Draw the diag. of each rect. to locate their ctrs. and draw the line determined by

the ctrs.

Pages 439-441 · WRITTEN EXERCISES

<u>A</u> <u>1</u>. L.A. = $2\pi \cdot 4 \cdot 5 = 40\pi$; T.A. = $40\pi + 2\pi \cdot 4^2 = 72\pi$; V = $\pi \cdot 4^2 \cdot 5 = 80\pi$

<u>2</u>. L.A. = $2\pi \cdot 8 \cdot 10 = 160\pi$; T.A. = $160\pi + 2 \cdot \pi \cdot 8^2 = 288\pi$;

   V = $\pi \cdot 8^2 \cdot 10 = 640\pi$

<u>3</u>. L.A. = $2\pi \cdot 4 \cdot 3 = 24\pi$; T.A. = $24\pi + 2\pi \cdot 4^2 = 56\pi$; V = $\pi \cdot 4^2 \cdot 3 = 48\pi$

<u>4</u>. L.A. = $2\pi \cdot 8 \cdot 6 = 96\pi$; T.A. = $96\pi + 2 \cdot \pi \cdot 8^2 = 224\pi$; V = $\pi \cdot 8^2 \cdot 6 = 384\pi$

<u>5</u>. $\pi r^3 = 64\pi$; $r^3 = 64$; $r = 4$ <u>6</u>. $2\pi \cdot r \cdot 6 = 18\pi$; $12r = 18$; $r = 1.5$

<u>7</u>. $\pi r^2 \cdot 8 = 72\pi$; $8r^2 = 72$; $r^2 = 9$; $r = 3$; L.A. = $2\pi \cdot 3 \cdot 8 = 48\pi$

<u>8</u>. $2\pi r^2 + 2\pi r^2 = 100\pi$; $r^2 = 25$; $r = 5$

	r	h	ℓ	L.A.	T.A.	V
<u>9</u>.	4	3	5	20π	36π	16π
<u>10</u>.	8	6	10	80π	144π	128π
<u>11</u>.	12	5	13	156π	300π	240π
<u>12</u>.	$4\sqrt{2}$	2	6	$24\pi\sqrt{2}$	$(32 + 24\sqrt{2})\pi$	$\dfrac{64\pi}{3}$
<u>13</u>.	12	9	15	180π	324π	432π
<u>14</u>.	15	8	17	255π	480π	600π

<u>15</u>. a. $\dfrac{20}{80} = \dfrac{1}{4}$ b. $\dfrac{36}{144} = \dfrac{1}{4}$ c. $\dfrac{16}{128} = \dfrac{1}{8}$

<u>16</u>. $\dfrac{1}{3}Bh : Bh = \dfrac{1}{3} : 1$ or $1 : 3$

<u>B</u> <u>17</u>. a. Answers will vary.   b. vol. of can = $\pi(2.5)^2 10 = 62.5\pi$ cm³; vol. of bottle =

   $\pi \cdot 2^2 \cdot 10 + \dfrac{1}{3}\pi \cdot 2^2 \cdot 6 = 40\pi + 8\pi = 48\pi$ cm³

<u>18</u>. vol. of cyl. = $\pi \cdot 6^2 \cdot 18 = 648\pi$; $\dfrac{1}{3}\pi \cdot 9^2 \cdot h = 648\pi$; $27h = 648$; $h = 24$; 24 cm

<u>19</u>. $\pi \cdot 6^2 \cdot 200 - \pi \cdot 5^2 \cdot 200 = 2200\pi$; 2200π cm³

<u>20</u>. $\pi(\dfrac{d}{2})^2 \cdot h = \pi \cdot 3^2 \cdot h + \pi \cdot 4^2 \cdot h$; $(\dfrac{d}{2})^2 = 9 + 16 = 25$; $\dfrac{d^2}{4} = 25$; $d^2 = 100$;

   $d = 10$; 10 cm

<u>21</u>. 9; 27

<u>22</u>. $2\pi r \cdot 8 + 2\pi r^2 = 40\pi$; $r^2 + 8r - 20 = 0$; $(r + 10)(r - 2) = 0$; $r = -10$ (reject) or

   $r = 2$; $r = 2$

<u>23</u>. $2\pi r \cdot 12 + 2\pi r^2 = 90\pi$; $r^2 + 12r - 45 = 0$; $(r + 15)(r - 3) = 0$; $r = -15$ (reject)

   or $r = 3$; $r = 3$

24. a. The space through which it moves is a cyl. with h = 10, r = 6;

$V = \pi \cdot 6^2 \cdot 10 = 360\pi$ b. The space through which it moves is a cyl. with

h = 6, r = 10; $V = \pi \cdot 10^2 \cdot 6 = 600\pi$

25. a. r = 3; h = 4; $\ell = \sqrt{4^2 + 3^2} = 5$;

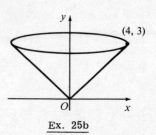

Ex. 25b

L.A. $= \pi \cdot 3 \cdot 5 = 15\pi$; $V = \frac{1}{3}\pi \cdot 3^2 \cdot 4 =$

12π b. r = 4; h = 3; $\ell = \sqrt{4^2 + 3^2} = 5$;

L.A. $= \pi \cdot 4 \cdot 5 = 20\pi$; $V = \frac{1}{3} \cdot \pi \cdot 4^2 \cdot 3$

$= 16\pi$ c. no

26. a. apothem of base = 3; $p = 3 \cdot 6\sqrt{3} = 18\sqrt{3}$;

L.A. $= 18\sqrt{3} \cdot 10 = 180\sqrt{3}$; $B = \frac{1}{2} \cdot 3 \cdot 18\sqrt{3} = 27\sqrt{3}$; $V = 27\sqrt{3} \cdot 10 = 270\sqrt{3}$

b. $s = \frac{12}{\sqrt{2}} = 6\sqrt{2}$; L.A. $= 4 \cdot 6\sqrt{2} \cdot 10 = 240\sqrt{2}$; $V = (6\sqrt{2})^2 10 = 720$

c. apothem of base = $3\sqrt{3}$; s = 6; p = 36; L.A. $= 36 \cdot 10 = 360$;

$V = \frac{1}{2} \cdot 3\sqrt{3} \cdot 36 \cdot 10 = 540\sqrt{3}$

27. $r = \frac{4\sqrt{2}}{2} = 2\sqrt{2}$; $V = \frac{1}{3} \cdot \pi(2\sqrt{2})^2 \cdot 6 = 16\pi$

28. a. $s = \frac{8}{\sqrt{2}} = 4\sqrt{2}$; $V = \frac{1}{3}(4\sqrt{2})^2 4 = \frac{128}{3} = 42\frac{2}{3}$

b. cone: $\sqrt{4^2 + 4^2} = 4\sqrt{2}$; pyramid: $\sqrt{(2\sqrt{2})^2 + 4^2} = 2\sqrt{6}$

C 29. r = 6; slant height of cone $= \sqrt{6^2 + 8^2} = 10$; L.A. of cone $= \pi \cdot 6 \cdot 10 = 60\pi$;

slant height of pyramid $= \sqrt{10^2 - 3^2} = \sqrt{91}$; L.A. of pyramid $= \frac{1}{2} \cdot 36 \cdot \sqrt{91} = 18\sqrt{91}$

30. $\triangle ABC$ is a rt. $\triangle$.   Let $\overline{AD}$ be the alt. to $\overline{BC}$.   The space resulting from the rotation

is 2 cones with r = AD.   One has height BD and one has height DC. $\sin \angle C = \frac{AD}{20} =$

$\frac{15}{25}$ so AD = 12; then BD $= \sqrt{15^2 - 12^2} = 9$ and DC = 16; $V = \frac{1}{3}\pi \cdot 12^2 \cdot 9 +$

$\frac{1}{3}\pi \cdot 12^2 \cdot 16 = \frac{144\pi}{3}(25) = 1200\pi$

31. Circumference of base $= \frac{120}{360} \cdot 2\pi \cdot 6 = 4\pi$, so r = 2; $\ell = 6$ so h $= \sqrt{6^2 - 2^2} = 4\sqrt{2}$;

$V = \frac{1}{3}\pi \cdot 2^2 \cdot 4\sqrt{2} = \frac{16\pi\sqrt{2}}{3}$

Page 441 · CALCULATOR KEY-IN

1. $V = \frac{1}{3}\pi(2.6)^2(\sqrt{(6.8)^2 - (2.6)^2}) \approx 44.5$ m³; ≈ 24.7 min

2. a. If the layer of paint were cut and unrolled, its shape would be approximately that of

a rect. solid with length = circumference of cylinder $= 2\pi r$, width = height of cylinder

= h, and height = thickness of paint layer = t.   Thus the volume of this rect. solid =

$2\pi r h t$.   The resulting shape would not be exactly a rect. solid because the circumference of the cylinder is less than the outer circumference of the layer of paint.   The figure would actually be a trapezoidal prism.   **b.** $V \approx 2\pi \cdot 10 \cdot 12(0.1) = 24\pi \approx$ 75.4   **c.** $V = \pi(10.1)^2 12 - \pi \cdot 10^2 \cdot 12 = 24.12\pi \approx 75.8$

Page 442 · COMPUTER KEY-IN

1-3. Programs and results may vary.   Sample answers are given.

1.
```
10   LET  R = 10
20   LET  H = 12
30   INPUT "THICKNESS: "; T
40   LET  V = (2 * 3.14159 * R * H) * T
50   PRINT "APPROX. VOLUME = "; V
60   END
```

2.
```
10   INPUT "RADIUS "; R
20   LET  H = 12
30   LET  V = (R * 3.14159 * R * H)
40   LET  CYL = (10 * 3.14159 * 10 * H)
50   PRINT V-CYL; " IS VOL. OF PAINT"
60   END
```

3.

Paint thickness	Approximate volume	Exact Volume
0.1	75.3981601	75.7751513
0.01	7.53981601	7.54358292
0.001	.753981601	.75401783

The exact volume is larger than the volume approximated by a rectangular solid.

Page 442 · CHALLENGE

Make a right circular cylinder whose radius is 1 cm and whose altitude is 2 cm.   Choose points A, B, C, and D so that quad. ABCD is a square.   Then determine points E and F so that $\overline{EF} \perp \overline{AB}$, as shown on the left, below.   Cut along two planes: one determined by C, D, and E; the other determined by C, D, and F.   The resulting solid looks like the diagram on the right, below.   Square ABCD passes through the square hole; circle O passes through the circular hole; triangle EFG passes through the triangular hole.

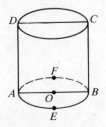
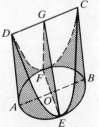

Pages 446-448 · WRITTEN EXERCISES

<u>A</u>

	1.	2.	3.	4.	5.	6.	7.	8.
Radius	3	5	$\frac{1}{2}$	$\frac{3}{4}$	4	9	$\sqrt{2}$	6
Area	36π	100π	π	$\frac{9\pi}{4}$	64π	324π	8π	144π
Volume	36π	$\frac{500\pi}{3}$	$\frac{\pi}{6}$	$\frac{9\pi}{16}$	$\frac{256\pi}{3}$	972π	$\frac{8\sqrt{2}\pi}{3}$	288π

<u>9.</u> 4; 8   <u>10.</u> 9; 27

<u>11.</u> Let x = radius of circle formed; r = 5; h = 2; $x^2 = 5^2 - 2^2$; $A = \pi x^2 = 21\pi$ cm^2

<u>12.</u> Let x = radius of circle formed; r = 8; h = 7; $x^2 = 8^2 - 7^2 = 15$; $A = 15\pi$ cm^2

<u>13.</u> vol. of sphere = $\frac{4}{3}\pi \cdot 2^3 = \frac{32\pi}{3}$; vol. of hemisphere = $\frac{1}{2} \cdot \frac{4}{3}\pi \cdot 4^3 = \frac{128\pi}{3}$ = 4 times vol. of sphere

<u>14.</u> no; volume of ice cream = $\frac{4}{3}\pi \cdot 3^3 = 36\pi$ cm^3; volume of cone = $\frac{1}{3}\pi \cdot (\frac{5}{2})^2 10 = \frac{125\pi}{6}$ cm^3

<u>B</u> <u>15.</u> area of floor = πr^2; area of ceiling = $\frac{1}{2} \cdot 4\pi r^2 = 2\pi r^2$; 6 cans are needed to paint ceiling.

<u>16.</u> vol. = $\pi \cdot 5^2 \cdot 20 + \frac{1}{2} \cdot \frac{4}{3}\pi \cdot 5^3 = 500\pi + \frac{250\pi}{3} = \frac{1750\pi}{3}$; $\frac{1750\pi}{3}$ m^3

<u>17.</u> area of hemisphere = $\frac{1}{2} \cdot 4\pi \cdot 5^2 = 50\pi$; area of cylinder = $2\pi \cdot 5 \cdot 20 = 200\pi$; 2 cans cover 50π m^2; 8 cans are needed to cover 200π m^2.

<u>18.</u> Let x = radius of water's surface. $x^2 = 25^2 - 15^2 = 400$; $A = 400\pi$

<u>19.</u> Let r = radius of earth; radius of ⊙ at latitude 45° N = $\frac{r}{\sqrt{2}} = \frac{r\sqrt{2}}{2}$; ratio of radii = $\frac{r\sqrt{2}}{2} : r = \sqrt{2} : 2$; ratio of areas = $(\sqrt{2})^2 : 2^2 = 2 : 4$ or 1 : 2

<u>20.</u> $\frac{4}{3}\pi \cdot 8^3 = \frac{1}{3}\pi \cdot 8^2 \cdot h$; $\frac{2048\pi}{3} = \frac{64\pi h}{3}$; h = 32 cm

<u>21.</u> yes; vol. of can = $\pi r^2 \cdot 8r = 8\pi r^3$; vol. of each ball = $\frac{4}{3}\pi r^3$; $6 \cdot \frac{4}{3}\pi r^3 = 8\pi r^3$

<u>22.</u> radius = r; h = 2r; $V = \pi r^2 \cdot 2r = 2\pi r^3$

<u>23.</u> Let r = radius of sphere = radius of cylinder; height of cylinder = 2r; area of sphere = $4\pi r^2$; L.A. of cylinder = $2\pi r \cdot 2r = 4\pi r^2$

<u>24.</u> $V = \pi r^2 \cdot 2r - 2 \cdot \frac{1}{3}\pi r^2 \cdot r = 2\pi r^3 - \frac{2}{3}\pi r^3 = \frac{4}{3}\pi r^3$

<u>25.</u> <u>a.</u> $\frac{4}{3}\pi \cdot 11^3 - \frac{4}{3}\pi \cdot 10^3 = \frac{4}{3}\pi (1331 - 1000) = \frac{1324\pi}{3}$; $\frac{1324\pi}{3}$ cm^3

<u>b.</u> $4\pi \cdot 10^2 \cdot 1 = 400\pi$; 400π cm^2 <u>c.</u> thin

26. radius of cylinder = $\sqrt{10^2 - 6^2}$ = 8; V = $\pi \cdot 8^2 \cdot 12$ = 768π

C 27. a. radius of cylinder = $\sqrt{10^2 - x^2}$ = $\sqrt{100 - x^2}$; V = $\pi(\sqrt{100 - x^2})^2 2x$ = $2\pi x(100 - x^2)$

b. $2\pi(\frac{10\sqrt{3}}{3})(100 - (\frac{10\sqrt{3}}{3})^2)$ = $2\pi(\frac{10\sqrt{3}}{3})(100 - \frac{100}{3})$ = $2\pi(\frac{10\sqrt{3}}{3})(\frac{200}{3})$ = $\frac{4000\pi\sqrt{3}}{9}$

c. Answers may vary.

28. a. h = 10 + x; r = $\sqrt{10^2 - x^2}$ = $\sqrt{100 - x^2}$; V = $\frac{1}{3}\pi(100 - x^2)(10 + x)$

b. V = $\frac{1}{3}\pi(100 - \frac{100}{9})(10 + \frac{10}{3})$ = $\frac{1}{3}\pi(\frac{800}{9})(\frac{40}{3})$ = $\frac{32000\pi}{81}$.

c. Answers may vary.

29. $\triangle$OXP is a rt. $\triangle$ with hyp. $\overline{OP}$.

OP $\cdot$ XZ = OX $\cdot$ PX (Ex. 33, page 251),

so 25 $\cdot$ XZ = 15 $\cdot$ 20 = 300; XZ = 12;

radius of $\odot$ of int. of 2 spheres = 12 cm;

A = 144π cm^2.

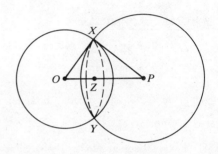

30. Draw $\overline{XY}$, a $\perp$ from ctr. of sphere to $\overline{VZ}$ where VZ =

slant height = $\sqrt{6^2 + 8^2}$ = 10.   Let r = radius of sphere;

XY = XP = r and VX = 8 - r; $\triangle$VPZ $\sim$ $\triangle$VYX;

$\frac{10}{8 - r}$ = $\frac{6}{r}$; 10r = 48 - 6r; 16r = 48; r = 3

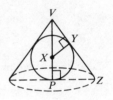

Pages 449-450 · COMPUTER KEY-IN

1-3. Answers may vary, due to round-off error.

1. Vol. of discs $\approx$ 4492.43; vol. of sphere $\approx$ 4188.79; approximately 7%

2.	Number of Discs	Height of Each Disc	Total Volume of Discs
	20	$\frac{1}{2}$	4343.20532
	50	$\frac{1}{5}$	4251.15763
	100	$\frac{1}{10}$	4220.05621
	1000	$\frac{1}{100}$	4191.88585

3. Vol. of inside discs $\approx$ 4157.22503; average $\approx$ 4188.64063

Page 450 · CALCULATOR KEY-IN

1. $A \approx 0.7(4\pi)(6380)^2 \approx 358{,}054{,}603$ km^2

2. a. $r = 3$; $V = \frac{4}{3}\pi \cdot 3^3 = 36\pi \approx 113.1$ cm^3

   b. $\frac{1}{2}$ vol. of cube $= \frac{1}{2} \cdot 216 = 108$

3. $\frac{4}{3}\pi \cdot 3^3 = \frac{1}{3}\pi \cdot 3^2 \cdot h$; $36\pi = 3\pi h$; $h = 12$; $\ell = \sqrt{12^2 + 3^2} = \sqrt{153}$; L.A. of cone $=$ $\pi \cdot 3\sqrt{153} \approx 116.6$ cm^2; A. of sphere $= 4\pi \cdot 3^2 \approx 113.1$ cm^2; $\frac{116.6 - 113.1}{113.1} \approx$ $.03 = 3\%$

Page 451 · APPLICATION

1. a. $V = \frac{4}{3}\pi \cdot 7^3 \approx 1436.0$; S.A. $= 4\pi \cdot 7^2 \approx 615.4$

   b. $V = 10^3 = 1000$; S.A. $= 6 \cdot 10^2 = 600$ c. $\frac{1436}{1000} \approx \frac{14}{10} = \frac{7}{5}$

2. $6n \div 3 = 2n$ vertices; n faces; $6n \div 2 = 3n$ edges

3. 0; no; no

4. 4 vertices are lost; the number of faces is the same; 12 hexagon edges are lost, but since they combine in twos, the frame loses 6 edges; vertices + faces - edges = $(2n - 4) + n - (3n - 6) = 2$.

5. Starting from lower left corner, count 5 partial figures to the right, 2 figures up; the second polygon up is a pentagon.

Pages 455-457 · WRITTEN EXERCISES

A   1. $\frac{6}{9} = \frac{10}{15}$; yes   2. $\frac{18}{8} \neq \frac{30}{15}$; no

    3. scale factor $= 3 : 4$ a. $3 : 4$ b. $3 : 4$ c. $3^2 : 4^2 = 9 : 16$

       d. $3^3 : 4^3 = 27 : 64$

    4. scale factor $= 12 : 18 = 2 : 3$ a. $2^2 : 3^2 = 4 : 9$ b. $2^2 : 3^2 = 4 : 9$

       c. $2^2 : 3^2 = 4 : 9$ d. $2^3 : 3^3 = 8 : 27$

    5. scale factor $= 12{,}800 : 3200 = 4 : 1$ a. $4 : 1$ b. $4^2 : 1^2 = 16 : 1$

       c. $4^3 : 1^3 = 64 : 1$

    6. ratio $\approx$ ratio of areas $= 1^2 : 200^2 = 1 : 40{,}000$

    7. ratio of volumes $= 1^3 : 48^3 = 1 : 110{,}592$; let $x =$ capacity of actual car in in.^{3};

       $\frac{90}{x} = \frac{1}{110{,}592}$; $x = 9{,}953{,}280$; 9,953,280 in.^{3} or 5760 ft^3

8. scale factor = $\sqrt{81} : \sqrt{144}$ = 9 : 12 or 3 : 4   <u>a.</u> 3 : 4   <u>b.</u> $3^2 : 4^2$ = 9 : 16

    <u>c.</u> $3^3 : 4^3$ = 27 : 64

9. scale factor = $\sqrt[3]{8} : \sqrt[3]{27}$ = 2 : 3   <u>a.</u> 2 : 3   <u>b.</u> 2 : 3   <u>c.</u> $2^2 : 3^2$ = 4 : 9

10. scale factor = $\sqrt[3]{3} : \sqrt[3]{375}$ = $\sqrt[3]{3} : 5\sqrt[3]{3}$ = 1 : 5   <u>a.</u> 1 : 5   <u>b.</u> $1^2 : 5^2$ = 1 : 25

    <u>c.</u> $1^2 : 5^2$ = 1 : 25

<u>B</u> 11. scale factor = 6 : 12 = 1 : 2; ratio of vol. = $1^3 : 2^3$ = 1 : 8; larger ball contains 8

     times the yarn at 6.5 times the cost of the smaller ball; it is the better buy.

12. scale factor = 6 : 10 = 3 : 5; ratio of volumes = $3^3 : 5^3$ = 27 : 125 = ratio of weights;

     let w = weight in kg of larger ball; $\frac{4}{w} = \frac{27}{125}$; 27w = 500; w = $\frac{500}{27}$; w $\approx$ 18.5 kg

13. scale factor = 5 : 4 : 3; ratio of volumes = $5^3 : 4^3 : 3^3$ = 125 : 64 : 27 = ratio of

     weights. Let m = weight in kg of middle snowball and b = weight in kg of bottom

     snowball; $\frac{m}{6} = \frac{64}{27}$; 27m = 384; m = $\frac{384}{27}$; $\frac{b}{6} = \frac{125}{27}$; 27b = 750; b = $\frac{750}{27}$; total

     weight = 6 + $\frac{384 + 750}{27}$ = 48 kg

14. scale factor = 3 : 1   <u>a.</u> ratio of areas of cross section = $3^2 : 1^2$ = 9 : 1; second

     column is 9 times as strong as first.   <u>b.</u> ratio of volumes = $3^3 : 1^3$ = 27 : 1; the

     second beam is 27 times heavier than the first.   <u>c.</u> the smaller (per lb. of column

     material, the larger supports $\frac{1}{3}$ the weight of the smaller.)

15. scale factor = $\sqrt{8} : \sqrt{18}$ = $2\sqrt{2} : 3\sqrt{2}$ = 2 : 3; ratio of volumes = $2^3 : 3^3$ = 8 : 27;

     let v = vol. of larger pyramid; $\frac{32}{v} = \frac{8}{27}$; 8v = 864; v = 108

16. scale factor = $\sqrt[3]{12} : \sqrt[3]{96}$ = $\sqrt[3]{12} : 2\sqrt[3]{12}$ = 1 : 2; ratio of lateral areas = $1^2 : 2^2$ = 1 : 4;

     let a = lateral area of larger cone; $\frac{15\pi}{a} = \frac{1}{4}$; a = 60π

17-18. The subscripts "t," "b," and "w" refer to "top," "bottom," and "whole."

17. <u>a.</u> scale factor = 9 : 12 = 3 : 4; $A_t : A_b = 3^2 : 4^2$ = 9 : 16   <u>b.</u> $L.A._t : L.A._w$ =

     $3^2 : 4^2$ = 9 : 16   <u>c.</u> $L.A._t : (L.A._t + L.A._b)$ = 9 : 16; $L.A._t : L.A._b$ = 9 : 7

     <u>d.</u> $V_t : V_w = 3^3 : 4^3$ = 27 : 64   <u>e.</u> $V_t : (V_t + V_b)$ = 27 : 64; $V_t : V_b$ = 27 : 37

18. <u>a.</u> scale factor = 10 : 14 = 5 : 7; $A_t : A_b = 5^2 : 7^2$ = 25 : 49   <u>b.</u> $L.A._t : L.A._w$ =

     $5^2 : 7^2$ = 25 : 49   <u>c.</u> $L.A._t : (L.A._t + L.A._b)$ = 25 : 49; $L.A._t : L.A._b$ = 25 : 24

     <u>d.</u> $V_t : V_w = 5^3 : 7^3$ = 125 : 343   <u>e.</u> $V_t : (V_t + V_b)$ = 125 : 343; $V_t : V_b$ =

     125 : 218

19. scale factor of top to whole = 9 : 15 = 3 : 5; ratio of vol. of top to vol. of whole =

$3^3 : 5^3$ = 27 : 125.   Let v = vol. of top; $\frac{v}{250} = \frac{27}{125}$; 125v = 6750; v = 54 cm^3;

vol. of bottom = 250 - 54 = 196 cm^3

20. ratio of areas = $4\pi a^2 : 4\pi b^2 = a^2 : b^2$

21. ratio of volumes = $\frac{4}{3}\pi a^3 : \frac{4}{3}\pi b^3 = a^3 : b^3$

22. scale factor = $h_1 : h_2$ so $r_1 : r_2 = h_1 : h_2$ and $r_1^2 : r_2^2 = h_1^2 : h_2^2$; ratio of volume =

$\frac{1}{3}\pi r_1^2 h_1 : \frac{1}{3}\pi r_2^2 h_2 = r_1^2 h_1 : r_2^2 h_2 = h_1^3 : h_2^3$.

23. scale factor = $r_1 : r_2$ so $\ell_1 : \ell_2 = r_1 : r_2$; ratio of lateral areas = $\pi r_1 \ell_1 : \pi r_2 \ell_2 =$

$r_1 \ell_1 : r_2 \ell_2 = r_1^2 : r_2^2$.

24. scale factor = $e_1 : e_2$ so $h_1 : h_2 = e_1 : e_2$; ratio of perimeters = $p_1 : p_2 =$

$5e_1 : 5e_2 = e_1 : e_2$; ratio of lateral areas = $p_1 h_1 : p_2 h_2 = e_1 \cdot e_1 : e_2 \cdot e_2 =$

$e_1^2 : e_2^2$.

25. ratio of area of bases = ratio of lateral areas = $e_1^2 : e_2^2$; ratio of volumes =

$B_1 h_1 : B_2 h_2 = e_1^2 \cdot e_1 : e_2^2 \cdot e_2 = e_1^3 : e_2^3$

C 26. Plane XYZ ∥ plane ABC and plane VAC intersects the ∥ planes in $\overleftrightarrow{XZ}$ and $\overleftrightarrow{AC}$.   If

2 ∥ planes are cut by a third plane, the lines of intersection are ∥.   Then $\overline{XZ}$ ∥ $\overline{AC}$

and $\triangle VXZ \sim \triangle VAC$ so $\frac{VZ}{VC} = \frac{VX}{VA} = \frac{1}{k}$ or VC = k $\cdot$ VZ and $\frac{XZ}{AC} = \frac{VX}{VA} = \frac{1}{k}$ or AC =

k $\cdot$ XZ.   Similarly, it can be shown that VB = k $\cdot$ VY, CB = k $\cdot$ ZY, and AB =

k $\cdot$ XY.   By the SSS $\sim$ Thm., the bases of V-XYZ and V-ABC are $\sim$ and corr.

lengths are prop., so V-XYZ $\sim$ V-ABC.

27. Let h = height of top; scale factor of top to whole = $\frac{h}{12}$; ratio of volumes = $\frac{h^3}{12^3} =$

$\frac{h^3}{1728}$; ratio of volumes of top to whole = ratio of volumes of top to top plus bottom;

ratio of top to bottom = $\frac{h^3}{1728 - h^3}$.   But volumes are =, so $\frac{h^3}{1728 - h^3}$ = 1;

h^3 = 1728 - h^3; $2h^3$ = 1728; h^3 = 864; h = $\sqrt[3]{864} = \sqrt[3]{4 \cdot 8 \cdot 27} = 6\sqrt[3]{4}$.

Page 457 · CALCULATOR KEY-IN

Ratio of top to original pyramid = $\frac{31}{481} \approx \frac{0.0644491}{1}$; ratio of volumes $\approx \frac{0.0002677}{1}$;

top which was destroyed was $\approx$ 0.02677% of original volume; $\approx$ 99.97% of original

volume remains.

Page 459 · CALCULATOR KEY-IN

1. $VO = \sqrt{5^2 - 4^2} = 3$; $OB = 4$; $OD = x$; $DB = 4 - x$; $\dfrac{y}{3} = \dfrac{4 - x}{4}$; $y = 3(\dfrac{4 - x}{4})$;

$A = 2xy = 2x(3(\dfrac{4 - x}{4})) = \dfrac{3x(4 - x)}{2}$.

2. Max. area, 6, occurs at $x = 2$.

Page 459 · COMPUTER KEY-IN

2. Graph shows greatest volume at $x = 2$.

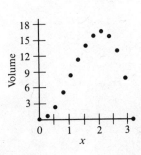

Page 461 · EXTRA

1. $V = \dfrac{1}{3}Bh = \dfrac{1}{3}(\dfrac{1}{2} \cdot 3 \cdot 4 \cdot 11) = 22$

2. $V = \pi \cdot 5^2 \cdot 8 = 200\pi$

3. $V = \dfrac{1}{3}\pi \cdot 4^2(3.5) = \dfrac{56\pi}{3}$

4. $h = \dfrac{15\sqrt{3}}{2}$; $V = 3^2 \cdot \dfrac{15\sqrt{3}}{2} = \dfrac{135\sqrt{3}}{2}$

5. $h = \dfrac{24}{2} = 12$; $12 \cdot B = 96$; $B = 8$; 8 cm^2

6. The area of each cross-section of the sphere equals the difference of the areas of the corresponding cross-sections of the cylinder and the double cone.   All three solids have equal heights, namely, 2r.   Then by Cavalieri's Principle, the volume of the sphere is equal to the difference between the volumes of the cylinder and the double cone.

Page 463 · CHAPTER REVIEW

1. lateral edge

2. $p = 8 \cdot 7 = 56$; L.A. $= 56 \cdot 12 = 672$

3. T.A. $= 28 \cdot 5 + 2 \cdot 8 \cdot 6 = 236$; $V = 8 \cdot 6 \cdot 5 = 240$

4. $81h = 891$; $h = 11$; T.A. $= 2 \cdot 81 + 36 \cdot 11 = 558$

5. $B = \dfrac{1}{2} \cdot 8 \cdot 4\sqrt{3} = 16\sqrt{3}$; $V = \dfrac{1}{3} \cdot 16\sqrt{3} \cdot 10 = \dfrac{160\sqrt{3}}{3}$

6. $\ell = \sqrt{5^2 - 3^2} = 4$; L.A. $= \dfrac{1}{2} \cdot 5 \cdot 6 \cdot 4 = 60$

7. $B = 30^2 = 900$; L.A. $= 1920 - 900 = 1020$; $\ell = \dfrac{2 \cdot 1020}{4 \cdot 30} = 17$

8. $h = \sqrt{17^2 - 15^2} = 8$; $V = \frac{1}{3} \cdot 900 \cdot 8 = 2400$

9. L.A. $= 2\pi \cdot 4 \cdot 3 = 24\pi$; T.A. $= 24\pi + 2\pi \cdot 4^2 = 56\pi$

10. L.A. $= \pi \cdot 6 \cdot 10 = 60\pi$ cm^2; T.A. $= 60\pi + \pi \cdot 6^2 = 96\pi$ cm^2; $h = \sqrt{10^2 - 6^2} = 8$;
    $V = \frac{1}{3}\pi \cdot 6^2 \cdot 8 = 96\pi$ cm^3

11. $\frac{1}{3}\pi r^2 \cdot 6 = 8\pi$; $r^2 = 4$; $r = 2$; $\ell = \sqrt{6^2 + 2^2} = \sqrt{40} = 2\sqrt{10}$

12. $V_1 = \pi r^2 h$; $V_2 = \pi(2r)^2 \left(\frac{h}{2}\right) = 2\pi r^2 h$; vol. is doubled.

13. $A = 4\pi \cdot 7^2 = 196\pi \approx 616$

14. $V = \frac{4}{3}\pi \left(\frac{12}{2}\right)^3 = 288\pi$; 288π ft^3

15. Let x = dist. from ctr. of sphere to plane; $x = \sqrt{29^2 - 21^2} = 20$

16. $4\pi r^2 = 484\pi$; $r^2 = 121$; $r = 11$; $V = \frac{4}{3}\pi \cdot 11^3 = \frac{5324\pi}{3}$; $\frac{5324\pi}{3}$ cm^3

17. $1 : 3$ 18. $1^2 : 3^2 = 1 : 9$

19. $\dfrac{\text{vol. of top}}{\text{vol. of whole}} = \dfrac{\text{vol. of top}}{\text{vol. of top + vol. of bottom}} = \dfrac{1}{27}$; 27 (vol. of top) = vol. of top +

    vol. of bottom; 26 (vol. of top) = vol. of bottom; $\dfrac{\text{vol. of small pyramid}}{\text{vol. of bottom part}} = 1 : 26$

20. scale factor $= \sqrt{48} : \sqrt{27} = 4\sqrt{3} : 3\sqrt{3} = 4 : 3$; ratio of volumes $= 4^3 : 3^3 = 64 : 27$

Page 464 · CHAPTER TEST

1. $V = (2k)^3 = 8k^3$; T.A. $= 6(2k)^2 = 24k^2$ 2. $V = \frac{1}{3} \cdot 10 \cdot 6 \cdot 4 = 80$; 80 cm^3

3. $V = \frac{1}{3}\pi \cdot 8^2 \cdot 6 = 128\pi$

4. $\ell = \sqrt{6^2 + 8^2} = 10$; L.A. $= \pi \cdot 8 \cdot 10 = 80\pi$; T.A. $= 80\pi + \pi \cdot 8^2 = 144\pi$

5. $p = 5 + 12 + 13 = 30$; T.A. $= 30 \cdot 20 + 2\left(\frac{1}{2} \cdot 5 \cdot 12\right) = 660$

6. $\frac{1}{2} \cdot 5 \cdot 12 \cdot 20 = 600$ 7. L.A. $= 2\pi \cdot 6 \cdot 4 = 48\pi$; 48π cm^2

8. $V = \pi \cdot 6^2 \cdot 4 = 144\pi$; 144π cm^3

9. $\frac{1}{2} \cdot 24\ell = 60$; $\ell = 5$; $h = \sqrt{5^2 - 3^2} = 4$; $V = \frac{1}{3} \cdot 6^2 \cdot 4 = 48$; 48 m^3

10. $A = 4\pi \cdot 6^2 = 144\pi$; 144π cm^2; $V = \frac{4}{3}\pi \cdot 6^3 = 288$; 288 cm^3

11. $\frac{12}{18} \neq \frac{18}{24}$; no

12. scale factor $= 6 : 18 = 1 : 3$; ratio of areas $= 1^2 : 3^2 = 1 : 9$; let a = total area of
    smaller pyramid $\frac{a}{648} = \frac{1}{9}$; $9a = 648$; $a = 72$

13. scale factor $= \sqrt[3]{1000} : \sqrt[3]{64} = 10 : 4 = 5 : 2$; ratio of lateral areas $= 5^2 : 2^2 = 25 : 4$

14. ratio of volumes $= \frac{1}{3}\pi \cdot 3^2 \cdot 4 : \pi \cdot 3^2 \cdot 4 = \frac{1}{3} : 1$ or $1 : 3$; $\ell = \sqrt{3^2 + 4^2} = 5$;

ratio of lateral areas $= \pi \cdot 3 \cdot 5 : 2\pi \cdot 3 \cdot 4 = 15 : 24$ or $5 : 8$

15. $4\pi r^2 = 9\pi$; $r^2 = \frac{9}{4}$; $r = \frac{3}{2}$; $V = \frac{4}{3}\pi\left(\frac{3}{2}\right)^3 = \frac{9\pi}{2}$

16. $2\pi \cdot 7^2 + 2\pi \cdot 7h = 168\pi$; $98\pi + 14\pi \cdot h = 168\pi$; $14\pi \cdot h = 70\pi$; $h = 5$; 5 cm

Page 465 · PREPARING FOR COLLEGE ENTRANCE EXAMS

1. A   2. C   3. C   4. C   5. B   6. C   7. B

Pages 466-467 · CUMULATIVE REVIEW: CHAPTERS 1-10

A 1. F   2. F   3. T   4. T   5. F   6. F   7. F   8. T

9. T   10. F   11. T   12. F   13. F   14. F   15. T

16. F   17. T   18. T

19. a. BC $= 9$; ED $= 8$; CD $= 2 \cdot$ BE $= 12$; p $= 18 + 16 + 12 = 46$

b. ratio of areas $= 1^2 : 2^2 = 1 : 4$

20. length of alt. $= \frac{1}{2} \cdot 4 \cdot \sqrt{3} = 2\sqrt{3}$ cm; area $= \frac{1}{2} \cdot 4 \cdot 2\sqrt{3} = 4\sqrt{3}$ cm^2

21. 1. $\overline{WZ} \perp \overline{ZY}$; $\overline{WX} \perp \overline{XY}$ (Given)   2. $\triangle YZW$ and $\triangle WXY$ are rt. $\triangle$. (Def. of $\perp$

lines; def. of rt. $\triangle$.)   3. $\overline{WX} \cong \overline{YZ}$ (Given)   4. $\overline{WY} \cong \overline{WY}$ (Refl. Prop.)

5. $\triangle YZW \cong \triangle WXY$ (HL)   6. $\angle YWZ \cong \angle WYX$ (Corr. parts of $\cong$ $\triangle$ are $\cong$.)

7. $\overline{WZ} \parallel \overline{XY}$ (If 2 lines are cut by a trans. and alt. int. $\angle$ are $\cong$, then the lines are $\parallel$.)

22. $4\pi r^2 \approx 4(3.14)(0.9)^2 = 10.1736$; 10 cm^2

23. $\ell = \sqrt{12^2 + 5^2} = \sqrt{169} = 13$; B $= 100$; p $= 40$; T.A. $= 100 + \frac{1}{2}p\ell =$

$100 + \frac{1}{2} \cdot 40 \cdot 13 = 360$; $V = \frac{1}{3} \cdot 10^2 \cdot 12 = 400$

B 24. a. $(2x + 10) + (3x - 10) + 4x = 180$; $9x = 180$; $x = 20$; m$\angle$R $= 2(20) + 10 = 50$;

m$\angle$S $= 3(20) - 10 = 50$; m$\angle$T $= 4(20) = 80$ b. isosceles; if 2 $\angle$ of a $\triangle$ are $\cong$,

then the sides opp. those $\angle$ are $\cong$; $\triangle$RST is not a rt. $\triangle$ since it has no rt. $\angle$.

25. $\frac{3}{2}x = x + 17$; $3x = 2x + 34$; $x = 34$; m$\angle$K $= 180 - (x + 17) = 180 - 51 = 129$

26. $\frac{x}{14 - x} = \frac{12}{9} = \frac{4}{3}$; $3x = 56 - 4x$; $7x = 56$; $x = 8$

27. $2\pi r^2 + 2\pi r^2 = 100\pi$; $4\pi r^2 = 100\pi$; $r^2 = 25$; $r = h = 5$; $V = \pi r^2 h = \pi r^3 = 125\pi$ cm^3

28. OA $=$ OB $= 8$; m$\angle$AOB $=$ m$\overset{\frown}{AB} = 60$; $\triangle$OAB is equilateral; AB $= 8$

29. Given: $\square$ABCD; $\overline{AC} \perp \overline{BD}$

    Prove: ABCD is a rhombus.

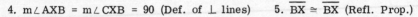

    Proof: 1. ABCD is a $\square$ (Given)   2. $\overline{AX} \cong \overline{CX}$ (The

    diag. of a $\square$ bis. each other.)   3. $\overline{AC} \perp \overline{BD}$ (Given)

    4. $m\angle AXB = m\angle CXB = 90$ (Def. of $\perp$ lines)   5. $\overline{BX} \cong \overline{BX}$ (Refl. Prop.)

    6. $\triangle AXB \cong \triangle CXB$ (SAS)   7. $\overline{AB} \cong \overline{BC}$ (Corr. parts of $\cong$ $\triangle$ are $\cong$.)   8. ABCD

    is a rhombus. (If 2 cons. sides of a $\square$ are $\cong$, then the $\square$ is a rhombus.)

30. $AB = BC = \dfrac{2\sqrt{2}}{\sqrt{2}} = 2$; $BD = 1$; $AD = \sqrt{2^2 + 1^2} = \sqrt{5}$; $AM = \dfrac{2}{3} \cdot AD = \dfrac{2\sqrt{5}}{3}$

31. Use Construction 13 with $a = z$ and $b = c = y$.   Then $\dfrac{z}{y} = \dfrac{y}{t}$; $tz = y^2$; $t = \dfrac{y^2}{z}$.

32. The locus is no pts., 1 pt. or 2 pts., depending on the int. of a line through the int.

    of the $\angle$ bis. of $\triangle$ABC and $\perp$ to the plane of $\triangle$ABC, and a sphere with ctr. A and

    rad. 4 cm.

33. $\tan 42° = \dfrac{12}{EF}$; $EF \approx \dfrac{12}{0.9004} \approx 13.3$; 13

34. $h = \sqrt{7^2 - (\frac{1}{2}(21 - 11))^2} = \sqrt{7^2 - 5^2} = \sqrt{24} = 2\sqrt{6}$; $A = \frac{1}{2}(2\sqrt{6})(11 + 21) = 32\sqrt{6}$

35. a. Length of $\overarc{AB} = \dfrac{90}{360} \cdot 2\pi \cdot 6 = 3\pi$; perimeter of sector AOB $= 6 + 6 + 3\pi =$

    $12 + 3\pi$ b. area of region = area of sector AOB - area of $\triangle$AOB $=$

    $\dfrac{90}{360} \cdot \pi \cdot 6^2 - \dfrac{1}{2} \cdot 6 \cdot 6 = 9\pi - 18$

36. Let $CX = x$ and $DX = 11 - x$, then $x(11 - x) = (7.5)(3.2)$; $x^2 - 11x + 24 = 0$;

    $(x - 8)(x - 3) = 0$; $x = 8$ or $x = 3$, reject $x = 3$; $CX = 8$

Pages 471-472 · WRITTEN EXERCISES

A 1. $|5 - (-2)| = 7$ 2. $|4 - (-3)| = 7$ 3. $|-2 - 3| = 5$

4. $|-1 - 3| = 4$ 5. $|5 - 1| = 4$ 6. $\sqrt{3^2 + 4^2} = \sqrt{25} = 5$

7. $\sqrt{(-7 - (-6))^2 + (-5 - (-2))^2} = \sqrt{(-1)^2 + (-3)^2} = \sqrt{1 + 9} = \sqrt{10}$

8. $\sqrt{(1 - 5)^2 + (-2 - 4)^2} = \sqrt{(-4)^2 + (-6)^2} = \sqrt{16 + 36} = \sqrt{52} = 2\sqrt{13}$

9. $\sqrt{(3 - (-1))^2 + (3 - (-1))^2} = \sqrt{(4)^2 + (4)^2} = \sqrt{16 + 16} = 4\sqrt{2}$

10. $\sqrt{(0 - (-8))^2 + (0 - (6))^2} = \sqrt{8^2 + (-6)^2} = \sqrt{64 + 36} = \sqrt{100} = 10$

11. $\sqrt{(5 - 3)^2 + (-2 - 2)^2} = \sqrt{2^2 + (-4)^2} = \sqrt{4 + 16} = \sqrt{20} = 2\sqrt{5}$

12. $\sqrt{(3 - 0)^2 + (4 - 0)^2} = \sqrt{3^2 + 4^2} = \sqrt{9 + 16} = \sqrt{25} = 5$

13. $\sqrt{(5 - (-2))^2 + (7 - (-2))^2} = \sqrt{7^2 + 9^2} = \sqrt{49 + 81} = \sqrt{130}$

14. $|3 - (-1)| = 4$

15. $\sqrt{(0 - (-6))^2 + (8 - 0)^2} = \sqrt{6^2 + 8^2} = \sqrt{36 + 64} = \sqrt{100} = 10$

16. $\sqrt{(3 - (-2))^2 + (-2 - 3)^2} = \sqrt{5^2 + (-5)^2} = \sqrt{25 + 25} = 5\sqrt{2}$

17. $\sqrt{(c - a)^2 + (d - b)^2}$ or $\sqrt{(a - c)^2 + (b - d)^2}$

18. $\sqrt{(-g - e)^2 + (-h + f)^2}$ or $\sqrt{(e + g)^2 + (h - f)^2}$

B 19. All the 6, 8, 10 △ with one vertex at (0, 0) and one leg on an axis determine 8 of the

points: (8, 6), (6, 8), (-6, 8), (-8, 6), (-8, -6), (-6, -8), (6, -8), (8, -6). The other

points are (10, 0), (0, 10), (-10, 0), and (0, -10).

20. All the 3, 4, 5 △ with a vertex at (-8, 1) and legs ∥ to the axes determine 8 of the

points: (-4, 4), (-5, 5), (-11, 5), (-12, 4), (-12, -2), (-11, -3), (-5, -3), (-4, -2).

The other points are (-3, 1), (-8, 6), (-13, 1), and (-8, -4).

21. AM $= \sqrt{(3 - (-3))^2 + (1 - 4)^2} = \sqrt{6^2 + (-3)^2} = \sqrt{36 + 9} = \sqrt{45} = 3\sqrt{5}$;

AY $= \sqrt{(0 - (-3))^2 + (-2 - 4)^2} = \sqrt{3^2 + (-6)^2} = \sqrt{9 + 36} = \sqrt{45} = 3\sqrt{5}$; $\overline{AM} \cong \overline{AY}$;

△ AMY is isos.

22. LA $= \sqrt{(-2 - 6)^2 + (4 - (-4))^2} = \sqrt{(-8)^2 + 8^2} = \sqrt{64 + 64} = 8\sqrt{2}$;

UT $= \sqrt{(4 - (-4))^2 + (6 - (-2))^2} = \sqrt{8^2 + 8^2} = \sqrt{64 + 64} = 8\sqrt{2}$; $\overline{LA} \cong \overline{UT}$

23. AB $= \sqrt{(5 - 3)^2 + (1 - (-1))^2} = \sqrt{2^2 + 2^2} = \sqrt{4 + 4} = 2\sqrt{2}$;

 AC $= \sqrt{(-1 - 3)^2 + (1 - (-1))^2} = \sqrt{(-4)^2 + 2^2} = \sqrt{16 + 4} = \sqrt{20} = 2\sqrt{5}$;

 BC $= \sqrt{(-1 - 5)^2 + (1 - 1)^2} = \sqrt{(-6)^2 + 0^2} = \sqrt{36} = 6$; since no 2 sides of $\triangle$ABC

 are $\cong$, $\triangle$ABC is scalene.

24. $\overline{BC} \parallel \overline{DE}$; length of median $= \frac{1}{2}$(BC + DE) $= \frac{1}{2}(|6 - (-4)| + |5 - 1|) =$

 $\frac{1}{2}(10 + 4) = \frac{1}{2}(14) = 7$

25. JA $= |4 - (-2)| = 6$; AN $= \sqrt{(2 - 4)^2 + (2 - (-2))^2} = \sqrt{(-2)^2 + 4^2} = \sqrt{4 + 16} = \sqrt{20} =$

 $2\sqrt{5}$; JN $= \sqrt{(2 - (-2))^2 + (2 - (-2))^2} = \sqrt{4^2 + 4^2} = \sqrt{16 + 16} = 4\sqrt{2}$; RF $= |4 - 1|$

 $= 3$; FK $= \sqrt{(6 - 8)^2 + (3 - 4)^2} = \sqrt{(-2)^2 + (-1)^2} = \sqrt{5}$; RK $= \sqrt{(6 - 8)^2 + (3 - 1)^2} =$

 $\sqrt{(-2)^2 + 2^2} = \sqrt{4 + 4} = 2\sqrt{2}$; $\frac{JA}{RF} = \frac{AN}{FK} = \frac{JN}{RK} = \frac{2}{1}$; $\triangle$JAN $\sim$ $\triangle$RFK (SSS)

26. AY $= \sqrt{(11 - 1)^2 + (1 - (-3))^2} = \sqrt{10^2 + 4^2} = \sqrt{100 + 16} = \sqrt{116} = 2\sqrt{29}$;

 RJ $= \sqrt{(9 - (-1)^2 + (-2 - (-6))^2} = \sqrt{10^2 + 4^2} = \sqrt{100 + 16} = \sqrt{116} = 2\sqrt{29}$;

 AR $= \sqrt{(-1 - 1)^2 + (-6 - (-3))^2} = \sqrt{(-2)^2 + (-3)^2} = \sqrt{4 + 9} = \sqrt{13}$;

 YJ $= \sqrt{(9 - 11)^2 + (-2 - 1)^2} = \sqrt{(-2)^2 + (-3)^2} = \sqrt{4 + 9} = \sqrt{13}$; $\overline{AY} \cong \overline{RJ}$ and

 $\overline{AR} \cong \overline{YJ}$; RAYJ is a $\square$. (If both pairs of opp. sides of a quad. are $\cong$, then the

 quad. is a $\square$.)

27. CB $= \sqrt{(8 - 5)^2 + (0 - 2)^2} = \sqrt{3^2 + (-2)^2} = \sqrt{9 + 4} = \sqrt{13}$;

 CR $= \sqrt{(-1 - 5)^2 + (-7 - 2)^2} = \sqrt{(-6)^2 + (-9)^2} = \sqrt{36 + 81} = \sqrt{117} = 3\sqrt{13}$;

 area $= $ CB $\cdot$ CR $= \sqrt{13}(3\sqrt{13}) = 3 \cdot 13 = 39$

28. congruent; KA $= \sqrt{(2 - 3)^2 + (6 - (-1))^2} = \sqrt{(-1)^2 + 7^2} = 5\sqrt{2}$;

 AT $= \sqrt{(5 - 2)^2 + (1 - 6)^2} = \sqrt{3^2 + (-5)^2} = \sqrt{9 + 25} = \sqrt{34}$; KT $=$

 $\sqrt{(5 - 3)^2 + (1 - (-1))^2} = \sqrt{2^2 + 2^2} = \sqrt{4 + 4} = 2\sqrt{2}$; IE $= \sqrt{(-3 - (-4))^2 + (-6 - 1)^2} =$

 $\sqrt{1^2 + (-7)^2} = \sqrt{50} = 5\sqrt{2}$; ES $= \sqrt{(-6 - (-3))^2 + (-1 - (-6))^2} = \sqrt{(-3)^2 + 5^2} =$

 $\sqrt{9 + 25} = \sqrt{34}$; IS $= \sqrt{(-6 - (-4))^2 + (-1 - 1)^2} = \sqrt{(-2)^2 + (-2)^2} = \sqrt{4 + 4} = 2\sqrt{2}$;

 $\overline{KA} \cong \overline{IE}$; $\overline{AT} \cong \overline{ES}$; $\overline{KT} \cong \overline{IS}$; $\triangle$KAT $\cong$ $\triangle$IES (SSS)

C 29. Let (4, y) be the coordinates of M. If $\overline{GH}$ is the base of $\triangle$GHM, then MH = MG;

 $\sqrt{(-2 - 4)^2 + (7 - y)^2} = \sqrt{(-2 - 4)^2 + (-3 - y)^2}$; $\sqrt{(-6)^2 + 49 - 14y + y^2} =$

 $\sqrt{(-6)^2 + 9 + 6y + y^2}$; $36 + 49 - 14y + y^2 = 36 + 9 + 6y + y^2$; $49 - 14y = 9 + 6y$;

 $20y = 40$; $y = 2$; if HG = HM, $|7 - (-3)| = 10 = \sqrt{(4 - (-2))^2 + (y - 7)^2}$;

 $\sqrt{6^2 + y^2 - 14y + 49} = 10$; $y^2 - 14y + 85 = 100$; $y^2 - 14y - 15 = 0$;

 $(y - 15)(y + 1) = 0$; $y = 15$ or $y = -1$; if HG = MG, $10 = \sqrt{(-2 - 4)^2 + (-3 - y)^2}$;

$\sqrt{(-6)^2 + 9 + 6y + y^2} = 10$; $y^2 + 6y + 45 = 100$; $y^2 + 6y - 55 = 0$;

$(y + 11)(y - 5) = 0$; $y = -11$ or $y = 5$; the 5 possible values are -11, -1, 2, 5,

and 15.

30. $JK = \sqrt{(-3 - (-6))^2 + (-2 - 4)^2} = \sqrt{3^2 + (-6)^2} = \sqrt{9 + 36} = \sqrt{45} = 3\sqrt{5}$;

$KM = \sqrt{(3 - (-3))^2 + (1 - 4)^2} = \sqrt{6^2 + (-3)^2} = \sqrt{36 + 9} = \sqrt{45} = 3\sqrt{5}$;

$JM = \sqrt{(3 - (-6))^2 + (1 - (-2))^2} = \sqrt{9^2 + 3^2} = \sqrt{81 + 9} = \sqrt{90} = 3\sqrt{10}$; $\overline{JK} \cong \overline{KM}$,

therefore $\triangle JKM$ is isosceles; $(JK)^2 + (KM)^2 = 45 + 45 = 90 = (JM)^2$, so $\triangle JKM$

is a rt. $\triangle$.

31. $\sqrt{(a - (-2))^2 + (b - 5)^2} = \sqrt{(a - 8)^2 + (b - 5)^2}$; $(a + 2)^2 + (b - 5)^2 =$

$(a - 8)^2 + (b - 5)^2$; $(a + 2)^2 = (a - 8)^2$; $a^2 + 4a + 4 = a^2 - 16a + 64$; $20a = 60$;

$a = 3$; also, $\sqrt{(a - 8)^2 + (b - 5)^2} = \sqrt{(a - 6)^2 + (b - 7)^2}$; $(-5)^2 + (b - 5)^2 =$

$(-3)^2 + (b - 7)^2$; $25 + b^2 - 10b + 25 = 9 + b^2 - 14b + 49$; $-10b + 50 =$

$-14b + 58$; $4b = 8$; $b = 2$

32. Assume temp. that (x, y) is equidistant from $(2, 2)$, $(-1, 8)$, and $(1, 4)$. Then

$\sqrt{(x - 2)^2 + (y - 2)^2} = \sqrt{(x - (-1))^2 + (y - 8)^2}$; $x^2 - 4x + 4 + y^2 - 4y + 4 =$

$x^2 + 2x + 1 + y^2 - 16y + 64$; $-4x - 4y + 8 = 2x - 16y + 65$; $6x - 12y = -57$;

$x - 2y = \frac{-57}{6} = \frac{-19}{2}$; also, $\sqrt{(x + 1)^2 + (y - 8)^2} = \sqrt{(x - 1)^2 + (y - 4)^2}$;

$x^2 + 2x + 1 + y^2 - 16y + 64 = x^2 - 2x + 1 + y^2 - 8y + 16$; $2x - 16y + 65 =$

$-2x - 8y + 17$; $4x - 8y = -48$; $x - 2y = -12$. Then $x - 2y = -\frac{19}{2} = -12$, which

is clearly false. Our temp. assumption that there is such a pt. must be incorrect.

It follows that there is no pt. equidistant from the given pts.

Pages 474-475 · APPLICATION

1. Check students' drawings.

2. a. $\sqrt{3^2 + 1^2} = \sqrt{9 + 1} = \sqrt{10}$ b. $\sqrt{4^2 + (-4)^2} = \sqrt{16 + 16} = 4\sqrt{2}$

   c. $\sqrt{(-5)^2 + 0^2} = \sqrt{25} = 5$ d. $\sqrt{(-3)^2 + (-4)^2} = \sqrt{9 + 16} = \sqrt{25} = 5$

3. a. $(2 + 4, 1 + 3) = (6, 4)$ b. $(-4 + 3, 7 + (-2)) = (-1, 5)$

   c. $(4 + (-4), -9 + 6) = (0, -3)$

4. $\overrightarrow{AC} = \overrightarrow{AB} + \overrightarrow{BC} = (2, 9) + (6, -3) = (2 + 6, 9 + (-3)) = (8, 6)$;

   $AC = \sqrt{8^2 + 6^2} = \sqrt{64 + 36} = \sqrt{100} = 10$

5. northwest; $\sqrt{(-5)^2 + 5^2} = \sqrt{25 + 25} = 5\sqrt{2}$ lb.

6. $\overrightarrow{KX} + \overrightarrow{KY} = (-1, 5) + (7, 3) = (-1 + 7, 5 + 3) = (6, 8)$; magnitude $= \sqrt{6^2 + 8^2} =$

$\sqrt{36 + 64} = \sqrt{100} = 10$

7. $\overrightarrow{KX} + \overrightarrow{KY} = (2, -3) + (-2, 3) = (2 + (-2), -3 + 3) = (0, 0)$; magnitude $= \sqrt{0^2 + 0^2} = 0$

8. yes; yes

Pages 477-478 · WRITTEN EXERCISES

A   1. (4, 3); 9   2. (87, 94); 6   3. (-3, 0); 7

 4. (-7, -8); $\frac{6}{5}$ 5. (j, -14); $\sqrt{17}$ 6. (-a, b); c

7-12. Form of equations may vary.

 7. $x^2 + y^2 = 4$ 8. $(x - 3)^2 + y^2 = 64$ 9. $(x - 2)^2 + (y + 1)^2 = 1$

10. $(x + 2)^2 + (y - 5)^2 = \frac{1}{9}$ 11. $(x + 4)^2 + (y + 7)^2 = g^2$ 12. $(x - p)^2 + (y - q)^2 = t^2$

13.   14.

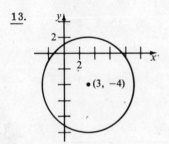

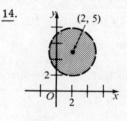

B 15-20. Form of equations may vary.

15. r = length of a ⊥ from the ctr. of the ⊙ to each axis = 5; $(x - 5)^2 + (y - 5)^2 = 25$

16. r = length of ⊥ from the ctr. of the ⊙ to the x-axis = q; $(x - p)^2 + (y - q)^2 = q^2$

17. $r = \sqrt{(6 - 0)^2 + (14 - 6)^2} = \sqrt{6^2 + 8^2} = \sqrt{36 + 64} = \sqrt{100} = 10$; $x^2 + (y - 6)^2 = 100$

18. $r = \sqrt{(3 - (-2))^2 + (8 - (-4))^2} = \sqrt{5^2 + 12^2} = \sqrt{25 + 144} = \sqrt{169} = 13$;

    $(x + 2)^2 + (y + 4)^2 = 169$

19. $r = \frac{1}{2} \cdot PD = \frac{1}{2}|4 - 0| = \frac{1}{2}(4) = 2$; ctr. = midpt. of $\overline{PD}$ = (0, 2); $x^2 + (y - 2)^2 = 4$

20. $r = \frac{1}{2} \cdot RS = \frac{1}{2}|3 - (-3)| = \frac{1}{2}(6) = 3$; ctr. = midpt. of $\overline{RS}$ = (0, 2);

    $x^2 + (y - 2)^2 = 9$

21. $(x - 2)^2 + (7 - 4)^2 = 25$; $x^2 - 4x + 4 + 9 = 25$; $x^2 - 4x - 12 = 0$;

    $(x - 6)(x + 2) = 0$; x = 6 or x = -2; 6 and -2

22. Every pt. in the locus is 4 units from (-3, 2); the locus is the ⊙ with ctr. (-3, 2),

    r = 4; $(x + 3)^2 + (y - 2)^2 = 16$.

<u>C</u> 23. The locus is a $\odot$, excluding pts. O and A, with $\overline{OA}$ as a diam.; ctr. = midpt. of $\overline{OA}$ = (0, 3); $r = \frac{1}{2} \cdot OA = \frac{1}{2} \cdot 6 = 3$; equation: $x^2 + (y - 3)^2 = 9$, $x \neq 0$.

24. If $\angle O$ is the rt. $\angle$, the locus is the line j through O, $\perp$ to $\overline{OM}$; if $\angle M$ is the rt. $\angle$, the locus is the line k through M, $\perp$ to $\overline{OM}$; if $\angle N$ is the rt. $\angle$, the locus is $\odot C$, excluding pts. O and M, with $\overline{OM}$ as diam.; ctr. = midpt. of $\overline{OM}$ = (0, 2); $r = \frac{1}{2} \cdot OM = \frac{1}{2} \cdot 4 = 2$; equation: $x^2 + (y - 2)^2 = 4$; $x \neq 0$.   Since O and M are on j and k, the locus is j, k, and C.

25. $(x^2 + 4x + 4) + (y^2 - 8y + 16) = 16 + 4 + 16$; $(x + 2)^2 + (y - 4)^2 = 36$; ctr. = (-2, 4); radius = 6

26. <u>a.</u>

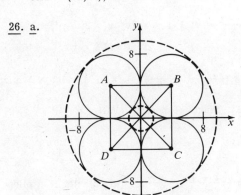

<u>b.</u> Draw ABCD, $\overline{AC}$ and $\overline{BD}$.   The distance from A to the ctr. of the $\odot$ = $4\sqrt{2}$.   The $\odot$ surrounding the 4 Ⓢ and tan. to them has ctr. at the origin and radius $4 + 4\sqrt{2}$;   equation: $x^2 + y^2 = (4 + 4\sqrt{2})^2$; $x^2 + y^2 = 48 + 32\sqrt{2}$.

<u>c.</u> The $\odot$ with ctr. at the origin and radius $4\sqrt{2} - 4$ is also tan. to all 4 Ⓢ; equation: $x^2 + y^2 = (4\sqrt{2} - 4)^2$; $x^2 + y^2 = 48 - 32\sqrt{2}$.

Pages 478-479 · COMPUTER KEY-IN

<u>1.</u> Programs may vary.

```
10   INPUT "HOW MANY POINTS: "; N
20   FOR I = 1 TO N
30   LET X = RND(1)
40   LET Y = RND(1)
50   LET D = SQR(X↑2 + Y↑2)
60   IF D < 1 THEN LET Q = Q + 1
70   NEXT I
80   PRINT Q; " POINTS INSIDE CIRCLE"
90   PRINT "4 * Q/N = "; 4 * Q/N
100  END
```

<u>2.</u> Results will vary.   Sample outputs are given.   For N = 100, 77 pts. inside $\odot$, A ≈ 3.08; for N = 500, 387 pts. inside $\odot$, A ≈ 3.096; for N = 1000, 792 pts. inside $\odot$, A ≈ 3.168.

<u>3.</u> $A = \pi r^2 = \pi(1) = \pi \approx 3.14159$

Pages 480-481 · WRITTEN EXERCISES

A 1. $(\frac{0 + 6}{2}, \frac{2 + 4}{2}) = (3, 3)$ 2. $(\frac{-2 + 4}{2}, \frac{6 + 3}{2}) = (1, 4\frac{1}{2})$

3. $(\frac{5 + 3}{2}, \frac{3 + 7}{2}) = (4, 5)$ 4. $(\frac{a + a + 2}{2}, \frac{4 + 0}{2}) = (a + 1, 2)$

5. $(\frac{2.3 + 1.5}{2}, \frac{3.7 - 2.9}{2}) = (1.9, 0.4)$ 6. $(\frac{a + c}{2}, \frac{b + d}{2})$

7. $\frac{x + 4}{2} = 4$; $x + 4 = 8$; $x = 4$; $\frac{y - 2}{2} = 4$; $y - 2 = 8$; $y = 10$; B (4, 10)

8. $\frac{x + 1}{2} = 5$; $x + 1 = 10$; $x = 9$; $\frac{y - 3}{2} = 1$; $y - 3 = 2$; $y = 5$; B (9, 5)

9. $\frac{x + 5}{2} = -4$; $x + 5 = -8$; $x = -13$; $\frac{y + 2}{2} = b$; $y + 2 = 2b$; $y = 2b - 2$;

B (-13, 2b - 2)

10. $\frac{x + r}{2} = t$; $x + r = 2t$; $x = 2t - r$; $\frac{y + s}{2} = v$; $y + s = 2v$; $y = 2v - s$;

B (2t - r, 2v - s)

B 11. $\overline{DE} \parallel \overline{CF}$; let M = midpt. of $\overline{DC}$; M is $(\frac{-1 - 4}{2}, \frac{4 - 3}{2}) = (-\frac{5}{2}, \frac{1}{2})$; let N = midpt.

of $\overline{EF}$; N is $(\frac{4 + 7}{2}, \frac{4 - 3}{2}) = (\frac{11}{2}, \frac{1}{2})$; length of median = MN =

$\sqrt{(\frac{11}{2} - (-\frac{5}{2}))^2 + (\frac{1}{2} - \frac{1}{2})^2} = \sqrt{8^2 + 0^2} = 8$

12. $\overline{RW} \parallel \overline{ST}$; let M = midpt. of $\overline{RS}$; M is $(\frac{-3 + 1}{2}, \frac{2 + 4}{2}) = (-1, 3)$; let N = midpt.

of $\overline{WT}$; N is $(\frac{-3 + 1}{2}, \frac{-1 - 10}{2}) = (-1, -\frac{11}{2})$; length of median = MN =

$\sqrt{(-1 - (-1))^2 + (-\frac{11}{2} - 3)^2} = \sqrt{0^2 + (-\frac{17}{2})^2} = \frac{17}{2} = 8\frac{1}{2}$

13. a. OK = $|6 - 0| = 6$; SE = $|8 - 2| = 6$; OK = SE; OS = $\sqrt{(2 - 0)^2 + (4 - 0)^2} =$

$\sqrt{2^2 + 4^2} = \sqrt{4 + 16} = \sqrt{20} = 2\sqrt{5}$; KE = $\sqrt{(8 - 6)^2 + (4 - 0)^2} = \sqrt{2^2 + 4^2} = \sqrt{4 + 16}$

$= \sqrt{20} = 2\sqrt{5}$; OS = KE   b. $\square$ c. $(\frac{0 + 8}{2}, \frac{0 + 4}{2}) = (4, 2)$

d. $(\frac{6 + 2}{2}, \frac{0 + 4}{2}) = (4, 2)$ e. The diag. of a $\square$ bisect each other.

14. a. $(\frac{0 - 6}{2}, \frac{8 + 0}{2}) = (-3, 4)$ b. MA = $\sqrt{(0 - (-3))^2 + (8 - 4)^2} = \sqrt{3^2 + 4^2} =$

$\sqrt{9 + 16} = \sqrt{25} = 5$; MT = $\sqrt{(-6 - (-3))^2 + (0 - 4)^2} = \sqrt{(-3)^2 + (-4)^2} = \sqrt{9 + 16} =$

$\sqrt{25} = 5$; MO = $\sqrt{(0 - (-3))^2 + (0 - 4)^2} = \sqrt{3^2 + (-4)^2} = \sqrt{9 + 16} = \sqrt{25} = 5$;

MA = MT = MO   c. The midpt. of the hyp. of a rt. $\triangle$ is equidistant from the

vertices.

<u>15.</u> <u>a.</u> P is $(\frac{0 + 4}{2}, \frac{0 + 8}{2}) = (2, 4)$; G is $(\frac{0 - 4}{2}, \frac{0 - 4}{2}) = (-2, -2)$; R is

$(\frac{-4 - 10}{2}, \frac{-4 + 10}{2}) = (-7, 3)$; T is $(\frac{-10 + 4}{2}, \frac{10 + 8}{2}) = (-3, 9)$; midpt. of $\overline{RP}$ =

$(\frac{-7 + 2}{2}, \frac{3 + 4}{2}) = (-\frac{5}{2}, \frac{7}{2})$; midpt. of $\overline{GT}$ is $(\frac{-2 - 3}{2}, \frac{-2 + 9}{2}) = (-\frac{5}{2}, \frac{7}{2})$

<u>b.</u> $\square$; if the diag. of a quad. bisect each other, the quad. is a $\square$.

<u>C</u> <u>16.</u> AM = $\sqrt{(\frac{a + c}{2} - a)^2 + (\frac{b + d}{2} - b)^2} = \sqrt{(\frac{c - a}{2})^2 + (\frac{d - b}{2})^2} =$

$\sqrt{\frac{(c - a)^2 + (d - b)^2}{4}} = \frac{1}{2}\sqrt{(c - a)^2 + (d - b)^2} = \frac{1}{2}AC$;

MC = $\sqrt{(c - \frac{a + c}{2})^2 + (d - \frac{b + d}{2})^2} = \sqrt{(\frac{c - a}{2})^2 + (\frac{d - b}{2})^2} =$

$\sqrt{\frac{(c - a)^2 + (d - b)^2}{4}} = \frac{1}{2}\sqrt{(c - a)^2 + (d - b)^2} = \frac{1}{2}AC$

<u>17.</u> Draw $\overline{PQ}$, with Q (7, 1). The vertical lines through (3, 1), (4, 1), (5, 1), and (6, 1)

divide $\overline{PQ}$, and thus $\overline{PD}$, into 5 $\cong$ seg. The pt. T, where the vertical line through

(4, 1) meets $\overline{PD}$, is the required pt.; T has coordinates (4, y); PT =

$\sqrt{(4 - 2)^2 + (y - 1)^2} = \frac{2}{5}\sqrt{(7 - 2)^2 + (11 - 1)^2}$; $\sqrt{2^2 + (y - 1)^2} = \frac{2}{5}\sqrt{25 + 100} =$

$\frac{2}{5} \cdot 5\sqrt{5} = 2\sqrt{5}$; $4 + (y - 1)^2 = 20$; $y^2 - 2y + 5 = 20$; $y^2 - 2y - 15 = 0$;

$(y + 3)(y - 5) = 0$; y = -3 (reject; (4, -3) is not on $\overline{PD}$) or y = 5;

T (4, 5) is the pt.

Pages 485-486 · WRITTEN EXERCISES

<u>A</u> <u>1.</u> $\frac{4 - 2}{3 - 1} = \frac{2}{2} = 1$

<u>2.</u> $\frac{-5 - 2}{-2 - 1} = \frac{-7}{-3} = \frac{7}{3}$

<u>3.</u> $\frac{5 - 2}{-2 - 1} = \frac{3}{-3} = -1$

<u>4.</u> $\frac{1 - 0}{5 - 0} = \frac{1}{5}$

<u>5.</u> $\frac{7 - 2}{2 - 7} = \frac{5}{-5} = -1$

<u>6.</u> slope not defined

<u>7.</u> $\frac{-6 - (-6)}{-6 - 6} = \frac{0}{12} = 0$

<u>8.</u> $\frac{3 - (-6)}{4 - 6} = \frac{9}{-2} = -\frac{9}{2}$

<u>9.</u> $\frac{0 - a}{b - 0} = \frac{-a}{b} = -\frac{a}{b}$

<u>10.</u> $\frac{n - q}{-m - p}$ or $\frac{q - n}{p + m}$

<u>11.</u> $\frac{v - s}{t - r}$

<u>12.</u> $\frac{f - f}{-d - (-e)} = \frac{0}{e - d} = 0$

<u>B</u> <u>13.</u> $\frac{3}{4} = \frac{y - 3}{10 - 2}$; $4(y - 3) = 24$; $4y - 12 = 24$; $4y = 36$; y = 9

<u>14.</u> $-\frac{5}{2} = \frac{6 - (-4)}{x - 7}$; $-5(x - 7) = 20$; $x - 7 = -4$; x = 3

15. $m = \dfrac{y - q}{r - p}$; $m(r - p) = y - q$; $y = m(r - p) + q$

16-17. Answers will vary.

16. a. $\dfrac{2}{3} = \dfrac{y - 0}{x - 0}$; $\dfrac{2}{3} = \dfrac{y}{x}$; $y = \dfrac{2}{3}x$; examples: $(-3, -2)$, $(3, 2)$, $(\dfrac{1}{2}, \dfrac{1}{3})$

    b. $-\dfrac{5}{2} = \dfrac{y - 7}{x + 3}$; $-5x - 15 = 2y - 14$; $2y = -5x - 1$; $y = \dfrac{-5x - 1}{2}$;

    examples: $(0, -\dfrac{1}{2})$, $(\dfrac{1}{5}, -1)$, $(-\dfrac{1}{5}, 0)$

17. a. $2 = \dfrac{y - 1}{x - 1}$; $2(x - 1) = y - 1$; $y - 1 = 2x - 2$; $y = 2x - 1$; examples: $(0, -1)$,

    $(-1, -3)$, $(\dfrac{1}{2}, 0)$ b. $-3 = \dfrac{y + 1}{x + 2}$; $-3(x + 2) = y + 1$; $y + 1 = -3x - 6$;

    $y = -3x - 7$; examples: $(0, -7)$, $(-3, 2)$, $(1, -10)$

18. slope of $\overline{RS} = \dfrac{1 - 3}{2 - 4} = \dfrac{-2}{-2} = 1$; slope of $\overline{TS} = \dfrac{1 - 6}{2 - (-3)} = \dfrac{-5}{5} = -1$;

    slope of $\overline{RS} = -\dfrac{1}{\text{slope of } \overline{TS}}$

19. slope of $\overline{RS} = \dfrac{4 - 1}{2 - (-1)} = \dfrac{3}{3} = 1$; slope of $\overline{TS} = \dfrac{4 - 1}{2 - 5} = \dfrac{3}{-3} = -1$;

    slope of $\overline{RS} = -\dfrac{1}{\text{slope of } \overline{TS}}$

20. slope of $\overline{RS} = \dfrac{2 - 6}{5 - 3} = \dfrac{-4}{2} = -2$; slope of $\overline{TS} = \dfrac{2 - 0}{5 - 1} = \dfrac{2}{4} = \dfrac{1}{2}$;

    slope of $\overline{RS} = -\dfrac{1}{\text{slope of } \overline{TS}}$

21. slope of $\overline{RS} = \dfrac{2 - (-4)}{2 - (-3)} = \dfrac{6}{5}$; slope of $\overline{TS} = \dfrac{-8 - 2}{14 - 2} = \dfrac{-10}{12} = -\dfrac{5}{6}$;

    slope of $\overline{RS} = -\dfrac{1}{\text{slope of } \overline{TS}}$

22. Yes; let r = rise in inches; $\dfrac{1}{12} = \dfrac{r}{120}$; $12r = 120$; $r = 10$; the rise is 10 in.

23. No; in order for the pts. to be collinear the slope of the segs. det. by any 2 must be =;

    slope of $\overline{DE} = \dfrac{4 - (-3)}{-2 - (-5)} = \dfrac{7}{3}$; slope of $\overline{FG} = \dfrac{23 - 9}{14 - 8} = \dfrac{14}{6} = \dfrac{7}{3}$; slope of $\overline{DF} =$

    $\dfrac{9 - (-3)}{8 - (-5)} = \dfrac{12}{13}$; D, E, F, and G are not collinear.

C 24. slope $= \dfrac{3 - (-1)}{4 - (-2)} = \dfrac{4}{6} = \dfrac{2}{3}$. Let the line intersect the x- and y-axes at $(x, 0)$ and

    $(0, y)$, resp. $\dfrac{-1 - 0}{-2 - x} = \dfrac{2}{3}$; $\dfrac{-1}{-2 - x} = \dfrac{2}{3}$; $-4 - 2x = -3$; $2x = -1$; $x = -\dfrac{1}{2}$;

    $\dfrac{-1 - y}{-2 - 0} = \dfrac{2}{3}$; $\dfrac{-1 - y}{-2} = \dfrac{2}{3}$; $-4 = -3 - 3y$; $3y = 1$; $y = \dfrac{1}{3}$; $(-\dfrac{1}{2}, 0)$ and $(0, \dfrac{1}{3})$

25. Draw a ∥ to the x-axis through H, making a 60° ∠ at H, and draw $\overline{JK}$ with K at (5, 1);

HK = 2; JK = HK$\sqrt{3}$; |a - 1| = $2\sqrt{3}$; $(a - 1)^2 = (2\sqrt{3})^2 = 12$; $a^2 - 2a + 1 = 12$;

$a^2 - 2a - 11 = 0$; a = $1 - 2\sqrt{3}$ (reject; if a = $1 - 2\sqrt{3}$, slope is neg.) or

a = $1 + 2\sqrt{3}$

26. Let A be (-3, 4), B be (0, k), C be (k, 10); if A, B, and C are collinear,

slope $\overline{AB}$ = slope $\overline{BC}$; $\dfrac{k - 4}{0 - (-3)} = \dfrac{10 - k}{k}$; $\dfrac{k - 4}{3} = \dfrac{10 - k}{k}$; $k^2 - 4k = 30 - 3k$;

$k^2 - k - 30 = 0$; (k - 6)(k + 5) = 0; k = 6 or k = -5

Pages 488-490 · WRITTEN EXERCISES

A 1. a. $\dfrac{3 - 0}{4 - (-2)} = \dfrac{3}{6} = \dfrac{1}{2}$ b. $\dfrac{1}{2}$ c. -2

2. a. $\dfrac{-1 - 1}{2 - (-3)} = \dfrac{-2}{5} = -\dfrac{2}{5}$ b. $-\dfrac{2}{5}$ c. $\dfrac{5}{2}$

3. $\overline{OE}$: $\dfrac{7 - 0}{2 - 0} = \dfrac{7}{2}$; $\overline{OG}$: 0; $\overline{GF}$: $\dfrac{7}{2}$; $\overline{EF}$: 0

4. $\overline{HI}$: $\dfrac{-1 - (-5)}{6 - 2} = \dfrac{4}{4} = 1$; $\overline{IJ}$: -1; $\overline{JK}$: 1; $\overline{KH}$: -1

5. a. $\overline{LM}$: $\dfrac{2 - (-1)}{-4 - (-3)} = \dfrac{3}{-1} = -3$; $\overline{PN}$: $\dfrac{4 - (-2)}{2 - 4} = \dfrac{6}{-2} = -3$ b. Two nonvert. lines are ∥

if their slopes are =.   c. $\overline{MN}$: $\dfrac{4 - 2}{2 - (-4)} = \dfrac{2}{6} = \dfrac{1}{3}$; $\overline{LP}$: $\dfrac{-2 - (-1)}{4 - (-3)} = \dfrac{-1}{7} = -\dfrac{1}{7}$

d. Two nonvert. lines are ∥ only if their slopes are =.   e. trapezoid

6. a. $\overline{RV}$: $\dfrac{-8 - (-6)}{0 - (-2)} = \dfrac{-2}{2} = -1$; $\overline{TV}$: $\dfrac{-8 - (-3)}{0 - 5} = \dfrac{-5}{-5} = 1$ b. Two nonvert. lines are

⊥ if the prod. of their slopes is -1.   c. If one ∠ of a ▱ is a rt. ∠, then the ▱ is

a rect.   d. $\dfrac{y - (-6)}{x - (-2)} = 1$; $\dfrac{y + 6}{x + 2} = 1$; y + 6 = x + 2; y = x - 4; $\dfrac{y - (-3)}{x - 5} = -1$;

$\dfrac{y + 3}{x - 5} = -1$; y + 3 = -x + 5; y = -x + 2; x - 4 = -x + 2; 2x = 6; x = 3;

y = 3 - 4 = -1; coord. of S = (3, -1)

7. $\overline{AB}$: $\dfrac{3 - 0}{7 - 0} = \dfrac{3}{7}$; alt. to $\overline{AB}$: $-\dfrac{7}{3}$; $\overline{AC}$: $\dfrac{-5 - 0}{2 - 0} = \dfrac{-5}{2} = -\dfrac{5}{2}$; alt. to $\overline{AC}$: $\dfrac{2}{5}$;

$\overline{BC}$: $\dfrac{-5 - 3}{2 - 7} = \dfrac{-8}{-5} = \dfrac{8}{5}$; alt. to $\overline{BC}$: $-\dfrac{5}{8}$

8. $\overline{AB}$: $\dfrac{-3 - 4}{-1 - 1} = \dfrac{-7}{-2} = \dfrac{7}{2}$; alt. to $\overline{AB}$: $-\dfrac{2}{7}$; $\overline{AC}$: $\dfrac{-5 - 4}{4 - 1} = \dfrac{-9}{3} = -3$; alt. to $\overline{AC}$: $\dfrac{1}{3}$;

$\overline{BC}$: $\dfrac{-5 - (-3)}{4 - (-1)} = \dfrac{-2}{5} = -\dfrac{2}{5}$; alt. to $\overline{BC}$: $\dfrac{5}{2}$

B 9-10. Let M, N, and P be the midpts. of $\overline{DE}$, $\overline{EF}$, and $\overline{DF}$, resp. so $\overline{DN}$, $\overline{EP}$, and $\overline{FM}$ are the medians.

9. M has coordinates $(\frac{8 + 0}{2}, \frac{0 + 0}{2})$ = (4, 0); N has coordinates $(\frac{6 + 8}{2}, \frac{6 + 0}{2})$ =

(7, 3); P has coordinates $(\frac{6 + 0}{2}, \frac{6 + 0}{2})$ = (3, 3); $\overline{DE}$: $\frac{0 - 0}{8 - 0}$ = 0; $\overline{EF}$: $\frac{6 - 0}{6 - 8}$ =

$\frac{6}{-2}$ = -3; $\overline{DF}$: $\frac{6 - 0}{6 - 0}$ = $\frac{6}{6}$ = 1; $\overline{DN}$: $\frac{3 - 0}{7 - 0}$ = $\frac{3}{7}$; $\overline{EP}$: $\frac{3 - 0}{3 - 8}$ = $\frac{3}{-5}$ = -$\frac{3}{5}$;

$\overline{FM}$: $\frac{6 - 0}{6 - 4}$ = $\frac{6}{2}$ = 3

10. M is $(\frac{9 + 3}{2}, \frac{1 - 5}{2})$ = (6, -2); N is $(\frac{5 + 9}{2}, \frac{5 + 1}{2})$ = (7, 3);

P is $(\frac{5 + 3}{2}, \frac{5 - 5}{2})$ = (4, 0); $\overline{DE}$: $\frac{1 - (-5)}{9 - 3}$ = $\frac{6}{6}$ = 1; $\overline{EF}$: $\frac{5 - 1}{5 - 9}$ = $\frac{4}{-4}$ = -1;

$\overline{DF}$: $\frac{5 - (-5)}{5 - 3}$ = $\frac{10}{2}$ = 5; $\overline{DN}$: $\frac{3 - (-5)}{7 - 3}$ = $\frac{8}{4}$ = 2; $\overline{EP}$: $\frac{0 - 1}{4 - 9}$ = $\frac{-1}{-5}$ = $\frac{1}{5}$;

$\overline{FM}$: $\frac{5 - (-2)}{5 - 6}$ = $\frac{7}{-1}$ = -7

11. $\frac{t - (-9)}{0 - 4}$ = $\frac{9 - 5}{-3 - (-1)}$; $\frac{t + 9}{-4}$ = $\frac{4}{-2}$; -2t - 18 = -16; -2t = 2; t = -1

12. $\frac{t - (-2)}{5 - t}$ = $\frac{9 - (-3)}{13 - 4}$; $\frac{t + 2}{5 - t}$ = $\frac{12}{9}$ = $\frac{4}{3}$; 3t + 6 = 20 - 4t; 7t = 14; t = 2

13. HIJK is a trap.   Proof: 1. slope of $\overline{HI}$ = $\frac{0 - 0}{5 - 0}$ = $\frac{0}{5}$ = 0; slope of $\overline{KJ}$ = $\frac{9 - 9}{7 - 1}$ =

$\frac{0}{6}$ = 0; slope of $\overline{KH}$ = $\frac{9 - 0}{1 - 0}$ = $\frac{9}{1}$ = 9; slope of $\overline{JI}$ = $\frac{9 - 0}{7 - 5}$ = $\frac{9}{2}$ (Def. of slope)

2. $\overline{HI}$ and $\overline{KJ}$ are ‖; $\overline{KH}$ and $\overline{JI}$ are not ‖. (Two nonvert. lines are ‖ if and only if their slopes are =.)   3. HIJK is a trap. (Def. of trap.)

14. HIJK is a rhombus.   Proof: 1. slope of $\overline{HI}$ = $\frac{-3 - 1}{2 - 0}$ = $\frac{-4}{2}$ = -2; slope of $\overline{KJ}$ =

$\frac{3 - (-1)}{-4 - (-2)}$ = $\frac{4}{-2}$ = -2; slope of $\overline{KH}$ = $\frac{1 - 3}{0 - (-4)}$ = $\frac{-2}{4}$ = -$\frac{1}{2}$; slope of $\overline{JI}$ = $\frac{-3 - (-1)}{2 - (-2)}$ =

$\frac{-2}{4}$ = -$\frac{1}{2}$ (Def. of slope)   2. $\overline{HI}$ ‖ $\overline{KJ}$; $\overline{KH}$ ‖ $\overline{JI}$ (Two nonvert. lines are ‖ if and only if their slopes are =.)   3. HIJK is a ▱. (Def. of ▱)   4. KH =

$\sqrt{(0 - (-4))^2 + (1 - 3)^2}$ = $\sqrt{4^2 + (-2)^2}$ = $\sqrt{16 + 4}$ = $\sqrt{20}$ = $2\sqrt{5}$;

HI = $\sqrt{(2 - 0)^2 + (-3 - 1)^2}$ = $\sqrt{2^2 + (-4)^2}$ = $\sqrt{4 + 16}$ = $\sqrt{20}$ = $2\sqrt{5}$ (Distance

Formula)   5. KH = HI (Subst. Prop.)   6. HIJK is a rhombus. (If 2 consecutive sides of a ▱ are ≅, then the ▱ is a rhombus.)

15. HIJK is a rect.   Proof: 1. slope of $\overline{HI}$ = $\frac{5 - 3}{7 - 8}$ = $\frac{2}{-1}$ = -2; slope of $\overline{KJ}$ =

$\frac{-1 - 1}{0 - (-1)}$ = $\frac{-2}{1}$ = -2; slope of $\overline{KH}$ = $\frac{5 - 1}{7 - (-1)}$ = $\frac{4}{8}$ = $\frac{1}{2}$; slope of $\overline{JI}$ = $\frac{3 - (-1)}{8 - 0}$ =

$\frac{4}{8}$ = $\frac{1}{2}$ (Def. of slope)   2. $\overline{HI}$ ‖ $\overline{KJ}$; $\overline{KH}$ ‖ $\overline{JI}$ (Two nonvert. lines are ‖ if and only if their slopes are =.)   3. (slope of $\overline{HI}$) · (slope of $\overline{KH}$) = -2 · $\frac{1}{2}$ = -1 (Subst. Prop.)

4. $\overline{HI} \perp \overline{KH}$ (Two nonvert. lines are $\perp$ if and only if the prod. of their slopes is -1.)

5. $\angle H$ is a rt. $\angle$. (Def. of $\perp$ lines)   6. HIJK is a rect. (If one $\angle$ of a $\square$ is a rt. $\angle$,

then the $\square$ is a rect.)

16. HIJK is a $\square$.   Proof: 1. slope of $\overline{HI}$ = $\frac{-6 - (-3)}{-5 - (-3)}$ = $\frac{-3}{-2}$ = $\frac{3}{2}$; slope of $\overline{KJ}$ =

$\frac{-5 - (-2)}{4 - 6}$ = $\frac{-3}{-2}$ = $\frac{3}{2}$; slope of $\overline{HK}$ = $\frac{-2 - (-3)}{6 - (-3)}$ = $\frac{1}{9}$; slope of $\overline{IJ}$ = $\frac{-5 - (-6)}{4 - (-5)}$ = $\frac{1}{9}$

2. $\overline{HI} \parallel \overline{KJ}$; $\overline{HK} \parallel \overline{IJ}$ (Two nonvert. lines are $\parallel$ if and only if their slopes are =.)

3. HIJK is a $\square$. (Def. of $\square$)

17. Let O be the $\odot$ with ctr. (0, 0) and radius 5; slope of $\overline{ON}$ = $\frac{-4 - 0}{3 - 0}$ = $\frac{-4}{3}$ = $-\frac{4}{3}$;

the tan. to $\odot$O at N is $\perp$ to $\overline{ON}$; slope of tan. = $- \dfrac{1}{\text{slope of } \overline{ON}}$ = $\frac{3}{4}$.

18. Let O be the $\odot$ with ctr. (-2, 1) and radius 10; slope of $\overline{OP}$ = $\frac{7 - 1}{6 - (-2)}$ = $\frac{6}{8}$ = $\frac{3}{4}$;

the tan. to $\odot$O at P is $\perp$ to $\overline{OP}$; slope of tan. = $- \dfrac{1}{\text{slope of } \overline{OP}}$ = $-\frac{4}{3}$.

19. a. true   b. true   c. true

20. Yes; Ex. 19a, b, and c, resp., demonstrate that the relation "is $\parallel$ to" is reflexive,

symmetric, and transitive.

21. Let T be (x_1, y_1), A be (x_2, y_2), and Y be (x_3, y_3); by the Midpt. Formula,

$\frac{x_1 + x_2}{2}$ = 8, $x_1 + x_2$ = 16; $\frac{x_1 + x_3}{2}$ = 7; $x_1 + x_3$ = 14; $\frac{x_2 + x_3}{2}$ = 15; $x_2 + x_3$ = 30;

$x_1 + x_2 + x_1 + x_3 = x_2 + x_3$; $2x_1$ = 0; x_1 = 0; x_2 = 16; x_3 = 14; $\frac{y_1 + y_2}{2}$ = 4,

$y_1 + y_2$ = 8; $\frac{y_2 + y_3}{2}$ = 7, $y_2 + y_3$ = 14; $\frac{y_1 + y_3}{2}$ = 3; $y_1 + y_3$ = 6;

$y_1 + y_2 + y_1 + y_3 = y_2 + y_3$; $2y_1$ = 0; y_1 = 0; y_2 = 8; y_3 = 6; T is (0, 0),

A is (16, 8), Y is (14, 6)

22. a. 1. slope of $\overleftrightarrow{TU}$ = $\frac{c - 0}{0 - a}$ = $\frac{c}{-a}$ = $-\frac{c}{a}$; slope of $\overleftrightarrow{US}$ = $\frac{0 - c}{b - 0}$ = $\frac{-c}{b}$ = $-\frac{c}{b}$ (Def. of

slope)   2. $\overleftrightarrow{TU} \perp \overleftrightarrow{US}$ (Given)   3. $\angle U$ is a rt. $\angle$; $\triangle SUT$ is a rt. $\triangle$. (Def. of $\perp$

lines; def. of rt. $\triangle$)   4. $(ST)^2 = (TU)^2 + (US)^2$ (Pyth. Thm.)   5. $(ST)^2$ =

$(a - b)^2 + (0 - 0)^2 = (a - b)^2$; $(TU)^2 = (a - 0)^2 + (0 - c)^2 = a^2 + c^2$; $(US)^2$ =

$(b - 0)^2 + (0 - c)^2 = b^2 + c^2$ (Distance Formula)   6. $(a - b)^2 = a^2 + c^2 + b^2 + c^2$;

$a^2 - 2ab + b^2 = a^2 + b^2 + 2c^2$; $-2ab = 2c^2$; $-ab = c \cdot c$; $(-\frac{c}{a})(-\frac{c}{b})$ = -1 (Subst.

Prop.; algebra)   7. (slope of $\overleftrightarrow{TU}$)(slope of $\overleftrightarrow{US}$) = -1 (Subst. Prop.)

<u>b</u>. 1. $(-\frac{c}{a}) \cdot (-\frac{c}{b}) = -1$ (Given)   2. $\frac{c^2}{ab} = -1$; $c^2 = -ab$; $2c^2 = -2ab$; $a^2 + b^2 + 2c^2$

$= a^2 - 2ab + b^2$; $a^2 + c^2 + b^2 + c^2 = (a - b)^2$ (By algebra)   3. $(ST)^2 = (a - b)^2$;

$(TU)^2 = a^2 + c^2$; $(US)^2 = b^2 + c^2$ (Distance Formula; see part (a))   4. $(ST)^2 =$

$(TU)^2 + (US)^2$ (Subst. Prop.)   5. $\triangle$ SUT is a rt. $\triangle$. (If the square of one side of a $\triangle$

$=$ the sum of the squares of the other 2 sides, then the $\triangle$ is a rt. $\triangle$.)   6. $\overleftrightarrow{TU} \perp \overleftrightarrow{US}$

(Def. of $\perp$ lines)

<u>Pages 494-496</u> · WRITTEN EXERCISES

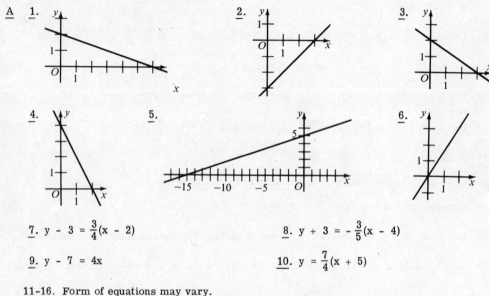

<u>7</u>. $y - 3 = \frac{3}{4}(x - 2)$ <u>8</u>. $y + 3 = -\frac{3}{5}(x - 4)$

<u>9</u>. $y - 7 = 4x$ <u>10</u>. $y = \frac{7}{4}(x + 5)$

<u>11-16</u>. Form of equations may vary.

<u>11</u>. $m = \frac{3 - 2}{5 - 1} = \frac{1}{4}$; $y - 2 = \frac{1}{4}(x - 1)$ <u>12</u>. $m = \frac{3 - 0}{4 - 2} = \frac{3}{2}$; $y = \frac{3}{2}(x - 2)$

<u>13</u>. $m = \frac{2 - (-2)}{-3 - 7} = \frac{4}{-10} = -\frac{2}{5}$; $y + 2 = -\frac{2}{5}(x - 7)$

<u>14</u>. $m = \frac{6 - 5}{-5 - 0} = \frac{1}{-5} = -\frac{1}{5}$; $y - 5 = -\frac{1}{5}x$

<u>15</u>. $y = \frac{5}{7}x - 9$ <u>16</u>. $y = -\frac{1}{2}x + 3$

<u>17</u>. $x + y = 3$

$\underline{x - y = -1}$

$2x \quad\quad = 2$; $x = 1$; $1 + y = 3$; $y = 2$; $(1, 2)$

<u>18</u>. $2x + 3y = 1$

$\underline{9x + 3y = 36}$

$-7x \quad\quad = -35$; $x = 5$; $10 + 3y = 1$; $3y = -9$; $y = -3$; $(5, -3)$

19. $3x + 2y = 8$

   $\underline{-3x + 9y = 36}$

   $11y = 44$; $y = 4$; $3x + 8 = 8$; $3x = 0$; $x = 0$; $(0, 4)$

20. $7x - 4y = -14$

   $\underline{6x + 4y = -12}$

   $13x \qquad = -26$; $x = -2$; $-14 - 4y = -14$; $-4y = 0$; $y = 0$; $(-2, 0)$

B 21. $y - 1 = \frac{5}{2}(x - 3)$; $2y - 2 = 5x - 15$; $5x - 2y = 13$; $y + 4 = \frac{5}{2}(x - 1)$;

   $2y + 8 = 5x - 5$; $5x - 2y = 13$

22. $y + 2 = -\frac{4}{3}(x - 3)$; $3y + 6 = -4x + 12$; $4x + 3y = 6$; $y - 2 = -\frac{4}{3}x$;

   $3y - 6 = -4x$; $4x + 3y = 6$

23-26. Form of equations may vary.

23. Line passes through $(0, 8)$ and $(4, 0)$; $m = \frac{0 - 8}{4 - 0} = \frac{-8}{4} = -2$; $y - 8 = -2x$

24. Line passes through $(0, 6)$ and $(-2, 0)$; $m = \frac{0 - 6}{-2 - 0} = \frac{-6}{-2} = 3$; $y - 6 = 3x$

25. slope of $\overline{AH} = \frac{2 - 2}{5 - 4} = \frac{0}{1} = 0$; slope of $\overline{OD} = \frac{0 - 0}{8 - 0} = \frac{0}{8} = 0$; $\overline{AH} \parallel \overline{OD}$; the line that

   contains the median contains M, the midpt. of $\overline{AO}$, and has slope = 0; M has

   coordinates $(\frac{4 + 0}{2}, \frac{2 + 0}{2}) = (2, 1)$; $y - 1 = 0(x - 2)$; $y = 1$

26. a. The diag. of a rhombus are $\perp$ so slope of $\overline{EK} = -\dfrac{1}{\text{slope of } \overline{BC}}$; slope of $\overline{BC} =$

   $\frac{-3 - 5}{7 - 3} = \frac{-8}{4} = -2$; slope of $\overline{EK} = \frac{1}{2}$ b. The diag. of a $\square$ bis. each other so $\overleftrightarrow{EK}$

   passes through $(\frac{3 + 7}{2}, \frac{5 - 3}{2}) = (5, 1)$; $y - 1 = \frac{1}{2}(x - 5)$

27. $m = 0$; $y - 8 = 0(x - 5)$; $y = 8$ 28. $y = 0$

29. Line is vert.; $x = 7$ 30. $x = 0$

31. $m = $ slope of $\overleftrightarrow{OM} = \frac{-2 - 0}{5 - 0} = \frac{-2}{5} = -\frac{2}{5}$; $y - 1 = -\frac{2}{5}(x - 4)$

32. $m = -\dfrac{1}{\text{slope of } \overleftrightarrow{OM}} = \frac{5}{2}$ (See Ex. 31, above); $y - 1 = \frac{5}{2}(x - 4)$

33. $m = -\dfrac{1}{\text{slope of } \overline{AN}}$; slope of $\overline{AN} = \frac{3 - (-5)}{4 - 0} = \frac{8}{4} = 2$; $m = -\frac{1}{2}$; $y = -\frac{1}{2}(x + 1)$

34. Let M be the midpt. of $\overline{JK}$; M has coordinates $(\frac{-1 + 3}{2}, \frac{4 - 2}{2}) = (1, 1)$; slope of

   $\overline{JK} = \frac{-2 - 4}{3 - (-1)} = \frac{-6}{4} = -\frac{3}{2}$; $m = \frac{2}{3}$; $y - 1 = \frac{2}{3}(x - 1)$

C 35. Let $O(-4, 7)$ be the ctr. of the $\odot$ and $P(0, 4)$ be the pt. of tangency; the tan. is $\perp$

   to $\overline{OP}$ so $m = -\dfrac{1}{\text{slope of } \overline{OP}}$; slope of $\overline{OP} = \frac{4 - 7}{0 - (-4)} = \frac{-3}{4} = -\frac{3}{4}$; $m = \frac{4}{3}$;

   $y - 4 = \frac{4}{3}x$.

<u>36</u>. <u>a</u>. The alt. from a given pt. passes through the pt. and is $\perp$ to the opp. side; let j, k,

and n be the alts. from L, O, and E, resp.; slope of $\overline{OE} = \dfrac{8 - 0}{6 - 0} = \dfrac{8}{6} = \dfrac{4}{3}$; slope of

$j = -\dfrac{3}{4}$; equation of j: $y = -\dfrac{3}{4}(x - 14)$; slope of $\overline{EL} = \dfrac{0 - 8}{14 - 6} = \dfrac{-8}{8} = -1$; slope of

$k = 1$; equation of k: $y = x$; slope of $\overline{OL} = \dfrac{0 - 0}{14 - 0} = \dfrac{0}{14} = 0$; n is vertical and

passes through (6, 8); equation of n: $x = 6$ <u>b</u>. $y = x$ and $x = 6$ intersect at

(6, 6)   <u>c</u>. $y = -\dfrac{3}{4}(x - 14)$; $y = -\dfrac{3}{4}(6 - 14) = -\dfrac{3}{4}(-8) = 6$; j passes through

S (6, 6)

<u>37</u>. <u>a</u>. A, B, and C are the midpts. of $\overline{OF}$, $\overline{EF}$, and $\overline{EO}$, resp.   A has coordinates

$(\dfrac{6 + 0}{2}, \dfrac{6 + 0}{2}) = (3, 3)$; slope of $\overleftrightarrow{EA} = \dfrac{3 - 0}{3 - 18} = \dfrac{3}{-15} = -\dfrac{1}{5}$; equation of $\overleftrightarrow{EA}$:

$y - 3 = -\dfrac{1}{5}(x - 3)$; B has coordinates $(\dfrac{18 + 6}{2}, \dfrac{0 + 6}{2}) = (12, 3)$; slope of $\overleftrightarrow{OB} =$

$\dfrac{3 - 0}{12 - 0} = \dfrac{3}{12} = \dfrac{1}{4}$; equation of $\overleftrightarrow{OB}$: $y = \dfrac{1}{4}x$; C has coordinates $(\dfrac{18 + 0}{2}, \dfrac{0 + 0}{2}) =$

(9, 0); slope of $\overleftrightarrow{FC} = \dfrac{0 - 6}{9 - 6} = \dfrac{-6}{3} = -2$; equation of $\overleftrightarrow{FC} = y - 6 = -2(x - 6)$

<u>b</u>. $y = -\dfrac{1}{5}(x - 3) + 3$; $y = \dfrac{1}{4}x$; $-\dfrac{1}{5}(x - 3) + 3 = \dfrac{1}{4}x$; $-4x + 12 + 60 = 5x$;

$-9x = -72$; $x = 8$; $y = \dfrac{1}{4}(8) = 2$; $\overleftrightarrow{EA}$ and $\overleftrightarrow{OB}$ intersect at (8, 2).   <u>c</u>. $y - 6 =$

$-2(8 - 6) = -4$; $y = 2$; $\overleftrightarrow{FC}$ passes through P (8, 2).   <u>d</u>. FP $=$

$\sqrt{(8 - 6)^2 + (2 - 6)^2} = \sqrt{2^2 + (-4)^2} = \sqrt{4 + 16} = \sqrt{20} = 2\sqrt{5}$; FC $=$

$\sqrt{(9 - 6)^2 + (0 - 6)^2} = \sqrt{3^2 + (-6)^2} = \sqrt{9 + 36} = \sqrt{45} = 3\sqrt{5}$; $\dfrac{2}{3}(3\sqrt{5}) = 2\sqrt{5}$;

FP $= \dfrac{2}{3}$FC

<u>38</u>. Let m and n be the $\perp$ bis. of $\overline{KI}$ and $\overline{KA}$, resp., intersecting $\overline{KI}$ at

$M(\dfrac{2 + (-4)}{2}, \dfrac{8 + (-4)}{2}) = (-1, 2)$ and $\overline{KA}$ at $N(\dfrac{4 + (-4)}{2}, \dfrac{4 + (-4)}{2}) = (0, 0)$;

slope of $\overline{KI} = \dfrac{8 - (-4)}{2 - (-4)} = \dfrac{12}{6} = 2$; slope of $m = -\dfrac{1}{2}$; equation of m: $y - 2 =$

$-\dfrac{1}{2}(x + 1)$; slope of $\overline{KA} = \dfrac{4 - (-4)}{4 - (-4)} = \dfrac{8}{8} = 1$; slope of $n = -1$; equation of n: $y = -x$;

$-x - 2 = -\dfrac{1}{2}(x + 1)$; $2x + 4 = x + 1$; $x = -3$; $y = -(-3) = 3$; m and n intersect at

(-3, 3); ctr. of $\odot$ = P (-3, 3); $r = PA = \sqrt{(-3 - 4)^2 + (3 - 4)^2} = \sqrt{(-7)^2 + (-1)^2} =$

$\sqrt{49 + 1} = \sqrt{50} = 5\sqrt{2}$; equation of $\odot$P: $(x + 3)^2 + (y - 3)^2 = 50$

Pages 500-501 · WRITTEN EXERCISES

A   1. upper left: (0, b); lower right: (a, 0)   2. (c + e, d)

3. upper left: (-f, 2f); upper right: (f, 2f)   4. $(\frac{g + h}{2}, j)$

5. (h + m, n)   6. (n - p, q)   7. $(\frac{s}{2}, \frac{s\sqrt{3}}{2})$

8. upper left: (3, 4); upper right: (8, 4)

9. C $(\sqrt{a^2 - b^2}, b)$; B $(a + \sqrt{a^2 - b^2}, b)$

10. a. $(\frac{2w + 2t}{2}, \frac{2z + 0}{2}) = (w + t, z)$ b. $(\frac{2u + 0}{2}, \frac{2v + 0}{2}) = (u, v)$

c. $(\frac{w + t + u}{2}, \frac{z + v}{2})$ d. $(\frac{2u + 2w}{2}, \frac{2v + 2z}{2}) = (u + w, v + z)$

e. $(\frac{2t + 0}{2}, \frac{0 + 0}{2}) = (t, 0)$ f. $(\frac{u + w + t}{2}, \frac{v + z}{2}) = (\frac{w + t + u}{2}, \frac{z + v}{2})$

g. $(\frac{w + t + u}{2}, \frac{z + v}{2})$

11-12. Answers may vary.

11. Let the x-coordinate of one vertex be a and use 30-60-90 △ to find the coordinates
of the other vertices.

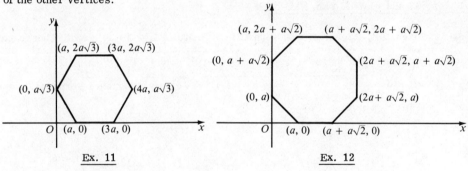

Ex. 11   Ex. 12

12. Let the coordinates of one vertex be (a, 0) and use 45-45-90 △ to find the coordinates
of the other vertices.

13. 1. HOJK is an isos. trap; $\overline{JK} \parallel \overline{OH}$ (Given)   2. slope of $\overline{JK}$ = slope of $\overline{OH}$ (Two
nonvert. lines are $\parallel$ if and only if their slopes are =.)   3. slope of $\overline{JK} = \frac{e - c}{d - b}$;
slope of $\overline{OH} = \frac{0 - 0}{a - 0} = 0$ (Def. of slope)   4. $\frac{e - c}{d - b} = 0$; e = c (Subst. Prop.;
algebra)   5. JO = $\sqrt{b^2 + c^2}$; KH = $\sqrt{(a - d)^2 + e^2}$ (Distance Formula)
6. JO = KH (Def. of isos. trap.)   7. $\sqrt{b^2 + c^2} = \sqrt{(a - d)^2 + e^2}$; $b^2 + c^2 =$
$(a - d)^2 + e^2$ (Subst. Prop.; algebra)   8. $b^2 = (a - d)^2$ (Subtr. Prop. of =)
9. b = a - d; d = a - b (By algebra (d > 0, a - b > 0))

Page 501 · CHALLENGE

Let ∠C be an obtuse ∠ and let ∠A be the smaller acute ∠ of △CBA.   Let I be the pt.

where the bisectors of ∠C, ∠B, and ∠A intersect.   At I draw 4 ∡ with measure

$45 - \frac{1}{4} m\angle A$, two of the ∡ with $\overrightarrow{IA}$ as a side, the other two with $\overrightarrow{IB}$ as a side.   Use R,

S, T, and U to name the pts. where the 4 new rays intersect the sides of △CBA as shown.

Draw $\overline{RS}$ and $\overline{TU}$. ∡ ARS, BTU, SIC, CIU, UIT, TIR, and RIS solve the problem.

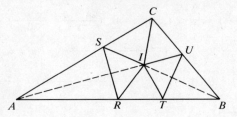

There are infinitely many solutions; you can replace $45 - \frac{1}{4} m\angle A$ above by 45 - k,

where k is any positive number less than $\frac{1}{2} m\angle A$.

Pages 503-504 · WRITTEN EXERCISES

<u>A</u> <u>1</u>. Given: $\overline{AB}$, its ⊥ bis. $\overline{CD}$, P on $\overline{CD}$.   Prove: PA = PB   Proof: Choose axes and

coordinates as shown.   1. PA = $\sqrt{(-a - 0)^2 + (0 - y)^2}$ = $\sqrt{(-a)^2 + (-y)^2}$ = $\sqrt{a^2 + y^2}$;

PB = $\sqrt{(a - 0)^2 + (0 - y)^2}$ = $\sqrt{a^2 + (-y)^2}$ = $\sqrt{a^2 + y^2}$ (Distance Formula)

2. PA = PB (Subst. Prop.)

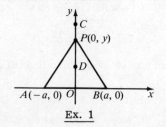

Ex. 1

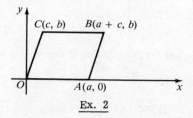

Ex. 2

<u>2</u>. Given: ▱OABC.   Prove $\overline{CA}$ and $\overline{OB}$ bis. each other.   Proof: Choose axes and

coordinates as shown.   1. midpt. of $\overline{CA}$ has coordinates $(\frac{c + a}{2}, \frac{b + 0}{2})$ =

$(\frac{a + c}{2}, \frac{b}{2})$; midpt. of $\overline{OB}$ has coordinates $(\frac{a + c}{2}, \frac{b + 0}{2})$ = $(\frac{a + c}{2}, \frac{b}{2})$ (Midpt.

Formula)   2. $\overline{CA}$ and $\overline{OB}$ bis. each other. (Def. of bisector)

<u>3</u>. Given: rect. OABC.   Prove: CA = OB.   Proof: Choose axes and coordinates as

shown.   1. CA = $\sqrt{(a - 0)^2 + (0 - b)^2}$ = $\sqrt{a^2 + (-b)^2}$ = $\sqrt{a^2 + b^2}$; OB =

$\sqrt{(a - 0)^2 + (b - 0)^2}$ = $\sqrt{a^2 + b^2}$ (Distance Formula)   2. CA = OB (Subst. Prop.)

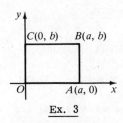

Ex. 3

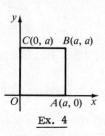

Ex. 4

<u>4</u>. Given: square OABC.   Prove: $\overline{CA} \perp \overline{OB}$.   Proof: Choose axes and coordinates as

shown.   1. slope of $\overline{CA}$ = $\dfrac{0 - a}{a - 0}$ = $\dfrac{-a}{a}$ = -1; slope of $\overline{OB}$ = $\dfrac{a - 0}{a - 0}$ = $\dfrac{a}{a}$ = 1 (Def. of

slope)   2. (slope of $\overline{CA}$)(slope of $\overline{OB}$) = -1 · 1 = -1 (Subst. Prop.)   3. $\overline{CA} \perp \overline{OB}$

(Two nonvert. lines are $\perp$ if and only if the product of their slopes is -1.)

<u>5</u>. Given: isos. trap. OABC.   Prove: CA = OB.   Proof: Choose axes and coordinates

as shown.   1. CA = $\sqrt{(2a + b - a)^2 + (0 - c)^2}$ = $\sqrt{(a + b)^2 + (-c)^2}$ = $\sqrt{(a + b)^2 + c^2}$;

OB = $\sqrt{(a + b - 0)^2 + (c - 0)^2}$ = $\sqrt{(a + b)^2 + c^2}$ (Distance Formula)   2. CA = OB

(Subst. Prop.)

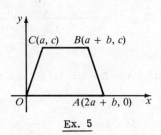

Ex. 5

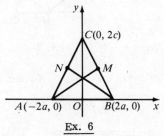

Ex. 6

<u>6</u>. Given: isos. $\triangle ABC$ with CA = CB and midpts. M and N of $\overline{CB}$ and $\overline{CA}$, resp.

Prove: AM = BN.   Proof: Choose axes and coordinates as shown.   1. Midpts. are

$M(\dfrac{0 + 2a}{2},\ \dfrac{2c + 0}{2})$ = (a, c) and $N(\dfrac{0 + (-2a)}{2},\ \dfrac{2c + 0}{2})$ = (-a, c) (Midpt. Formula)

2. AM = $\sqrt{(a - (-2a))^2 + (c - 0)^2}$ = $\sqrt{(3a)^2 + c^2}$ = $\sqrt{9a^2 + c^2}$; BN =

$\sqrt{(2a - (-a))^2 + (0 - c)^2}$ = $\sqrt{(3a)^2 + (-c)^2}$ = $\sqrt{9a^2 + c^2}$ (Distance Formula)

3. AM = BN (Subst. Prop.)

<u>7</u>. Given: rect. RECT with M, N, P, and Q the midpts. of $\overline{RE}$, $\overline{EC}$, $\overline{TC}$, and $\overline{RT}$, resp.

Prove: MNPQ is a rhombus.   Proof: Choose axes and coordinates as shown.

1. Midpts. are $M(\dfrac{a + (-a)}{2}, \dfrac{b + b}{2}) = (\dfrac{0}{2}, \dfrac{2b}{2}) = (0, b)$; $N(\dfrac{a + a}{2}, \dfrac{b + (-b)}{2}) =$

$(\dfrac{2a}{2}, \dfrac{0}{2}) = (a, 0)$; $P(\dfrac{a + (-a)}{2}, \dfrac{-b + (-b)}{2}) = (\dfrac{0}{2}, \dfrac{-2b}{2}) = (0, -b)$;

$Q(\dfrac{-a + (-a)}{2}, \dfrac{b + (-b)}{2}) = (\dfrac{-2a}{2}, \dfrac{0}{2}) = (-a, 0)$ (Midpt. Formula)   2. slope of $\overline{QM} =$

$\dfrac{b - 0}{0 - (-a)} = \dfrac{b}{a}$; slope of $\overline{PN} = \dfrac{0 - (-b)}{a - 0} = \dfrac{b}{a}$ (Def. of slope)   3. $\overline{QM} \parallel \overline{PN}$ (Two

nonvert. lines are $\parallel$ if and only if their slopes are =.)   4. QM =

$\sqrt{(0 - (-a))^2 + (b - 0)^2} = \sqrt{a^2 + b^2}$; $PN = \sqrt{(a - 0)^2 + (0 - (-b))^2} = \sqrt{a^2 + b^2}$

(Distance Formula)   5. QM = PN (Subst. Prop.)   6. MNPQ is a $\square$. (If 2 sides

of a quad. are both $\cong$ and $\parallel$, then the quad. is a $\square$.)   6. MN =

$\sqrt{(a - 0)^2 + (0 - b)^2} = \sqrt{a^2 + (-b)^2} = \sqrt{a^2 + b^2}$ (Distance Formula)   7. MN = QM

(Subst. Prop.)   8. MNPQ is a rhombus. (If 2 consecutive sides of a $\square$ are $\cong$,

then the $\square$ is a rhombus.)

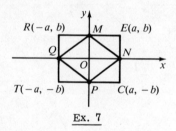

R(−a, b)   M   E(a, b)   C(0, 2b)

Q   N   N   M

T(−a, −b)   P   C(a, −b)   A(−2a, 0) P   B(2a, 0) x

Ex. 7   Ex. 8

<u>8</u>. Answers may vary.   Given: isos. $\triangle ABC$ with CA = CB and M, N, and P the midpts.

of $\overline{CB}$, $\overline{CA}$, and $\overline{AB}$, resp.   Prove: $\triangle MNP$ is isos.   Proof: Choose axes and

coordinates as shown.   1. Midpts. are $M(\dfrac{0 + 2a}{2}, \dfrac{2b + 0}{2}) = (\dfrac{2a}{2}, \dfrac{2b}{2}) = (a, b)$;

$N(\dfrac{0 + (-2a)}{2}, \dfrac{2b + 0}{2}) = (\dfrac{-2a}{2}, \dfrac{2b}{2}) = (-a, b)$; $P(\dfrac{2a + (-2a)}{2}, \dfrac{0 + 0}{2}) = (\dfrac{0}{2}, \dfrac{0}{2}) =$

$(0, 0)$ (Midpt. Formula)   2. $PN = \sqrt{(-a - 0)^2 + (b - 0)^2} = \sqrt{(-a)^2 + b^2} = \sqrt{a^2 + b^2}$;

$PM = \sqrt{(a - 0)^2 + (b - 0)^2} = \sqrt{a^2 + b^2}$ (Distance Formula)   3. PN = PM (Subst.

Prop.)   4. $\triangle MNP$ is isos. (Def. of isos. $\triangle$)

<u>9</u>. Given: $\triangle OAB$ and M and N the midpts. of $\overline{OB}$ and $\overline{OA}$, resp.   Prove: (1) $\overline{MN} \parallel \overline{BA}$;

(2) $MN = \dfrac{1}{2}BA$ Proof: Choose axes and coordinates as shown.   (1) 1. Midpts. are

$M(\dfrac{2b + 0}{2}, \dfrac{2c + 0}{2}) = (\dfrac{2b}{2}, \dfrac{2c}{2}) = (b, c)$; $N(\dfrac{2a + 0}{2}, \dfrac{0 + 0}{2}) = (\dfrac{2a}{2}, \dfrac{0}{2}) = (a, 0)$

(Midpt. Formula)   2. slope of $\overline{MN}$ = $\dfrac{0 - c}{a - b}$ = $-\dfrac{c}{a - b}$; slope of $\overline{BA}$ = $\dfrac{0 - 2c}{2a - 2b}$ =

$\dfrac{-2c}{2(a - b)}$ = $-\dfrac{c}{a - b}$ (Def. of slope)   3. slope of $\overline{MN}$ = slope of $\overline{BA}$ (Subst. Prop.)

4. $\overline{MN} \parallel \overline{BA}$ (Two nonvert. lines are $\parallel$ if and only if their slopes are =.)

(2) 1. BA = $\sqrt{(2a - 2b)^2 + (0 - 2c)^2}$ = $\sqrt{(2(a - b))^2 + (2(-c))^2}$ = $\sqrt{4(a - b)^2 + 4c^2}$ =

$2\sqrt{(a - b)^2 + c^2}$; MN = $\sqrt{(a - b)^2 + (0 - c)^2}$ = $\sqrt{(a - b)^2 + (-c)^2}$ = $\sqrt{(a - b)^2 + c^2}$

(Distance Formula)   2. $\dfrac{1}{2}$BA = $\sqrt{(a - b)^2 + c^2}$ (Mult. Prop. of =)   3. MN =

$\dfrac{1}{2}$BA (Subst. Prop.)

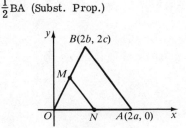

Ex. 9

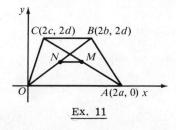

Ex. 11

10. a. Given: ROST and M, N, P, and Q the midpts. of $\overline{RO}$, $\overline{OS}$, $\overline{ST}$, and $\overline{RT}$, resp.

Prove: MNPQ is a $\square$.   Proof: 1. Midpts. are M$\left(\dfrac{2b + 0}{2}, \dfrac{2c + 0}{2}\right)$ = $\left(\dfrac{2b}{2}, \dfrac{2c}{2}\right)$ =

(b, c); N$\left(\dfrac{2a + 0}{2}, \dfrac{0 + 0}{2}\right)$ = $\left(\dfrac{2a}{2}, \dfrac{0}{2}\right)$ = (a, 0); P$\left(\dfrac{2d + 2a}{2}, \dfrac{2e + 0}{2}\right)$ = (d + a, e);

Q$\left(\dfrac{2b + 2d}{2}, \dfrac{2c + 2e}{2}\right)$ = (b + d, c + e) (Midpt. Formula)   2. slope of $\overline{MQ}$ =

$\dfrac{c + e - c}{b + d - b}$ = $\dfrac{e}{d}$; slope of $\overline{NP}$ = $\dfrac{e - 0}{d + a - a}$ = $\dfrac{e}{d}$; slope of $\overline{MN}$ = $\dfrac{0 - c}{a - b}$ = $-\dfrac{c}{a - b}$;

slope of $\overline{QP}$ = $\dfrac{e - (c + e)}{d + a - (b + d)}$ = $-\dfrac{c}{a - b}$ (Def. of slope.)   3. slope of $\overline{MQ}$ =

slope of $\overline{NP}$; slope of $\overline{MN}$ = slope of $\overline{QP}$ (Subst. Prop.)   4. $\overline{MQ} \parallel \overline{NP}$; $\overline{MN} \parallel \overline{QP}$

(Two nonvert. lines are $\parallel$ if and only if their slopes are =.)   5. MNPQ is a $\square$.

(Def. of $\square$)   b. If MNPQ is a rect., then $\overline{MN} \perp \overline{NP}$ and slope of $\overline{MN}$ =

$-\dfrac{1}{\text{slope of } \overline{NP}}$; $\left(-\dfrac{c}{a - b}\right)$ = $-\dfrac{1}{\frac{e}{d}}$; $\dfrac{c}{a - b}$ = $\dfrac{d}{e}$; c = $\dfrac{d(a - b)}{e}$

11. The seg. joining the midpts. of the diag. of a trap. is $\parallel$ to the bases of the trap. and

has length = half the difference of the lengths of the bases.   Given: trap. OABC

with bases $\overline{CB}$ and $\overline{OA}$, OA > CB, and M and N the midpts. of $\overline{CA}$ and $\overline{OB}$, resp.

Prove: (1) $\overline{NM} \parallel \overline{OA}$ (and $\overline{CB}$);   (2) NM = $\dfrac{1}{2}$(OA - CB).   Proof: Choose axes and

coordinates as shown above.   (1) 1. Midpts. are M$\left(\dfrac{2a + 2c}{2}, \dfrac{0 + 2d}{2}\right)$ = (a + c, d);

$N(\dfrac{2b + 0}{2}, \dfrac{2d + 0}{2}) = (\dfrac{2b}{2}, \dfrac{2d}{2}) = (b, d)$ (Midpt. Formula)   2. slope of $\overline{NM}$ =

$\dfrac{d - d}{a + c - b} = \dfrac{0}{a + c - b} = 0$; slope of $\overline{OA} = \dfrac{0 - 0}{2a - 0} = \dfrac{0}{2a} = 0$ (Def. of slope)

3. slope of $\overline{NM}$ = slope of $\overline{OA}$ (Subst. Prop.)   4. $\overline{NM} \parallel \overline{OA}$ (and $\overline{CB}$) (Two nonvert.

lines are $\parallel$ if and only if their slopes are =.)   (2) 1. OA = $|2a - 0| = 2|a| = 2a$;

CB = $|2b - 2c| = 2|b - c| = 2(b - c)$; NM = $|(a + c) - b| = a + c - b$ ($\overline{OA}$, $\overline{CB}$,

and $\overline{NM}$ are vert. lines; $a > 0$, $b > c$, and $a > b$)   2. OA - CB = 2a - 2(b - c) =

2a - 2b + 2c (Subtr. Prop. of =)   3. $\dfrac{1}{2}$(OA - CB) = a + c - b (Mult. Prop. of =)

4. NM = $\dfrac{1}{2}$(OA - CB) (Subst. Prop.)

12. Given: $\triangle$ORS with coordinates as shown; M, N, and J midpts of $\overline{RS}$, $\overline{OR}$, and $\overline{OS}$;

$\overline{OM}$ and $\overline{SN}$ intersect at P.   Prove: OP = $\dfrac{2}{3} \cdot$ OM; RP = $\dfrac{2}{3} \cdot$ RJ; SP = $\dfrac{2}{3} \cdot$ SN

Proof: 1. Midpts. are $M(\dfrac{6b + 6a}{2}, \dfrac{6c + 0}{2}) = (3b + 3a, 3c)$; $N(\dfrac{6b + 0}{2}, \dfrac{6c + 0}{2})$ =

$(3b, 3c)$; $J(\dfrac{6a + 0}{2}, \dfrac{0 + 0}{2}) = (3a, 0)$ (Midpt. Formula)   2. slope of $\overleftrightarrow{OM}$ =

$\dfrac{3c - 0}{3b + 3a - 0} = \dfrac{3c}{3b + 3a} = \dfrac{c}{b + a}$; slope of $\overleftrightarrow{SN} = \dfrac{3c - 0}{3b - 6a} = \dfrac{c}{b - 2a}$; slope of $\overleftrightarrow{RJ}$ =

$\dfrac{0 - 6c}{3a - 6b} = \dfrac{2c}{2b - a}$ (Def. of slope)   3. equation of $\overleftrightarrow{OM}$: $y = \dfrac{c}{b + a}$ x; equation of $\overleftrightarrow{SN}$:

$y = \dfrac{c}{b - 2a}(x - 6a)$; equation of $\overleftrightarrow{RJ}$: $y = \dfrac{2c}{2b - a}(x - 3a)$ (Point-Slope Form)

4. $\overleftrightarrow{OM}$ and $\overleftrightarrow{SN}$ intersect at P(2b + 2a, 2c) [Use Subst. Method: $\dfrac{c}{b + a}$ x =

$\dfrac{c}{b - 2a}(x - 6a)$; cx(b - 2a) = c(x - 6a)(b + a); xbc - 2acx = xbc + xac - 6abc -

$6a^2c$; -3acx = -6abc - $6a^2c$; x = 2b + 2a; $y = \dfrac{c}{b + a}(2b + 2a) = 2c$]   5. P is on

$\overleftrightarrow{RJ}$. $(y = \dfrac{2c}{2b - a}(2b + 2a - 3a) = \dfrac{2c}{2b - a}(2b - a) = 2c)$ 6. OM =

$\sqrt{(3b + 3a - 0)^2 + (3c - 0)^2} = \sqrt{(3(b + a))^2 + (3c)^2} = \sqrt{9((b + a)^2 + c^2)}$ =

$3\sqrt{(b + a)^2 + c^2}$; OP = $\sqrt{(2b + 2a - 0)^2 + (2c - 0)^2} = \sqrt{(2(b + a))^2 + (2c)^2}$ =

$\sqrt{4((b + a)^2 + c^2)} = 2\sqrt{(b + a)^2 + c^2}$; SN = $\sqrt{(3b - 6a)^2 + (3c - 0)^2}$ =

$\sqrt{(3(b - 2a))^2 + 9c^2} = \sqrt{9((b - 2a)^2 + c^2)} = 3\sqrt{(b - 2a)^2 + c^2}$; SP =

$\sqrt{(2b + 2a - 6a)^2 + (2c - 0)^2} = \sqrt{(2b - 4a)^2 + (2c)^2} = \sqrt{(2(b - 2a))^2 + 4c^2}$ =

$\sqrt{4((b - 2a)^2 + c^2)} = 2\sqrt{(b - 2a)^2 + c^2}$; RJ = $\sqrt{(3a - 6b)^2 + (0 - 6c)^2}$ =

$\sqrt{(3(a - 2b))^2 + (3(-2c))^2} = \sqrt{9(a - 2b)^2 + 9(4c^2)} = \sqrt{9((a - 2b)^2 + 4c^2)}$ =

$3\sqrt{(a - 2b)^2 + 4c^2}$; RP = $\sqrt{(2b + 2a - 6b)^2 + (2c - 6c)^2} = \sqrt{(2a - 4b)^2 + (-4c)^2}$ =

$\sqrt{(2(a - 2b))^2 + (2(-2c))^2} = \sqrt{4(a - 2b)^2 + 4(4c^2)} = \sqrt{4((a - 2b)^2 + 4c^2)}$ =

$2\sqrt{(a - 2b)^2 + 4c^2}$ (Distance Formula)   7. $\dfrac{2}{3}$OM = $2\sqrt{(b + a)^2 + c^2}$;

$\frac{2}{3}$SN = $2\sqrt{(b - 2a)^2 + c^2}$; $\frac{2}{3}$RJ = $2\sqrt{(a - 2b)^2 + 4c^2}$ (Mult. Prop. of =)   8. OP =

$\frac{2}{3}$OM; SP = $\frac{2}{3}$SN; RP = $\frac{2}{3}$RJ (Subst. Prop.)

13. a. 1. slope of $\overline{CG}$ = $\dfrac{2c - \dfrac{(3b^2 + 3c^2 - 3ab)}{c}}{2a + 2b - 3a}$ = $\dfrac{2c^2 - 3b^2 - 3c^2 + 3ab}{c(2b - a)}$ =

$\dfrac{-3b^2 - c^2 + 3ab}{2bc - ac}$; slope of $\overline{GH}$ = $\dfrac{\dfrac{6ab - 6b^2}{c} - 2c}{6b - (2a + 2b)}$ = $\dfrac{6ab - 6b^2 - 2c^2}{c(4b - 2a)}$ =

$\dfrac{3ab - 3b^2 - c^2}{2bc - ac}$ (Def. of slope)   2. slope of $\overline{CG}$ = slope of $\overline{GH}$ (Subst. Prop.)

3. C, G, and H are collinear. (Suppose C, G, and H are not collinear. Then $\overleftrightarrow{CG}$

and $\overleftrightarrow{GH}$ are 2 $\parallel$ lines that intersect at G.   C, G, and H must be collinear.)

b. 1. CG = $\sqrt{(2a + 2b - 3a)^2 + (2c - \dfrac{3b^2 + 3c^2 - 3ab}{c})^2}$ =

$\sqrt{(2b - a)^2 + (\dfrac{2c^2 - 3b^2 - 3c^2 + 3ab}{c})^2}$ = $\sqrt{(2b - a)^2 + (\dfrac{-3b^2 - c^2 + 3ab}{c})^2}$;

CH = $\sqrt{(6b - 3a)^2 + (\dfrac{6ab - 6b^2}{c} - \dfrac{3b^2 + 3c^2 - 3ab}{c})^2}$ =

$\sqrt{(3(2b - a))^2 + (\dfrac{9ab - 9b^2 - 3c^2}{c})^2}$ = $\sqrt{9(2b - a)^2 + (\dfrac{3(3ab - 3b^2 - c^2)}{c})^2}$ =

$\sqrt{9((2b - a)^2 + (\dfrac{3ab - 3b^2 - c^2}{c})^2)}$ = $3\sqrt{(2b - a)^2 + (\dfrac{-3b^2 - c^2 + 3ab}{c})^2}$ (Distance

Formula)   2. $\frac{1}{3}$CH = $\sqrt{(2b - a)^2 + (\dfrac{-3b^2 - c^2 + 3ab}{c})^2}$ (Mult. Prop. of =)

3. CG = $\frac{1}{3}$CH (Subst. Prop.)

Pages 505-506 · CHAPTER REVIEW

1.

2. XY = $\sqrt{(2 - (-2))^2 + (4 - (-4))^2}$ = $\sqrt{4^2 + 8^2}$ =

$\sqrt{16 + 64}$ = $\sqrt{80}$ = $4\sqrt{5}$; YZ = $\sqrt{(2 - 2)^2 + (-6 - 4)^2}$ =

$\sqrt{0^2 + (-10)^2}$ = $\sqrt{100}$ = 10; XZ =

$\sqrt{(2 - (-2))^2 + (-6 - (-4))^2}$ = $\sqrt{4^2 + (-2)^2}$ =

$\sqrt{16 + 4}$ = $\sqrt{20}$ = $2\sqrt{5}$

3. $(YZ)^2$ = 100 = 80 + 20 = $(XY)^2 + (XZ)^2$, so $\triangle XYZ$ is a rt. $\triangle$. (If the square of one

side of a $\triangle$ = the sum of the squares of the other 2 sides, then the $\triangle$ is a rt. $\triangle$)

4. (-3, 0); 10   5. (5, -1); 7

6. r = dist. to x-axis = 3; $(x - 2)^2 + (y + 3)^2$ = 9

7. r = $\sqrt{(-3 - (-6))^2 + (3 - (-1))^2}$ = $\sqrt{3^2 + 4^2}$ = $\sqrt{9 + 16}$ = $\sqrt{25}$;

$(x + 6)^2 + (y + 1)^2$ = 25

8. $(\dfrac{7 + 1}{2}, \dfrac{-2 + (-1)}{2})$ = $(\dfrac{8}{2}, -\dfrac{3}{2})$ = $(4, -\dfrac{3}{2})$

9. $(\frac{-4 + 2}{2}, \frac{5 + (-5)}{2}) = (\frac{-2}{2}, \frac{0}{2}) = (-1, 0)$ 10. $(\frac{a + (-a)}{2}, \frac{b + b}{2}) = (\frac{0}{2}, \frac{2b}{2}), (0, b)$

11. $\frac{x + 11}{2} = 0$; $x + 11 = 0$; $x = -11$; $\frac{y + (-1)}{2} = 5$; $y - 1 = 10$; $y = 11$; R(-11, 11)

12. $\frac{-6 - (-1)}{15 - (-5)} = \frac{-5}{20} = -\frac{1}{4}$

13. $\frac{y - (-13)}{0 - 9} = \frac{2}{3}$; $\frac{y + 13}{-9} = \frac{2}{3}$; 3y + 39 = -18; 3y = -57; y = -19

14. Answers may vary; for example: $5 = \frac{y - (-2)}{x - 0}$; $5 = \frac{y + 2}{x}$; y + 2 = 5x; y = 5x - 2;

    (2, 8), (1, 3), (-1, -7)

15. 0

16. slope of $\overline{TQ}$ = $\frac{-2 - 4}{-1 - 7} = \frac{-6}{-8} = \frac{3}{4}$; slope of $\overline{SR}$ = $\frac{-2 - 1}{6 - 10} = \frac{-3}{-4} = \frac{3}{4}$; slope of $\overline{TS}$ =

    $\frac{1 - 4}{10 - 7} = \frac{-3}{3} = -1$; slope of $\overline{QR}$ = $\frac{-2 - (-2)}{6 - (-1)} = \frac{0}{7} = 0$; $\overline{TQ} \parallel \overline{SR}$; $\overline{TS}$ is not $\parallel$ to $\overline{QR}$;

    QRST is a trap.

17. $\frac{3}{4}$; $-\frac{4}{3}$

18. U is on $\overline{UT}$ so slope of $\overline{UT}$ = slope of $\overline{QT}$ = $\frac{3}{4}$; $\frac{4 - y}{7 - x} = \frac{3}{4}$; 16 - 4y = 21 - 3x;

    3x - 4y = 5; also, if $\overline{UR} \parallel \overline{ST}$; $\frac{-2 - y}{6 - x} = -1$; -2 - y = -6 + x; y = 4 - x;

    substituting, 3x - 4(4 - x) = 5; 3x - 16 + 4x = 5; 7x = 21; x = 3;

    y = 4 - 3 = 1; U(3, 1)

19.

20-21. Form of equation may vary.

20. y - 2 = -2(x - 5)

21. m = $\frac{-1 - (-3)}{-8 - (-2)} = \frac{2}{-6} = -\frac{1}{3}$; $y + 3 = -\frac{1}{3}(x + 2)$

22. 4x - 6y = 12; -6y = -4x + 12; $y = \frac{4}{6}x - 2$; $m = \frac{2}{3}$; b = -2

23. 4x + 20y = 32

    4x - 3y = 9
    _____
    23y = 23; y = 1; x + 5 = 8; x = 3; (3, 1)

24. A(d, 0); C(0, e)

25. m∠TRS = 60; let $\overline{SX}$ be the alt. to $\overline{RT}$; △ SRX is a 30°-60°-90° △; SX = a$\sqrt{3}$; S has

    coordinates (a, a$\sqrt{3}$) or (a, -a$\sqrt{3}$).

26. Given: Rect. DOEF; OE = 2 · EF; G the midpt. of $\overline{DF}$.   Prove: $\overline{OG} \perp \overline{EG}$

    Proof: Choose axes and coordinates with E(2e, 0), F(2e, h), D(0, h), O(0, 0).

    1. G is the midpt. of $\overline{DF}$, so G has coordinates (e, h) (Given and Midpt. Formula)

2. slope of $\overline{OG} = \dfrac{h - 0}{e - 0} = \dfrac{h}{e}$; slope of $\overline{EG} = \dfrac{0 - h}{2e - e} = \dfrac{-h}{e} = -\dfrac{h}{e}$ (Def. of slope)

3. (slope of $\overline{OG}$) $\cdot$ (slope of $\overline{EG}$) $= \dfrac{h}{e}\left(-\dfrac{h}{e}\right) = -\dfrac{h^2}{e^2}$ (Subst. Prop.)   4. OE $= 2 \cdot$ EF

(Given)   5. OE $= |2e - 0| = |2e| = 2e$; EF $= |h - 0| = |h| = h$ ($\overline{OE}$ is horiz.;

$\overline{EF}$ is vert.)   6. $2e = 2h$; $e = h$ (Subst. Prop.; Div. Prop. of =)

7. (slope of $\overline{OG}$) $\cdot$ (slope of $\overline{EG}$) $= -\dfrac{h^2}{h^2} = -1$ (Subst. Prop.)   8. $\overline{OG} \perp \overline{EG}$ (Two

nonvert. lines are $\perp$ if and only if the product of their slopes is -1.)

<u>27.</u> Given: Rect. DOEF; G the midpt. of $\overline{DF}$ Prove: $\triangle$ OEG is isos.   Proof: Choose

axes and coordinates with E(2e, 0), F(2e, h), D(0, h), and O(0, 0)   1. G is the

midpt. of $\overline{DF}$, so G has coordinates (e, h) (Given and the Midpt. Formula)

2. OG $= \sqrt{(e - 0)^2 + (h - 0)^2} = \sqrt{e^2 + h^2}$; EG $= \sqrt{(e - 2e)^2 + (h - 0)^2} =$

$\sqrt{(-e)^2 + h^2} = \sqrt{e^2 + h^2}$ (Distance Formula)   3. OG = EG (Subst. Prop.)

4. $\triangle$ OEG is isos. (Def. of isos. $\triangle$)

<u>28.</u> Given: $\square$ OABC and M and N the midpts. of

$\overline{CB}$ and $\overline{OA}$, resp.   Prove: $\overline{MN} \parallel \overline{CO} \parallel \overline{BA}$.

Proof: Choose axes and coordinates as shown.

1. M has coordinates $\left(\dfrac{c + 2a + c}{2}, \dfrac{d + d}{2}\right) =$

$\left(\dfrac{2a + 2c}{2}, \dfrac{2d}{2}\right) = (a + c, d)$; N has coordinates $\left(\dfrac{0 + 2a}{2}, \dfrac{0 + 0}{2}\right) = \left(\dfrac{2a}{2}, \dfrac{0}{2}\right) = (a, 0)$

(Midpt. Formula)   2. slope of $\overline{MN} = \dfrac{0 - d}{a - (a + c)} = \dfrac{-d}{-c} = \dfrac{d}{c}$; slope of $\overline{CO} =$

$\dfrac{d - 0}{c - 0} = \dfrac{d}{c}$; slope of BA $= \dfrac{d - 0}{2a + c - 2a} = \dfrac{d}{c}$ (Def. of slope)   3. $\overline{MN} \parallel \overline{CO} \parallel \overline{BA}$

(Two nonvert. lines are $\parallel$ if and only if their slopes are =.)

Page 507 · CHAPTER TEST

<u>1.</u> 2   <u>2.</u> II

<u>3.</u> $\sqrt{(2 - (-2))^2 + (4 - 1)^2} = \sqrt{4^2 + 3^2} = \sqrt{16 + 9} = \sqrt{25} = 5$

<u>4.</u> $\left(\dfrac{-2 + 2}{2}, \dfrac{1 + 4}{2}\right) = \left(\dfrac{0}{2}, \dfrac{5}{2}\right) = \left(0, \dfrac{5}{2}\right)$

<u>5.</u> r = 5 (See Ex. 3, above); $(x - 2)^2 + (y - 4)^2 = 25$

<u>6, 8, 10.</u> Form of equations may vary.

<u>6.</u> m $= \dfrac{4 - 1}{2 - (-2)} = \dfrac{3}{4}$; $y - 1 = \dfrac{3}{4}(x + 2)$

<u>7.</u> slope of $\overleftrightarrow{MN} = \dfrac{3}{4}$ (See Ex. 6, above); slope of $\overleftrightarrow{LM} = -\dfrac{4}{3}$

<u>8.</u> m = $-\frac{4}{3}$ (See Ex. 7, above); y + 2 = $-\frac{4}{3}$(x - 1)

<u>9.</u> m = $\frac{3}{4}$ (See Ex. 6, above); $\frac{3}{4} = \frac{y - 1}{-1 - 3}$; $\frac{3}{4} = \frac{y - 1}{-4}$; 4y - 4 = -12; 4y = -8; y = -2

<u>10.</u> m = slope of $\overleftrightarrow{MN}$ = $\frac{3}{4}$ (See Ex. 6, above); y = $\frac{3}{4}$x - 4

<u>11.</u> $\frac{x + 2}{2}$ = -2; x + 2 = -4; x = -6; $\frac{y + 4}{2}$ = 1; y + 4 = 2; y = -2; Z(-6, -2)

<u>12.</u> 5x - 3y = -1

6x - 3y = -3

-x   = 2; x = -2; -10 - 3y = -1; -3y = 9; y = -3; (-2, -3)

<u>13.</u> 3; (-6, 0)   <u>14.</u> (f - g, h)

<u>15.</u> JL = $\sqrt{(-3 - (-12))^2 + (-3 - 0)^2}$ = $\sqrt{9^2 + (-3)^2}$ = $\sqrt{81 + 9}$ = $\sqrt{90}$ = $3\sqrt{10}$;

KL = $\sqrt{(-3 - 0)^2 + (-3 - 6)^2}$ = $\sqrt{(-3)^2 + (-9)^2}$ = $\sqrt{9 + 81}$ = $\sqrt{90}$ = $3\sqrt{10}$; JL = KL;

△ JKL is isos.

<u>16.</u> slope of $\overline{JL}$ = $\frac{-3 - 0}{-3 - (-12)}$ = $\frac{-3}{9}$ = $-\frac{1}{3}$; slope of $\overline{KL}$ = $\frac{-3 - 6}{-3 - 0}$ = $\frac{-9}{-3}$ = 3;

(slope of $\overline{JL}$) · (slope of $\overline{KL}$) = $-\frac{1}{3}$(3) = -1; $\overline{JL} \perp \overline{KL}$; △ JKL is a rt. △.

<u>17.</u> Given: square OABC.   Prove: $\overline{CA}$ and $\overline{OB}$ bis. each other.   Proof: Choose axes

and coordinates as shown.   1. midpt. of $\overline{CA}$ is $(\frac{0 + a}{2}, \frac{a + 0}{2})$ = $(\frac{a}{2}, \frac{a}{2})$;

midpt. of $\overline{OB}$ is $(\frac{a + 0}{2}, \frac{a + 0}{2})$ = $(\frac{a}{2}, \frac{a}{2})$ (Midpt. Formula)   2. $\overline{CA}$ passes

through midpt. of $\overline{OB}$; $\overline{OB}$ passes through midpt. of $\overline{CA}$. $((\frac{a}{2}, \frac{a}{2})$ is on $\overline{CA}$ and $\overline{OB}$.)

3. $\overline{CA}$ and $\overline{OB}$ bis. each other. (Def. of segment bisector)

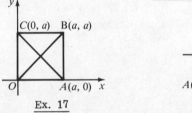
Ex. 17

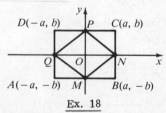
Ex. 18

<u>18.</u> Given: rect. ABCD and M, N, P, and Q the midpts. of $\overline{AB}$, $\overline{CB}$, $\overline{DC}$, and $\overline{DA}$, resp.

Prove: MNPQ is a rhombus.   Proof: Choose axes and coordinates as shown.

1. M has coordinates $(\frac{a + (-a)}{2}, \frac{-b + (-b)}{2})$ = $(\frac{0}{2}, \frac{-2b}{2})$ = (0, -b); N has coordinates

$(\frac{a + a}{2}, \frac{b + (-b)}{2})$ = $(\frac{2a}{2}, \frac{0}{2})$ = (a, 0); P has coordinates $(\frac{a + (-a)}{2}, \frac{b + b}{2})$ =

$(\frac{0}{2}, \frac{2b}{2})$ = (0, b); Q has coordinates $(\frac{-a + (-a)}{2}, \frac{b + (-b)}{2})$ = $(\frac{-2a}{2}, \frac{0}{2})$ = (-a, 0)

(Midpt. Formula)   2. slope of $\overline{QM} = \frac{-b - 0}{0 - (-a)} = \frac{-b}{a} = -\frac{b}{a}$; slope of $\overline{PN} = \frac{0 - b}{a - 0} =$

$\frac{-b}{a} = -\frac{b}{a}$ (Def. of slope)   3. $\overline{QM} \parallel \overline{PN}$ (Two nonvert. lines are $\parallel$ if and only if their

slopes are =.)   4. QM $= \sqrt{(0 - (-a))^2 + (-b - 0)^2} = \sqrt{a^2 + (-b)^2} = \sqrt{a^2 + b^2}$;

PN $= \sqrt{(a - 0)^2 + (0 - b)^2} = \sqrt{a^2 + (-b)^2} = \sqrt{a^2 + b^2}$ (Distance Formula)   5. QM =

PN (Subst. Prop.)   8. MNPQ is a $\square$. (If one pr. of opp. sides of a quad. are both

$\cong$ and $\parallel$, then the quad. is a $\square$.)   7. MN $= \sqrt{(a - 0)^2 + (0 - (-b))^2} = \sqrt{a^2 + b^2}$

(Distance Formula)   8. MN = QM (Subst. Prop.)   9. MNPQ is a rhombus. (If 2

consecutive sides of a $\square$ are $\cong$, then the $\square$ is a rhombus.)

Page 508 · MIXED REVIEW

1. a. $\frac{AE}{CE} = \frac{8}{12} = \frac{2}{3}$; $\frac{BE}{DE} = \frac{6}{9} = \frac{2}{3}$; $\angle AEB \cong \angle CED$; $\triangle AEB \sim \triangle CED$ (SAS); $\angle B \cong \angle D$

(Def. of $\sim$ polygons)   b. $\frac{12}{x} = \frac{2}{3}$; 2x = 36; x = 18   c. ratio of lengths = 2 : 3;

ratio of areas $= 2^2 : 3^2 = 4 : 9$

2. b = -4; m $= \frac{-4 - 5}{0 - (-3)} = \frac{-9}{3} = -3$; y = -3x - 4 (Form of equation may vary.)

3. $12^2 + 35^2 = 144 + 1225 = 1369 = 37^2$; right

4. T. A. $= 2\pi \cdot 10^2 + 2\pi(10)(8.2) = 200\pi + 164\pi = 364\pi$; V $= \pi(10^2)(8.2) = 820\pi$

5. $x^2 = 9(9 + 11) = 180$; x $= \sqrt{180} = 6\sqrt{5}$; 10(10 + y) = 180; 100 + 10y = 180;

   10y = 80; y = 8

6. no; no (Figures may vary.)

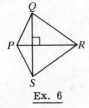

Ex. 6

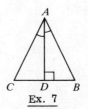

Ex. 7

7. Given: $\triangle ABC$; $\overrightarrow{AD}$ bis. $\angle A$; $\overline{AD} \perp \overline{BC}$.   Prove: $\triangle ABC$ is isos.   Proof: 1. $\overrightarrow{AD}$

   bis. $\angle A$. (Given)   2. $\angle BAD \cong \angle CAD$ (Def. of $\angle$ bis.)   3. $\overline{AD} \perp \overline{BC}$ (Given)

   4. $\angle BDA \cong \angle CDA$ (Adj. $\angle$ formed by $\perp$ lines are $\cong$.)   5. $\overline{AD} \cong \overline{AD}$ (Refl. Prop.)

   6. $\triangle BDA \cong \triangle CDA$ (ASA)   7. $\overline{AB} \cong \overline{AC}$ (Corr. parts of $\cong \triangle$ are $\cong$.)

   8. $\triangle ABC$ is isos. (Def. of isos. $\triangle$)

8. length of side $= 2\sqrt{2}$; p $= 8\sqrt{2}$ cm; A $= (2\sqrt{2})^2 = 8$; A $= 8$ cm^2

9. $\dfrac{x}{12} = \dfrac{10}{18} = \dfrac{5}{9};\ 9x = 60;\ x = 6\dfrac{2}{3}$

10. $(x + y) + (x - y) = 180;\ 2x = 180;\ x = 90$

11. $180 - x = \dfrac{1}{2}(104 + 78) = 91;\ x = 89$ **12.** Construction 10

13. Given: Trap. OABC with coordinates as shown;

median $\overline{MN}$.   Prove: $\overline{MN} \parallel \overline{OA};\ \overline{MN} \parallel \overline{CB}$

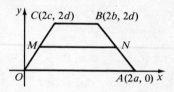

Proof: 1. M and N are midpts. of $\overline{OC}$ and $\overline{BA}$,

resp. (Given, def. of median of trap.)   2. M

has coordinates (c, d); N has coordinates (a + b, d) (Midpt. Formula)   3. slope

of $\overline{OA} = \dfrac{0 - 0}{2a - 0} = 0$; slope of $\overline{OA}$ = slope of $\overline{CB} = 0$ (By def. of trapezoid)

4. slope of $\overline{MN} = \dfrac{d - d}{a + b - c} = 0$ 5. $\overline{OA} \parallel \overline{MN} \parallel \overline{CB}$ (Two nonvert. lines are $\parallel$

if and only if their slopes are =.)

14. If $x = 1$, then $x \neq 0$.   If $x = 0$, then $x \neq 1$; true.

15. $BC = \sqrt{3^2 - 1^2} = \sqrt{8} = 2\sqrt{2}$ **a.** $\cos A = \dfrac{AB}{AC} = \dfrac{1}{3}$ **b.** $\sin C = \dfrac{AB}{AC} = \dfrac{1}{3}$

   c. $\tan A = \dfrac{BC}{AB} = \dfrac{2\sqrt{2}}{1} = 2\sqrt{2}$ **d.** $\cos C = \dfrac{BC}{AC} = \dfrac{2\sqrt{2}}{3}$

16. $4\pi r^2 = 144\pi;\ r^2 = 36;\ r = 6;\ V = \dfrac{4}{3}\pi r^3 = \dfrac{4}{3}\pi(216) = 288\pi\ \text{cm}^3$

Page 509 · ALGEBRA REVIEW

1. $(-6)^3 = -216$

2. $15^0 = 1$

3. $2^3 \cdot 2^2 = 2^5 = 32$

4. $4^2 \cdot 3^3 = 16 \cdot 27 = 432$

5. $2^{-4} = \dfrac{1}{2^4} = \dfrac{1}{16}$

6. $r^5 \cdot r^8 = r^{13}$

7. $\dfrac{r^9}{r^4} = r^5$

8. $\dfrac{t^3}{t^4} = t^{-1} = \dfrac{1}{t}$

9. $a \cdot a^{-1} = a^{1-1} = a^0 = 1$

10. $a^3 \cdot a^{-5} = a^{-2} = \dfrac{1}{a^2}$

11. $x^{-1} \cdot x^{-2} = x^{-3} = \dfrac{1}{x^3}$

12. $(-3)^{-2} = \dfrac{1}{(-3)^2} = \dfrac{1}{9}$

13. $(3^2)^2 = 3^{2 \cdot 2} = 3^4 = 81$

14. $\left(\dfrac{7}{9}\right)^0 = 1$

15. $(-1)^8 = 1$

16. $(-1)^{99} = -1$

17. $\left(\dfrac{1}{2}\right)^{-3} = 2^3 = 8$

18. $(2x)^3 = 2^3 \cdot x^3 = 8x^3$

19. $(3y^2)(2y^4) = 6 \cdot y^{2+4} = 6y^6$

20. $(x^2y)^5 = x^{2 \cdot 5}y^5 = x^{10}y^5$

21. $(m^{-5})(m^5) = m^0 = 1$

22. $\dfrac{d^{10}}{d^{-10}} = d^{10-(-10)} = d^{20}$

23. $7^5 \cdot 7^{-11} \cdot 7^7 = 7^{5-11+7} = 7^1 = 7$

24. $x^{-6} \cdot x^{-2} \cdot x^3 = x^{-6-2+3} = x^{-5} = \dfrac{1}{x^5}$

25. $(x^2)^{-2} = x^{2(-2)} = x^{-4} = \dfrac{1}{x^4}$

26. $(x^{-2})^2 = x^{-2(2)} = x^{-4} = \dfrac{1}{x^4}$

27. $(4x^3y^2)^2 = 4^2 \cdot x^{3 \cdot 2} \cdot y^{2 \cdot 2} = 16x^6y^4$

28. $(3x)^2(2xy^3) = 3^2 \cdot x^2 \cdot 2xy^3 = 18 \cdot x^{2+1} \cdot y^3 = 18x^3y^3$

29. $(-2s^5t)(-4st)^2 = -2s^5t((-4)^2s^2t^2) = -2s^5t(16s^2t^2) = -32s^7t^3$

30. $4^{-1} \cdot 3^{-2} = \dfrac{1}{4 \cdot 3^2} = \dfrac{1}{4 \cdot 9} = \dfrac{1}{36}$

31. $\left(\dfrac{2}{3}\right)^{-3} = \left(\dfrac{3}{2}\right)^3 = \dfrac{27}{8}$

32. $\left(\dfrac{7}{5}\right)^{-2} = \left(\dfrac{5}{7}\right)^2 = \dfrac{25}{49}$

Pages 513-515 · WRITTEN EXERCISES

<u>A</u> 1. <u>a.</u>

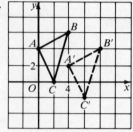

<u>b.</u> yes   <u>c.</u> x + 4 = 12; x = 8;

y - 2 = 6; y = 8; (8, 8)

2. <u>a.</u>

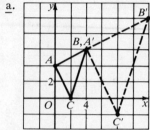

<u>b.</u> no   <u>c.</u> 2x + 4 = 12; 2x = 8;

x = 4; 2y - 2 = 6; 2y = 8; y = 4;

(4, 4)

3. <u>a.</u>

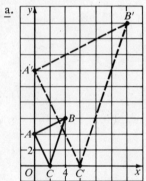

<u>b.</u> no   <u>c.</u> 3x = 12; x = 4;

3y = 6; y = 2; (4, 2)

4. <u>a.</u>

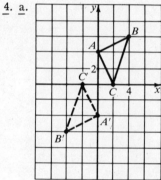

<u>b.</u> yes   <u>c.</u> -x = 12; x = -12;

-y = 6; y = -6; (-12, -6)

5. <u>a.</u>

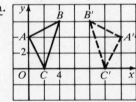

<u>b.</u> yes   <u>c.</u> 12 - x = 12; x = 0;

y = 6; (0, 6)

6. <u>a.</u>

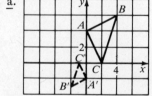

<u>b.</u> no   <u>c.</u> $-\frac{1}{2}$x = 12; x = -24;

$-\frac{1}{2}$y = 6; y = -12; (-24, -12)

7. a. yes   b. yes   c. no

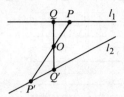

8. For each P on $\overline{XY}$, map P to the pt.
P' where the $\parallel$ to $\overline{YZ}$ through P
intersects $\overline{XZ}$.

B 9. Let O be the intersection of the diagonals of ABCD.   For each P on $\overline{DC}$, map P to

the pt. P' where $\overrightarrow{PO}$ intersects $\overline{AB}$; no

10. a. yes   b-c, e. Answers may vary.   Examples are given.   d. no   e. Map R to

A, S to B, T to C, and U to D.   Map $\overline{RS}$ onto $\overline{AB}$ as follows: for P on RS, map P

onto P' such that AP' = RP.   Map $\overline{ST}$ onto $\overline{BC}$, $\overline{UT}$ onto $\overline{DC}$, and $\overline{RU}$ onto $\overline{AD}$ in

the same way.

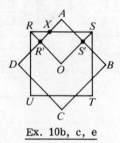

Ex. 10b, c, e

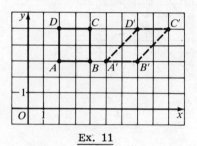

Ex. 11

11. ABCD: A = 4, P = 8; A'B'C'D': A = 4, P = 4 + $4\sqrt{2}$

12. Overlooking the thickness of the paper, the equator is mapped onto itself.

13. yes   14. less   15. no

16. Let A' and B' be the images of A and B under U.   AB > 0 but since A' = B',
A'B' = 0.   U does not preserve distance.

C 17. P' has coordinates $(-x_1, y_1)$; Q' has coordinates $(-x_2, y_2)$; P'Q' =

$\sqrt{(-x_2 - (-x_1))^2 + (y_2 - y_1)^2} = \sqrt{(x_1 - x_2)^2 + (y_2 - y_1)^2}$;

PQ = $\sqrt{(x_2 - x_1)^2 + (y_2 - y_1)^2} = \sqrt{(x_1 - x_2)^2 + (y_2 - y_1)^2}$; PQ = P'Q', so R

is an isometry.

18. Suppose that B' is not on $\overleftrightarrow{A'C'}$, that is, that A', B', and C' are not collinear.

Consider $\triangle A'B'C$.   By the $\triangle$ Ineq., A'C' > A'B' + B'C'; but I is an isometry so it

follows that AC > AB + BC.   This contradicts the Seg. Add. Post.   It follows that

A', B', and C' are collinear and B' is on $\overleftrightarrow{A'C'}$.

Pages 518-520 · WRITTEN EXERCISES

 1.
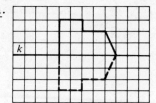

2.
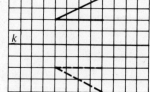

3.
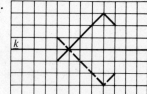

4.
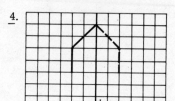

5.
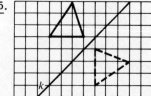

6.
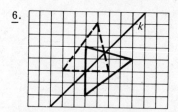

7. a. (2, -4)   b. (-2, 4)   8. a. (4, 0)   b. (-4, 0)

9. a. (0, 2)   b. (0, -2)   10. a. (-2, -1)   b. (2, 1)

11. a. (-3, 2)   b. (3, -2)   12. a. (0, 0)   b. (0, 0)

B 13. (4, 2)   14. (0, 4)   15. (-2, 0)

16. (1, -2)   17. (-2, -3)   18. (0, 0)

19. 1. P = P' is on j, the ⊥ bis. of $\overline{QQ'}$. (Given)   2. PQ = P'Q' (If a pt. lies on the ⊥ bis. of a seg., then it is equidistant from the endpts. of the seg.)

20. Let X and Y be the pts. where $\overline{PP'}$ and $\overline{QQ'}$ intersect j, resp.   1. XP = XP' and YP = YP'; XY = XY (If a pt. is on the ⊥ bis. of a seg., then the pt. is equidistant from the endpts. of the seg; Refl. Prop.)   2. △YPX ≅ △YP'X (SSS)   3. ∠PYX ≅ ∠P'YX (Corr. parts of ≅ ⧍ are ≅.)   4. ∠PYQ ≅ ∠P'YQ' (If 2 ⦟ are comp. of ≅ ⦟, then the 2 ⦟ are ≅.)   5. YQ = YQ' (Def. of reflection)   6. △PYQ ≅ △P'YQ' (SAS)   7. PQ = PQ' (Corr. parts of ≅ ⧍ are ≅.)

21. 1. O is on j, the ⊥ bis. of $\overline{PP'}$ and $\overline{QQ'}$. (Given)   2. OP = OP'; OQ = OQ' (If a pt. is on the ⊥ bis. of a seg., then it is equidistant from the endpts. of the seg.)   3. OP + OQ = OP' + OQ'; PQ = P'Q' (Add. Prop. of =, Seg. Add. Post.)

22. Construct k, the ⊥ to t through A, intersecting t at P, and construct $\overline{PA'}$ on k so that AP = PA'; A' = R_t(A).

23. Construct t the ⊥ bis. of $\overline{BB'}$.

24. a. ∠1 and ∠3 are vert. ∠ so ∠1 ≅ ∠3; if Y is the pt. where $\overline{HH'}$ intersects the wall, then △PYH ≅ △PYH' (SAS), so ∠3 ≅ ∠2; ∠1 ≅ ∠2 by the Trans. Prop.

    b. BP + PH = BP + PH' ($\overline{PH}$ and $\overline{PH'}$ are corr. sides of ≅ △); BP + PH' = BH'

25. Let P and Q be the pts. where $\overline{H'H''}$ and $\overline{HH'}$, resp., intersect the walls and let R and S be the pts. where $\overrightarrow{BH''}$ and $\overrightarrow{RH'}$, resp., intersect the walls.   △RPH'' ≅ △RPH' and △SQH ≅ △SQH' (SAS) so BR + RS + SH = BR + RS + SH' = BR + RH' = BR + RH'' = BH''.

26-28. Answers may vary.

26.

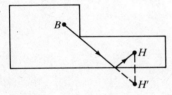

27. Find H' as in Ex. 26, above. Then find H'', the image of H' under reflection in the line of the left side wall. Aim for H''.

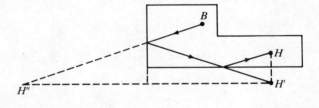

28. First find H', the image of H under reflection in the upper wall, then H'', the image of H' under reflection in the lower wall, then H''', the image of H'' under reflection in the line of the left side wall.   Aim for H'''

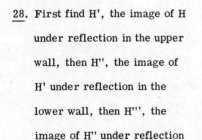

29. yes

30. (0, 3) and (1, 5) are on the given line.   Their images under reflection in the y-axis are (0, 3) and (-1, 5); slope of image line = $\frac{5 - 3}{-1 - 0}$ = $\frac{2}{-1}$ = -2; equation: y = -2x + 3 (Form of equation may vary.)

31. (0, 5) and (-5, 0) are on the given line. Their images under reflection in the x-axis

are (0, -5) and (-5, 0); slope of image line = $\dfrac{0 - (-5)}{-5 - 0} = \dfrac{5}{-5} = -1$; y-intercept is -5;

equation: y = -x - 5. (Form of equation may vary.)

C 32. (-y, -x)

33. a. (6, 3)   b. (10, -2)   c. (13, 1)   d. (5 + (5 - x), y) = (10 - x, y)

34. a. (4, 9)   b. (0, 14)   c. (-3, 11)   d. (x, 6 + (6 - y)) = (x, 12 - y)

35-41. k is the ⊥ bis. of $\overline{AA'}$. Let M be the midpt. and m the slope of $\overline{AA'}$. Form of

equations may vary.

35. M has coordinates $(\dfrac{2 + (-2)}{2}, \dfrac{3 + 3}{2}) = (\dfrac{0}{2}, \dfrac{6}{2}) = (0, 3)$; m = 0; slope of k is

undefined; equation: x = 0 (k is the y-axis.)

36. M has coordinates $(\dfrac{5 + 9}{2}, \dfrac{0 + 0}{2}) = (\dfrac{14}{2}, \dfrac{0}{2}) = (7, 0)$; m $= \dfrac{0 - 0}{9 - 5} = \dfrac{0}{4} = 0$; slope

of k is undefined; equation: x = 7

37. M has coordinates $(\dfrac{1 + 3}{2}, \dfrac{4 + 4}{2}) = (\dfrac{4}{2}, \dfrac{8}{2}) = (2, 4)$; m $= \dfrac{4 - 4}{3 - 1} = \dfrac{0}{2} = 0$; slope

of k is undefined; equation: x = 2

38. M has coordinates $(\dfrac{4 + 4}{2}, \dfrac{0 + 6}{2}) = (\dfrac{8}{2}, \dfrac{6}{2}) = (4, 3)$; slope of $\overline{AA'}$ is undefined;

slope of k = 0; equation: y = 3

39. M has coordinates $(\dfrac{5 + 1}{2}, \dfrac{1 + 5}{2}) = (\dfrac{6}{2}, \dfrac{6}{2}) = (3, 3)$; m $= \dfrac{5 - 1}{1 - 5} = \dfrac{4}{-4} = -1$; slope

of k = 1; equation: y - 3 = 1(x - 3); y = x

40. M has coordinates $(\dfrac{0 + 4}{2}, \dfrac{2 + 6}{2}) = (\dfrac{4}{2}, \dfrac{8}{2}) = (2, 4)$; m $= \dfrac{6 - 2}{4 - 0} = \dfrac{4}{4} = 1$; slope

of k = -1; equation: y - 4 = -1(x - 2); y - 4 = -x + 2; y = -x + 6

41. M has coordinates $(\dfrac{-1 + 4}{2}, \dfrac{2 + 5}{2}) = (\dfrac{3}{2}, \dfrac{7}{2})$; m $= \dfrac{5 - 2}{4 - (-1)} = \dfrac{3}{5}$; slope of k = $-\dfrac{5}{3}$;

equation: y $- \dfrac{7}{2} = -\dfrac{5}{3}(x - \dfrac{3}{2})$; y $= -\dfrac{5}{3}x + \dfrac{5}{2} + \dfrac{7}{2}$; y $= -\dfrac{5}{3}x + 6$

Page 521 · APPLICATION

1. 45   2. yes

3. (Figure not drawn to scale)   Let B be highest pt. on

wall that can be seen at D, highest pt. of mirror.

∠BDC ≅ ∠ADE; m∠C = 90 = m∠E; △BDC ~ △ADE;

$\dfrac{CD}{DE} = \dfrac{BC}{AE}$; $\dfrac{CD}{30} = \dfrac{300}{100}$; CD = 90; height of B =

150 + 30 + 90 = 270; 270 cm

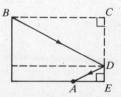

4. Let $\overline{AB}$ be the person, E the eyes, and $\overline{CD}$ the mirror (and the person's image).

Draw $\overline{CF} \perp \overline{AB}$ (and $\overline{CD}$) and $\overline{DH} \perp \overline{AB}$ (and $\overline{CD}$).

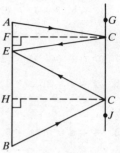

1. $\angle ACG \cong \angle ECD$; $\angle BDJ \cong \angle EDC$ (The $\angle$ between

a mirror and a reflected light ray is $\cong$ to the $\angle$

between the mirror and the initial light ray.)

2. $\angle ACF \cong \angle ECF$; $\angle EDH \cong \angle BDH$ (If 2 $\&$ are

comp. of $\cong$ $\&$, then the 2 $\&$ are $\cong$.)   3. $\triangle ACF \cong$

$\triangle ECF$; $\triangle EDH \cong \triangle BDH$ (ASA)   4. AF = FE;

EH = HB (Corr. parts of $\cong$ $\&$ are $\cong$.)   5. FH = FE + EH = $\frac{1}{2}$AE + $\frac{1}{2}$EB = $\frac{1}{2}$AB

(Seg. Add. Post.; Subst. Prop.)   6. FH = CD (Opp. sides of a $\square$ are $\cong$.)

7. CD = $\frac{1}{2}$AB (Subst. Prop.)

5-6. Let M be the midpt. of $\overline{AD}$.

5. 1. $\overleftrightarrow{EM}$ is the $\perp$ bis. of $\overline{AD}$. (Given)   2. $\triangle BAM \cong \triangle BDM$ (SAS)   3. m$\angle$ DBM =

m$\angle$ ABM = x (Corr. parts of $\cong$ $\&$ are $\cong$.)   4. m$\angle$ EBD + x = 180 ($\angle$ Add. Post.)

5. m$\angle$ CBE = x (Given)   6. m$\angle$ CBE + m$\angle$ EBD = 180 (Subst. Prop.)   7. $\angle$ CBD

is a straight $\angle$ and D lies on $\overleftrightarrow{BC}$. (Protractor Postulate).

6. 1. $\overleftrightarrow{EM}$ is the $\perp$ bis. of $\overline{AD}$. (Given)   2. AB = BD; AE = DE (If a pt. lies on

the $\perp$ bis. of a seg., then the pt. is equidistant from the endpts. of the seg.)

3. AE + EC = DE + EC > CD (Subst. Prop.; $\triangle$ Ineq. Thm.)   4. AB + BC =

BD + BC = CD (Subst. Prop.; Seg. Add. Post.)   5. AE + EC > AB + BC

(Subst. Prop.)

Pages 524-525 · WRITTEN EXERCISES

A 1. a, b.

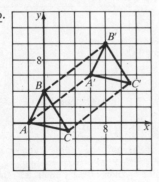

2. a, b.

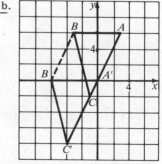

c. yes; yes   c. yes; yes

<u>3</u>. $0 + a = 5$; $a = 5$; $0 + b = 1$; $b = 1$; T: $(x, y) \rightarrow (x + 5, y + 1)$; T: $(3, 3) \rightarrow$

$(3 + 5, 3 + 1) = (8, 4)$

<u>4</u>. $1 + a = 3$; $a = 2$; $1 + b = 0$; $b = -1$; T: $(x, y) \rightarrow (x + 2, y - 1)$; T: $(0, 0) \rightarrow$

$(0 + 2, 0 - 1) = (2, -1)$

<u>5</u>. $-2 + a = 2$; $a = 4$; $3 + b = 6$; $b = 3$; T: $(x, y) \rightarrow (x + 4, y + 3)$; $x + 4 = 0$;

$x = -4$; $y + 3 = 0$; $y = -3$; $(-4, -3)$

<u>6</u>. $-1 + a = 5$; $a = 6$; $5 + b = 7$; $b = 2$; T: $(x, y) \rightarrow (x + 6, y + 2)$; $x + 6 = -1$;

$x = -7$; $y + 2 = 5$; $y = 3$; $(-7, 3)$

<u>7</u>.
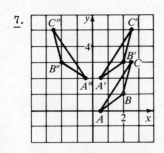

<u>8</u>.
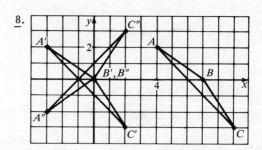

<u>B</u> <u>9</u>. The glide maps (x, y) to $(x, y + 4)$; the reflection maps $(x, y + 4)$ to $(-x, y + 4)$;

the glide reflection maps (x, y) to $(-x, y + 4)$

<u>10</u>. The glide maps (x, y) to $(x - 7, y)$; the reflection maps $(x - 7, y)$ to $(x - 7, -y)$;

the glide reflection maps (x, y) to $(x - 7, -y)$.

<u>11</u>. Construct a $\parallel$ to $\overline{CD}$ through A and

construct $\overline{AA'} \cong \overline{CD}$. Draw $\odot A'$ with

the same radius as $\odot A$. Let T be the

translation that maps A to A'. $\odot A'$

int. $\odot B$ at 2 pts. Choose one and call

it Y. Construct a $\parallel$ to $\overline{CD}$ through Y,

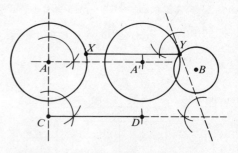

intersecting $\odot A$ at 2 pts. Choose X such that $T(X) = Y$; then $\overline{XY} \parallel \overline{CD}$ and

$XY = CD$.

<u>12</u>. Let j and k be the upper and lower lines. Draw $\overrightarrow{EF}$ intersecting j at G. Construct

$\overline{GH}$ on $\overline{GF}$ so that $GH = EF$. Construct a $\parallel$ to j through H, int. k at Y. Construct

a $\parallel$ to $\overline{GH}$ through Y, int. j at X. $\overline{XY}$ is the required seg. This procedure has the

same result as gliding $\overline{EF}$ first along $\overrightarrow{FE}$ to int. j, then along j until $\overline{EF}$ intersects k.

13. R: $(x, y) \to (x + 1, y + 2)$; S: $(x + 1, y + 2) \to (x - 4, y + 9)$;

   T: $(x, y) \to (x - 4, y + 9)$

14. R: $(x, y) \to (x - 5, y - 3)$; S: $(x - 5, y - 3) \to (x - 1, y - 9)$;

   T: $(x, y) \to (x - 1, y - 9)$

15. The midpts. of $\overline{AA'}$, $\overline{BB'}$, and $\overline{CC'}$ are on the reflecting line. Let X be the image of A under the glide, k the reflecting line, and P the pt. where $\overline{XA'}$ intersects k. k is the $\perp$ bis. of $\overline{XA'}$ so P is the midpt. of $\overline{XA'}$ and $A'P = \frac{1}{2}A'X$. Draw $\overline{AA'}$, intersecting k at Q. Since k $\parallel$ $\overleftrightarrow{AX}$, $\triangle A'QP \sim \triangle A'AX$ and $\frac{A'Q}{A'A} = \frac{A'P}{A'X} = \frac{1}{2}$. Then Q is the midpt. of $\overline{AA'}$ and the midpt. of $\overline{AA'}$ is on k. (The proofs for $\overline{BB'}$ and $\overline{CC'}$ are similar.)

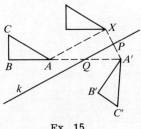

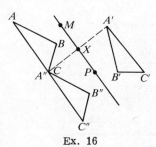

Ex. 15   Ex. 16

16. Construct the $\perp$ bis. of any 2 of $\overline{AA'}$, $\overline{BB'}$ and $\overline{CC'}$ (fig. uses $\overline{AA'}$ and $\overline{CC'}$) to locate midpts. M and P; $\overleftrightarrow{MP}$ is the reflecting line. To find the image of A under the glide, construct a $\perp$ to $\overleftrightarrow{MP}$ from A', intersecting $\overleftrightarrow{MP}$ at X. Construct $\overline{XA''} \cong \overline{A'X}$. Locate B'' and C'' similarly.

C 17. Let T be the translation and k be the reflecting line of a glide reflection G. Let P' and Q' be the images of pts. P and Q under T, and P'' and Q'' the images of P' and Q' under the reflection. T is an isometry so $P'Q' = PQ$; reflection in a line is an isometry so $P''Q'' = P'Q'$. Then by the Trans. Prop., $P''Q'' = PQ$ and G is an isometry.

18. a. P' has coordinates $(x_1 + a, y_1 + b)$; Q' has coordinates $(x_2 + a, y_2 + b)$; PQ = $\sqrt{(x_2 - x_1)^2 + (y_2 - y_1)^2}$; $P'Q' = \sqrt{((x_2 + a) - (x_1 + a))^2 + ((y_2 + b) - (y_1 + b))^2} = \sqrt{(x_2 - x_1)^2 + (y_2 - y_1)^2}$; $PP' = \sqrt{((x_1 + a) - x_1)^2 + ((y_1 + b) - y_1)^2} = \sqrt{a^2 + b^2}$; $QQ' = \sqrt{((x_2 + a) - x_2)^2 + ((y_2 + b) - y_2)^2} = \sqrt{a^2 + b^2}$

b. slope of $\overline{PP'} = \dfrac{y_1 + b - y_1}{x_1 + a - x_1} = \dfrac{b}{a}$; slope of $\overline{QQ'} = \dfrac{y_2 + b - y_2}{x_2 + b - x_2} = \dfrac{b}{a}$

c. slope of $\overline{PQ} = \dfrac{y_2 - y_1}{x_2 - x_1}$; slope of $\overline{P'Q'} = \dfrac{(y_2 + b) - (y_1 + b)}{(x_2 + a) - (x_1 + a)} = \dfrac{y_2 - y_1}{x_2 - x_1}$

d. PP'Q'Q is a $\square$. ($\overline{PQ}$ and $\overline{P'Q'}$ are $\parallel$, $\overline{PP'}$ and $\overline{QQ'}$ are $\parallel$.)

Pages 527-529 · WRITTEN EXERCISES

A   1-5. Answers may vary.   Examples are given.

1. $R_{0,440}$ 2. $R_{0,345}$ 3. $R_{A,90}$ 4. $R_{B,0}$ 5. $R_{0,180}$

6. F   7. C   8. B   9. D   10. C   11. E   12. C; D

13. D   14. rotation   15. reflection   16. half-turn   17. translation

18. rotation   19. half-turn   20. reflection   21. translation

B   22. 6   23. (3) and (8)

24.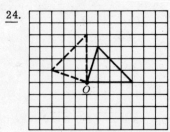

25.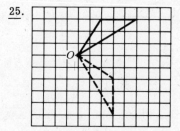

26.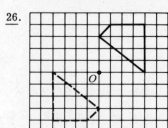

27. C is the midpt. of the seg. joining

(1, 1) and (7, 3); C is given by

$(\dfrac{1 + 7}{2},\ \dfrac{1 + 3}{2}) = (\dfrac{8}{2},\ \dfrac{4}{2}) = (4, 2)$

28. Construct the $\perp$ bisectors of $\overline{AA'}$ and

$\overline{BB'}$, intersecting at O.

c. slope of $\overleftrightarrow{AB} = \dfrac{1 - 3}{4 - 0} = \dfrac{-2}{4} = -\dfrac{1}{2}$;

slope of $\overleftrightarrow{A'B'} = \dfrac{4 - 0}{-1 - (-3)} = \dfrac{4}{2} = 2$

$\overleftrightarrow{AB} \perp \overleftrightarrow{A'B'}$

d. A rotation is an isometry.

29. a, b.
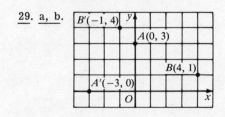

30. a. P   b. (6, 4)   c. (3, 4)   d. (5, 0)   e. (8, 3)   f. (6 - x, 4 - y)

31. Extend $\overrightarrow{OF}$ to intersect ℓ' at G. $\triangle$GF'O is a rt. $\triangle$; m$\angle$OGF' = 90 - x; let Y be

the pt. where ℓ and ℓ' intersect; $\triangle$GYF is a rt. $\triangle$; m$\angle$GYF = 90 - (90 - x) = x

<u>32.</u> <u>a.</u> $R_{C,-60}$ <u>b.</u> isometry   <u>c.</u> $R_{C,-60}$ maps $\overleftrightarrow{AD}$ to $\overleftrightarrow{BE}$; meas. of acute ∠ between $\overleftrightarrow{AD}$ and $\overleftrightarrow{BE}$ = 60 (If $R_{0,x}$ maps ℓ to ℓ', one of the ∠ between ℓ and ℓ' has meas. x.)

<u>33.</u> <u>a.</u> $R_{C,90}$ <u>b.</u> A rotation is an isometry.   <u>c.</u> Since $\overline{BE}$ is the image of $\overline{AD}$ under $R_{C,90}$ the meas. of the ∠ between $\overline{BE}$ and $\overline{AD}$ is 90; by def. $\overline{AD} \perp \overline{BE}$.

<u>C</u> <u>34.</u> <u>a.</u>

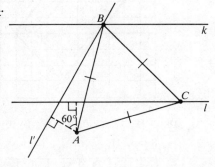

<u>b.</u> $\overline{AB}$ is the image of $\overline{AC}$ under $R_{A,60}$ so by Ex. 31, above, m∠A = 60; AB = AC since a rotation is an isometry. Then m∠B = m∠C = $\frac{1}{2}$(180 - 60) = 60. An equiangular △ is also equilateral.

<u>c.</u> yes; construct a ⊥ to ℓ and k through A; reflect △ABC in the ⊥.

<u>35.</u> Locate X and Z as you did B and C in Ex. 34, above, using $R_{A,90}$ instead of $R_{A,60}$. With ctrs. X and Z and rad. AX, draw arcs int. at Y. Draw $\overline{XY}$, $\overline{YZ}$, $\overline{ZA}$ and $\overline{AX}$.

Page 529 · CHALLENGE

The locus of the cat is C. Let $\overline{CD}$ be ⊥ $\overline{AJ}$, intersecting $\overline{AJ}$ at D. Then CD = $\frac{1}{2}$(AX + JY) = $\frac{1}{2}$(AM + MJ) = $\frac{1}{2}$ · AJ. Since $\overline{CD} \parallel \overline{AX} \parallel \overline{JY}$ and C is the midpt. of $\overline{XY}$, D is midpt. of $\overline{AJ}$; $\overline{CD}$ bisects $\overline{AJ}$ and all $\overline{XY}$, so the cat stays on $\overline{CD}$ at distance CD from $\overline{AJ}$.

Pages 532-533 · WRITTEN EXERCISES

<u>A</u> <u>1.</u> (12, 0); (8, 4); (4, -4)

<u>2.</u> (18, 0); (12, 6); (6, -6)

<u>3.</u> (3, 0); (2, 1); (1, -1)

<u>4.</u> (-3, 0); (-2, -1); (-1, 1)

<u>5.</u> (-12, 0); (-8, -4); (-4, 4)

<u>6.</u> (6, 0); (4, 2); (2, -2)

<u>7.</u> (6, 0); (7, -1); (8, 1)

<u>8.</u> (6, 0); (2, 4); (-2, -4)

<u>9.</u> k = $\frac{8}{2}$ = 4; expansion

<u>10.</u> k = $\frac{4}{2}$ = 2; expansion

<u>11.</u> k = $\frac{1}{3}$; contraction

<u>12.</u> k = $\frac{-2}{4}$ = -$\frac{1}{2}$; contraction

<u>13.</u> k = $\dfrac{\frac{2}{3}}{\frac{1}{6}}$ = 4; expansion

<u>14.</u> k = $\frac{18}{-6}$ = -3; expansion

B 15. P'(-3, 3); Q'(0, -3); R'(12, 0);   16. P'(8, 0); Q'(0, 10); R'(-6, 4);
       S'(6, 6)   S'(2, -6)

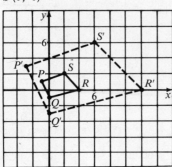   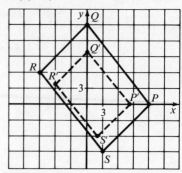

17. P'(-6, 0); Q'(-6, -8); R'(-12, -12);   18. P'(1, 1); Q'(0, 0); R'(-2, 0);
    S'(-10, 2)   S'(-3, 1)

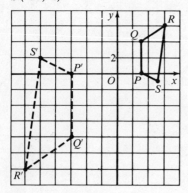   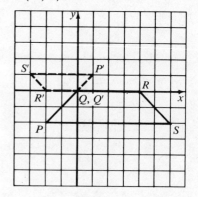

19. a. 3 : 1   b. 9 : 1   20. a. 1 : 4   b. 1 : 8

21. a. $\frac{2}{3}$ b. $\frac{1}{2}$ c. $D_{G, -\frac{1}{2}}$ d. N; P

22. a. slope of $\overline{PQ} = \frac{d - b}{c - a}$; slope of $\overline{P'Q'} = \frac{kd - kb}{kc - ka} = \frac{k(d - b)}{k(c - a)} = \frac{d - b}{c - a}$ b. parallel

C 23. $P'Q' = \sqrt{(ka - kc)^2 + (kb - kd)^2} = \sqrt{k^2(a - c)^2 + k^2(b - d)^2} =$

$\sqrt{k^2[(a - c)^2 + (b - d)^2]} = |k| \sqrt{(a - c)^2 + (b - d)^2} = |k| \cdot PQ$

24. (a, b) is on $\overleftrightarrow{AA'}$ and $\overleftrightarrow{BB'}$; slope of $\overleftrightarrow{AA'} = \frac{8 - 4}{1 - 3} = \frac{4}{-2} = 2$; equation of $\overleftrightarrow{AA'}$:

y - 4 = -2(x - 3); y = -2x + 10; slope of $\overleftrightarrow{BB'} = 0$; equation of $\overleftrightarrow{BB'}$: y = 2;

2 = -2x + 10; 2x = 8; x = 4; (a, b) = (4, 2); $A'B' = \sqrt{(1 - 1)^2 + (8 - 2)^2} = 6$;

AB = |4 - 2| = 2; k = $\frac{6}{2}$ = 3

Pages 538-540 · WRITTEN EXERCISES

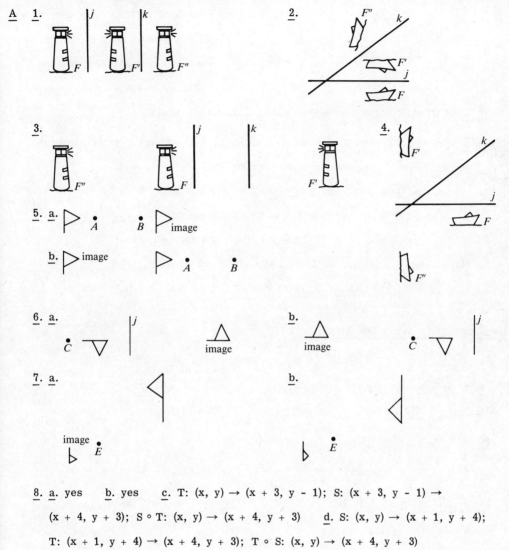

__A__ __1.__

__2.__

__3.__

__4.__

__5.__ __a.__

__b.__

__6.__ __a.__   __b.__

__7.__ __a.__   __b.__

__8.__ __a.__ yes   __b.__ yes   __c.__ T: (x, y) → (x + 3, y - 1); S: (x + 3, y - 1) →

(x + 4, y + 3); S ∘ T: (x, y) → (x + 4, y + 3)   __d.__ S: (x, y) → (x + 1, y + 4);

T: (x + 1, y + 4) → (x + 4, y + 3); T ∘ S: (x, y) → (x + 4, y + 3)

__9.__ __a.__ Q   __b.__ S   __c.__ M   __d.__ Q

__B__ __10.__ __a.__ L   __b.__ L   __c.__ Q   __11.__ Q   __12.__ (-3, -1)   __13.__ (1, 2)   __14.__ (9, 2)

__15.__ (-5, -1)   __16.__ (4, -8)   __17.__ (-1, 2)   __18.__ (3, -3)   __19.__ (-1, 1)

__20.__ __a.__ Q = (-2, 5)   __b.__ 90   __c.__ slope of $\overline{OP}$ = $\frac{2 - 0}{5 - 0}$ = $\frac{2}{5}$; slope of $\overline{OQ}$ = $\frac{5 - 0}{-2 - 0}$ =

$\frac{5}{-2}$ = - $\frac{5}{2}$; two nonvertical lines are ⊥ if and only if the product of their slopes is -1.

21. a, b.

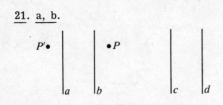

c. A product of reflections in 2 ∥ lines is a translation. The translation glides all pts. through twice the dist. between the lines; distance between a and b = distance between c and d.

22. Find B' such that R_R: B → B'. Line j is the ⊥ bis. of $\overline{AB'}$.

C 23. a. The seg. that joins the midpts. of 2 sides of a △ has a length = to half the length of the third side.   b. yes   c. yes; translation

24. translation; $\overline{P'Q'}$ ∥ $\overline{PQ}$ and $\overline{P''Q''}$ ∥ $\overline{P'Q'}$ so $\overline{PQ}$ ∥ $\overline{P''Q''}$; P'Q' = 2 · PQ and P''Q'' = $\frac{1}{2}$ · P'Q' so P''Q'' = PQ; then PP''Q''Q is a ▱ and $D_{B,\frac{1}{2}} \circ D_{A,2}$ is a translation.

25. a. $R_{0,90}$: one (the origin); R_y: infinitely many (all pts. on the y-axis); $D_{0,3}$: one (the origin); T: none   b. Let (x, y) be the fixed pt. $D_{A,\frac{1}{4}}(x, y) =$ $(1 + \frac{1}{4}(x - 1), \frac{y}{4})$; $D_{0,2} \circ D_{A,\frac{1}{4}}$ (x, y) = $(2 + \frac{1}{2}(x - 1), \frac{y}{2})$ = (x, y); (x, y) = (3, 0)

Pages 542-543 · WRITTEN EXERCISES

A 1. $\frac{1}{4}$ 2. $\frac{1}{9}$ 3. $\frac{3}{2}$ 4. 5   5. C   6. D   7. A   8. D

9. C   10. B   11. A   12. B   13. C   14. P   15. I

16. H_0 17. H_0 18. (x + 4, y)   19. (x + 6, y + 8)

B 20. S^{-1}: (x, y) → (x - 5, y - 2)   21. S^{-1}: (x, y) → (x + 3, y + 1)

22. S^{-1}: (x, y) → $(\frac{1}{3}x, \frac{1}{3}y)$ 23. S^{-1}: (x, y) → (4x, 4y)

24. S^{-1}: (x, y) → (x - 4, $\frac{1}{4}y$)   25. S^{-1}: (x, y) → (y, x)

26. T: (x, y) → (x + 2, y + $\frac{1}{2}$)   27. $R_{0,72}$

C 28. a. 2 units left; 2 units right   b. $R_k \circ R_k$ = I and $R_j \circ R_j$ = I; $(R_k \circ R_j) \circ (R_j \circ R_k)$ = $R_k \circ (R_j \circ R_j) \circ R_k = R_k \circ I \circ R_k = R_k \circ R_k = I$

29. a. S and T are inverses   b. $H_A \circ H_A$ = I and $H_B \circ H_B$ = I; $(H_A \circ H_B) \circ (H_B \circ H_A)$ = $H_A \circ (H_B \circ H_B) \circ H_A = H_A \circ I \circ H_A = H_A \circ H_A = I$

30. 1, 2.   A product of reflections in ⊥ lines is a half turn about the pt. where the lines int.   3, 5. Subst. Prop.   6. Def. of identity mapping   7. A product of reflections in ∥ lines is a translation

Pages 546-547 · WRITTEN EXERCISES

<u>A</u> <u>1</u>. <u>a</u>. 5   <u>b</u>. no   <u>c</u>. Let O be the ctr. of the circumscribed ⊙ of the starfish;

$R_{0,72}$; $R_{0,144}$; $R_{0,216}$; $R_{0,288}$

<u>2</u>. <u>a</u>. 6   <u>b</u>. yes   <u>c</u>. Let O be the ctr. of the circumscribed ⊙ of the snowflake;

$R_{0,60}$; $R_{0,120}$; $R_{0,180}$; $R_{0,240}$; $R_{0,300}$

<u>3</u>. <u>a</u>. 4   <u>b</u>. yes   <u>c</u>. Let O be the ctr. of the circumscribed ⊙ of the flower;

$R_{0,90}$; $R_{0,180}$; $R_{0,270}$

<u>4</u>. <u>a</u>. 13   <u>b</u>. no   <u>c</u>. Let O be the ctr. of the circumscribed ⊙ of the cactus;

$R_{0,\frac{360n}{13}}$ for n = 1, 2, 3, ..., 12

<u>5-7</u>. Answers may vary depending on the manner in which the letters are formed.

<u>5</u>. A B C D E K M T U V W Y   <u>6</u>. H I O X

<u>7</u>. H I N O S X Z

<u>8-11</u>. Figures may vary.   Examples are given.

<u>8</u>.
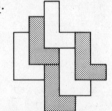

<u>9</u>.
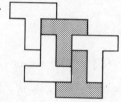

<u>10</u>.
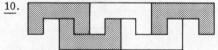

<u>11</u>.
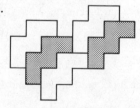

<u>12</u>.
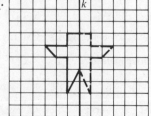

<u>13</u>.
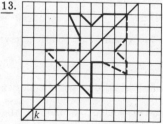

14.
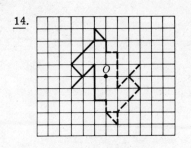

15.

16.

17.

18. a. yes   b. yes   c. no (There is no integer n for which 108 · n = 360)   d. yes

19. a. 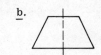   b.   c. not possible

20. a. 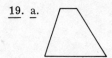   b. 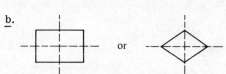   or   c. not possible

21. a. 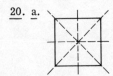   b.   c.

    regular octagon

22. a. 90°; 180°, and 270° rotational symmetries   b. 60°:6; 45°:8; 30°:12

23. a. at the midpts. of the sides   b. translational   24. a. no   b. yes

25. Let ABCDEF be a hexagon with symmetry pt. O. H_0 maps $\overline{AB}$ to $\overline{DE}$ so, since a
    rotation is an isometry, $\overline{AB} \cong \overline{DE}$.   Also by the def. of a rotation, $\overline{OA} \cong \overline{OD}$ and
    $\overline{OB} \cong \overline{OE}$.   Then $\triangle OAB \cong \triangle ODE$ and $\angle OAB \cong \angle ODE$.   Then $\overline{AB} \parallel \overline{DE}$.
    Similarly, $\overline{BC} \parallel \overline{EF}$ and $\overline{CD} \parallel \overline{FA}$.

26. Let P be a pt. on the figure and P' its image under $R_{0,60}$; P' must be on the figure;
    let P'' be its image under $R_{0,60}$.   P'' is also on the figure and is the image of P
    under $R_{0,120}$.   Thus, the figure has 120° rotational symmetry.   Similarly, it has
    180°, 240°, and 300° rotational symmetry, as well as 360° rotational symmetry.

27. By the same reasoning as in Ex. 26, above, the fig. must have 100°, 150°, 200°, 250°,
    300°, 350° and 360° rotational symmetries.   But having 350° and 360° rotational
    symmetries means that the fig. also has 10° rotational symmetry.   Then it must
    have 10°, 20°, 30°, ..., 360° rotational symmetries.

Pages 548-549 · EXERCISES

1. Let k be the alt. to the base.

∘	I	R_k
I	I	R_k
R_k	R_k	I

2. a. I, R_j, R_k, H_0 c. yes

b.

∘	I	R_j	R_k	H_0
I	I	R_j	R_k	H_0
R_j	R_j	I	H_0	R_k
R_k	R_k	H_0	I	R_j
H_0	H_0	R_k	R_j	I

3.

∘	I	$R_{0,120}$	$R_{0,240}$
I	I	$R_{0,120}$	$R_{0,240}$
$R_{0,120}$	$R_{0,120}$	$R_{0,240}$	I
$R_{0,240}$	$R_{0,240}$	I	$R_{0,120}$

4.

∘	I	$R_{0,90}$	H_0	$R_{0,270}$
I	I	$R_{0,90}$	H_0	$R_{0,270}$
$R_{0,90}$	$R_{0,90}$	H_0	$R_{0,270}$	I
H_0	H_0	$R_{0,270}$	I	$R_{0,90}$
$R_{0,270}$	$R_{0,270}$	I	$R_{0,90}$	H_0

5. a. 2 (H_0 and I)   b. all 4   6. yes; yes

7. a.

∘	I	$R_{0,120}$	$R_{0,240}$	R_j	R_k	R_ℓ
I	I	$R_{0,120}$	$R_{0,240}$	R_j	R_k	R_ℓ
$R_{0,120}$	$R_{0,120}$	$R_{0,240}$	I	R_ℓ	R_j	R_k
$R_{0,240}$	$R_{0,240}$	I	$R_{0,120}$	R_k	R_ℓ	R_j
R_j	R_j	R_k	R_ℓ	I	$R_{0,120}$	$R_{0,240}$
R_k	R_k	R_ℓ	R_j	$R_{0,240}$	I	$R_{0,120}$
R_ℓ	R_ℓ	R_j	R_k	$R_{0,120}$	$R_{0,240}$	I

b. Answers may vary; for example, $R_j \circ R_k = R_{0,240}$; $R_k \circ R_j = R_{0,120}$

8.

∘	I	$R_{0,90}$	H_o	$R_{0,270}$	R_j	R_k	R_ℓ	R_m
I	I	$R_{0,90}$	H_o	$R_{0,270}$	R_j	R_k	R_ℓ	R_m
$R_{0,90}$	$R_{0,90}$	H_o	$R_{0,270}$	I	R_ℓ	R_m	R_k	R_j
H_o	H_o	$R_{0,270}$	I	$R_{0,90}$	R_k	R_j	R_m	R_ℓ
$R_{0,270}$	$R_{0,270}$	I	$R_{0,90}$	H_o	R_m	R_ℓ	R_j	R_k
R_j	R_j	R_m	R_k	R_ℓ	I	H_o	$R_{0,270}$	$R_{0,90}$
R_k	R_k	R_ℓ	R_j	R_m	H_o	I	$R_{0,90}$	$R_{0,270}$
R_ℓ	R_ℓ	R_j	R_m	R_k	$R_{0,90}$	$R_{0,270}$	I	H_o
R_m	R_m	R_k	R_ℓ	R_j	$R_{0,270}$	$R_{0,90}$	H_o	I

The symmetry group of the square is
not a commutative group.

9. a. no; there is no identity, and the product of 2 line symmetries is not a line

symmetry.   b. yes; the rotational symmetries   c. I and H_o

10. a. S^3 maps each fish to the 3rd fish of the same color to its right; yes.   b. T^{-1}

maps each fish to the fish of the same color directly below; yes.   c. S ∘ T maps

each fish to the fish of the same color above and to the right; yes   d. infinitely

many   e. yes

Pages 551-552 · CHAPTER REVIEW

1. ≅   2. (6, 1)   3. ($\frac{3}{2}$, 5)   4. no

5.
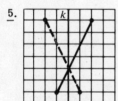

6.
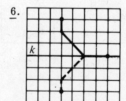

7.
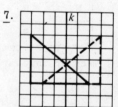

8. (7, 5)   9. (5, 0)   10. a. (2, -4)   b. (x + 2, y - 4)   c. (1, 6)

11. (12, 2)

12. a. 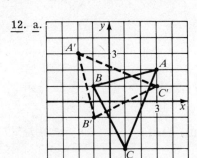   b.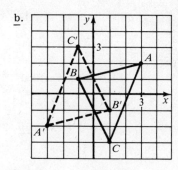

13. a, c   14. (0, 4)   15. (0, -1)   16. (2, 4)   17. (-3, -1)

18. (3, -1)   19. (1, 3)   20. (x + 1, y - 6)   21. 0, $\frac{1}{5}$ 22. I

23. -75 (or 285)   24. no   25. yes   26. yes   27. a regular pentagon

Page 553 · CHAPTER TEST

1. translation   2. reflection   3. glide reflection   4. rotation

5. (2, 4)   6. (2, -4)   7. (2, 1)   8. (-4, 2)   9. (-4, -2)

10. (2, 2)   11. (4, 2)   12. (2, -4)   13. (2, -2)   14. (-2, -4)

15. H_0 16. R_x 17. $D_{0,-1}$ 18. (2, 1)   19. (6, 3)   20. (-2, -1)

21. (2, 1)   22. true   23. false   24. true   25. true   26. true

Page 554 · PREPARING FOR COLLEGE ENTRANCE EXAMS

1. B   2. A   3. E   4. C   5. C   6. E   7. A   8. E

9. B   10. D

Pages 555-559 · CUMULATIVE REVIEW: CHAPTERS 1-12

True-False Exercises

A   1. F   2. F   3. T   4. T   5. F   6. T   7. T   8. T

9. T   10. F   11. T   12. F   13. F   14. T   15. F   16. T

17. F

B   18. F   19. F   20. T   21. F   22. F   23. T   24. T   25. T

26. T

Multiple Choice Exercises

A   1. b   2. d   3. a   4. d   5. c   6. c   7. d   8. a

9. a   10. b

B 11. d   12. c   13. b   14. c   15. b

Completion Exercises

A 1. $-\frac{3}{2}$ 2. 124   3. vertical   4. 1331   5. (-6, 1)   6. (4, -1)

7. right   8. $2\sqrt{13}$ 9. n - 3   10. 4   11. 33   12. 20π

13. 512 cm³   14. 12; 9   15. SAS, ASA, HL, AAS   16. Add. Prop. of =

17. 6   18. 96   19. $6\sqrt{3}$

B 20. 12.5   21. 22.5   22. $81\pi\sqrt{7}$; 108π 23. $10\sqrt{3}$ 24. $\frac{16\pi}{5}$ m²

25. $\frac{15}{17}$ 26. 7; -1   27. $27\sqrt{7}$ 28. $36\sqrt{3}$ cm²; $18\sqrt{2}$ cm³

29. (-5, 2)   30. 1:7

Always-Sometimes-Never Exercises

A 1. N   2. A   3. S   4. A   5. S   6. A   7. S   8. S

9. N   10. N   11. S   12. A   13. N   14. A   15. N

B 16. S   17. N   18. A   19. S   20. S   21. A   22. N   23. S

Construction Exercises

A 1. Construction 11   2. Construction 8

3-10. Methods may vary.

3. Construct an equilateral △ and bis. one ∠ to construct a 30° ∠. Construct $\overline{AB}$ with length x and construct a 30° ∠ at A. Construct $\overline{AC}$ with length x on the other side of ∠A. Draw $\overline{BC}$.

4. Draw a line and construct $\overline{AB}$, $\overline{BC}$, and $\overline{CD}$ each with length x. Construct $\overline{ED}$ (with E on $\overrightarrow{DC}$) with length y. Construct the ⊥ bis. of $\overline{AE}$, int. $\overline{AE}$ at F; AF = $\frac{1}{2}$(3x - y)

5. Construct $\overline{AB}$ so that AB = y. Construct a ⊥ to $\overline{AB}$ at A and one at B. With ctr. B and rad. x, draw an arc intersecting the first ⊥ at D. With ctr. A and rad. x, draw an arc intersecting the second ⊥ at C. Draw $\overline{DC}$.

B 6. Draw a line and construct $\overline{AB}$, $\overline{BC}$, and $\overline{CD}$ each with length x. Use Construction 14 to construct the geom. mean of AD and y.

7. Draw a line and construct $\overline{AB}$ and $\overline{BC}$ each with length x. At C, construct a ⊥ to $\overline{AC}$ and construct $\overline{CD}$ on the ⊥ with length y. Draw $\overline{AD}$.

8. Construct $\overline{AB}$ with length y. With ctrs. A and B and radii x and y, resp., draw arcs intersecting at C. With ctrs. A and C and radius y, draw arcs intersecting at D. Draw $\overline{BC}$, $\overline{CD}$, and $\overline{AD}$.

9. Construct the ⊥ bis. of $\overline{AB}$, intersecting $\overline{AB}$ at C.   Use Construction 12 to divide $\overline{AC}$ into 5 ≅ parts, $\overline{AW}$, $\overline{WX}$, $\overline{XY}$, $\overline{YZ}$, and $\overline{ZC}$.   Construct $\overline{DE} \cong \overline{AY}$.   Construct a ⊥ to $\overline{DE}$ at D and one at E.   Construct $\overline{DG}$ and $\overline{EF}$ both ≅ to $\overline{YC}$ on the ⊥s.   Draw $\overline{GF}$.

10. Draw a seg. $\overline{AC}$ and choose B on $\overline{AC}$.   Construct $\overline{BD} \perp \overline{AC}$.   Construct $\overrightarrow{BF}$, the bis. of ∠DBC and $\overrightarrow{BG}$, the bis. of ∠FBC; m∠ABG = $157\frac{1}{2}$.

Proof Exercises

A   1. 1. $\overline{OP} \cong \overline{OQ}$; $\overline{OS} \cong \overline{OR}$ (Given)   2. ∠POS ≅ ∠QOR (Vert. ∡ are ≅.)

3. △POS ≅ △QOR (SAS)   4. $\overline{PS} \cong \overline{QR}$ (Corr. parts of ≅ ⧌ are ≅.)

2. 1. $\overline{PQ} \parallel \overline{RS}$ (Given)   2. ∠OPQ ≅ ∠ORS; ∠OQP ≅ ∠OSR (If 2 ∥ lines are cut by a trans., then alt. int. ∡ are ≅.)   3. △OQP ∼ △OSR (AA)   4. $\dfrac{PO}{RO} = \dfrac{PQ}{RS}$ (Corr. sides of ∼ ⧌ are in prop.)

3. 1. $\overline{PR} \perp \overline{QS}$ (Given)   2. ∠POS and ∠QOR are rt. ∡; △POS and △QOR are rt. ⧌. (Def. of ⊥ lines; def. of rt. △)   3. $\overline{PS} \cong \overline{QR}$; $\overline{OS} \cong \overline{OR}$ (Given)

4. △POS ≅ △QOR (HL)   5. ∠PSO ≅ ∠QRO (Corr. parts of ≅ ⧌ are ≅.)

B   4. 1. ∠OSR ≅ ∠ORS; ∠OPQ ≅ ∠OQP (Given)   2. OS = OR; OP = OQ (If 2 ∡ of a △ are ≅, then the sides opp. those ∡ are ≅.)   3. OS + OQ = OR + OP (Add. Prop. of =)   4. OS + OQ = SQ; OR + OP = RP (Seg. Add. Post.)   5. SQ = RP (Subst. Prop.)   6. SR = SR (Refl. Prop.)   7. △PSR ≅ △QRS (SAS)

5. Given: rect. ABCD; $\overline{AC}$ and $\overline{BD}$ intersect at X.

Prove: AX = XC = BX = XD   Proof: 1. ABCD is a rect. (Given)   2. AC = BD (The diag. of a rect. are ≅.)   3. $\overline{AC}$ and $\overline{BD}$ bis. each other. (The diag. of a ▱ bis. each other.)

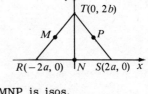

4. X is the midpt. of $\overline{AC}$ and $\overline{BD}$. (Def. of bis.)   5. AX = XC = $\frac{1}{2}$AC; BX = XD = $\frac{1}{2}$BD (Midpt. Thm.)   6. $\frac{1}{2}$AC = $\frac{1}{2}$BD (Mult. Prop. of =)   7. AX = XC = BX = XD (Subst. Prop.)

6. Let R(-2a, 0), S(2a, 0), and T(0, 2b) be the vertices of an isos. △. Then M(-a, b), N(0, 0), and P(a, b) are the midpts. of $\overline{TR}$, $\overline{RS}$, and $\overline{TS}$, resp.; NM = $\sqrt{(0 - (-a))^2 + (0 - b)^2} = \sqrt{a^2 + b^2}$; NP = $\sqrt{(a - 0)^2 + (b - 0)^2} = \sqrt{a^2 + b^2}$; then $\overline{NM} \cong \overline{NP}$ and △MNP is isos.

C 7. Let ABCD be a trap. with bases $\overline{AB}$ and $\overline{CD}$ and assume

temp. that ABCD has 2 pairs of ≃ sides.

Case 1: $\overline{AB} \simeq \overline{DC}$ and $\overline{AD} \simeq \overline{BC}$. Since $\overline{AB} \parallel \overline{DC}$ and

$\overline{AB} \simeq \overline{DC}$, ABCD must be a ▱ and $\overline{AD} \parallel \overline{BC}$. This

contradicts the def. of a trap.   Case 2: $\overline{AB} \simeq \overline{AD}$ and $\overline{BC} \simeq \overline{DC}$.   Draw $\overline{AC}$.

△ADC ≃ △ABC (SSS) so ∠D ≃ ∠B, ∠DAC ≃ ∠BAC, and ∠ACD ≃ ∠ACB.   Since

$\overline{AB} \parallel \overline{DC}$, ∠ACD ≃ ∠BAC ≃ ∠DAC.   Then m∠A = m∠DAC + m∠BAC =

m∠ACB + m∠ACD = m∠C.   If both pairs of opp. ∡ of ABCD are ≃, ABCD is

a ▱ and $\overline{AD} \parallel \overline{BC}$. This contradicts the def. of a trap.   Case 3: ($\overline{AB} \simeq \overline{BC}$ and

$\overline{AD} \simeq \overline{DC}$) is similar to Case 2.   All three cases lead to a contradiction.   Our temp.

assumption must be incorrect.   It follows that a trap. cannot have 2 prs. of ≃ sides.

8. Given: ⊙O and ⊙P intersect in A and B; $\overline{XY}$ a

common tan. with X on ⊙O and Y on ⊙P.   Let

Z be the pt. where $\overleftrightarrow{AB}$ intersects $\overline{XY}$.

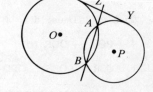

Prove: ZX = ZY.   Proof: 1. $(ZX)^2$ = ZA · ZB;

$(ZY)^2$ = ZA · ZB (When a sec. seg. and a tan.

seg. are drawn to a ⊙ from an outside pt., the product of the length of the secant seg.

and the length of its ext. seg. = the square of the length of the tan. seg.)   2. $(ZX)^2$ =

$(ZY)^2$ (Subst. Prop.)   3. ZX = ZY (By algebra)

End-of-Book Examinations

Page 560 · CHAPTER 1

1. b 2. d 3. c 4. d 5. a 6. a 7. b
8. b 9. a 10. b 11. a

Page 561 · CHAPTER 2

1. d 2. a 3. b 4. a 5. c 6. b 7. d
8. b 9. d 10. c 11. a 12. c

Page 562 · CHAPTER 3

1. ASA 2. AAS 3. ASA 4. HL 5. SSS 6. AAS 7. SAS
8. HL 9. c 10. d 11. a 12. d 13. b 14. c 15. a

Page 563 · CHAPTER 4

1. a 2. d 3. a 4. d 5. b 6. b 7. a
8. c 9. b 10. c 11. a

Page 564 · CHAPTER 5

1. c 2. d 3. a 4. d 5. b 6. b 7. b
8. a 9. b 10. d 11. c

Page 565 · CHAPTER 6

1. a 2. b 3. c 4. d 5. c 6. d 7. b
8. a 9. c 10. d 11. c 12. a

Page 566 · CHAPTER 7

1. c 2. b 3. c 4. c 5. c 6. a 7. b
8. d 9. a 10. b 11. d 12. a 13. d

Page 567 · CHAPTER 8

1. c 2. d 3. b 4. b 5. c 6. d 7. a
8. d 9. d 10. d 11. a 12. c

Page 568 · CHAPTER 9

<u>1</u>. a   <u>2</u>. d   <u>3</u>. b   <u>4</u>. c   <u>5</u>. b   <u>6</u>. a   <u>7</u>. d

<u>8</u>. c   <u>9</u>. c   <u>10</u>. b   <u>11</u>. d   <u>12</u>. d   <u>13</u>. b

Page 569 · CHAPTER 10

<u>1</u>. d   <u>2</u>. b   <u>3</u>. a   <u>4</u>. c   <u>5</u>. b   <u>6</u>. b   <u>7</u>. a

<u>8</u>. b   <u>9</u>. a   <u>10</u>. d   <u>11</u>. c   <u>12</u>. a   <u>13</u>. d

Page 570 · CHAPTER 11

<u>1</u>. d   <u>2</u>. a   <u>3</u>. c   <u>4</u>. d   <u>5</u>. d   <u>6</u>. b   <u>7</u>. d

<u>8</u>. c   <u>9</u>. c   <u>10</u>. c   <u>11</u>. a   <u>12</u>. b

Page 571 · CHAPTER 12

<u>1</u>. c   <u>2</u>. c   <u>3</u>. b   <u>4</u>. c   <u>5</u>. a   <u>6</u>. d   <u>7</u>. b

<u>8</u>. c   <u>9</u>. c   <u>10</u>. c   <u>11</u>. b   <u>12</u>. b   <u>13</u>. d

Pages 577-578 · EXERCISES

1. I like the city and you like the country.   2. I do not like the city.

3. You do not like the country.   4. I like the city or you like the country.

5. I like the city or you do not like the country.

6. It is not true that "I like the city and you like the country."

7. I do not like the city or you do not like the country.

8. I do not like the city and you like the country.

9. It is not true that "I like the city or you like the country."

10. I do not like the city and you do not like the country.

11. p ∨ q   12. ~ q   13. ~ (p ∨ q)   14. ~ p ∧ ~ q   15. ~ (p ∧ q)

16. ~ p ∨ ~ q   17. Yes   18. Yes

19.

p	q	~ q	p ∨ ~ q
T	T	F	T
T	F	T	T
F	T	F	F
F	F	T	T

20.

p	q	~ p	~ p ∨ q
T	T	F	T
T	F	F	F
F	T	T	T
F	F	T	T

21.

p	~ p	~ (~ p)
T	F	T
F	T	F

22.

p	q	p ∧ q	~ (p ∧ q)
T	T	T	F
T	F	F	T
F	T	F	T
F	F	F	T

23.

p	~ p	p ∨ ~ p
T	F	T
F	T	T

24.

p	~ p	p ∧ ~ p
T	F	F
F	T	F

25.

p	q	r	q ∨ r	p ∧ (q ∨ r)
T	T	T	T	T
T	T	F	T	T
T	F	T	T	T
T	F	F	F	F
F	T	T	T	F
F	T	F	T	F
F	F	T	T	F
F	F	F	F	F

26.

p	q	r	p ∧ q	p ∧ r	(p ∧ q) ∨ (p ∧ r)
T	T	T	T	T	T
T	T	F	T	F	T
T	F	T	F	T	T
T	F	F	F	F	F
F	T	T	F	F	F
F	T	F	F	F	F
F	F	T	F	F	F
F	F	F	F	F	F

Pages 579-580 · EXERCISES

1. If you like to paint, then you are an artist.

2. If you are an artist, then you draw landscapes.

3. If you are not an artist, then you do not draw landscapes.

4. It is not true that "If you like to paint, then you are an artist."

5. If you like to paint and you are an artist, then you draw landscapes.

6. You like to paint, and if you are an artist, then you draw landscapes.

7. If you draw landscapes or you are an artist, then you like to paint.

8. You draw landscapes, or if you are an artist, then you like to paint.

9. b → w   10. w → ~ s   11. (~ b ∨ ~ w) → s   12. s ∧ (b → w)

13. ~ (b → s)   14. ~ b → (w ∧ s)

15. a.

p	q	~ p	~ q	~ p → ~ q
T	T	F	F	T
T	F	F	T	T
F	T	T	F	F
F	F	T	T	T

Yes; no   b. Yes; yes

16.

p	q	~ q	p → ~ q
T	T	F	F
T	F	T	T
F	T	F	T
F	F	T	T

17.

p	q	p → q	~ (p → q)
T	T	T	F
T	F	F	T
F	T	T	F
F	F	T	F

18.

p	q	~ q	p ∧ ~ q
T	T	F	F
T	F	T	T
F	T	F	F
F	F	T	F

19. ~ (p → q) and p ∧ ~ q are

logically equivalent.

20.

p	q	p → q	q → p	(p → q) ∧ (q → p)
T	T	T	T	T
T	F	F	T	F
F	T	T	F	F
F	F	T	T	T

Pages 581-582 · EXERCISES

1. (1) Given; (2) Step 1 and Simplification; (3) Given; (4) Steps 2 and 3 and Modus Ponens

2. (1) Given; (2) Given; (3) Steps 1 and 2 and Modus Ponens; (4) Given; (5) Steps 3 and
   4 and Modus Ponens

3.

Statements	Reasons
1. p ∨ q	1. Given
2. ~ p	2. Given
3. q	3. Steps 1 and 2 and Disjunctive Syllogism
4. q → s	4. Given
5. s	5. Steps 3 and 4 and Modus Ponens

4.

Statements	Reasons
1. a → b	1. Given
2. ~ b	2. Given
3. ~ a	3. Steps 1 and 2 and Modus Tollens
4. a ∨ c	4. Given
5. c	5. Steps 3 and 4 and Disjunctive Syllogism

<u>5.</u>

Statements	Reasons
1. a ∧ b	1. Given
2. a	2. Step 1 and Simplification
3. a → ~ c	3. Given
4. ~ c	4. Steps 2 and 3 and Modus Ponens
5. c ∨ d	5. Given
6. d	6. Steps 4 and 5 and Disjunctive Syllogism

<u>6.</u>

Statements	Reasons
1. p ∧ q	1. Given
2. p	2. Step 1 and Simplification
3. p → ~ s	3. Given
4. ~ s	4. Steps 2 and 3 and Modus Ponens
5. r → s	5. Given
6. ~ r	6. Steps 4 and 5 and Modus Tollens

<u>7.</u> Given: j → d; d → c; j ∧ w.   Prove: c.   Proof:

Statements	Reasons
1. j ∧ w	1. Given
2. j	2. Step 1 and Simplification
3. j → d	3. Given
4. d	4. Steps 2 and 3 and Modus Ponens
5. d → c	5. Given
6. c	6. Steps 4 and 5 and Modus Ponens

<u>8.</u> Given: a ∧ r; b ∨ c; a → ~ b.   Prove: c.   Proof:

Statements	Reasons
1. a ∧ r	1. Given
2. a	2. Step 1 and Simplification
3. a → ~ b	3. Given
4. ~ b	4. Steps 2 and 3 and Modus Ponens
5. b ∨ c	5. Given
6. c	6. Steps 4 and 5 and Disjunctive Syllogism

9. Given: $t \vee r$; $t \rightarrow p$; $r \rightarrow s$; $\sim p$.   Prove: s.   Proof:

Statements	Reasons
1. $t \rightarrow p$	1. Given
2. $\sim p$	2. Given
3. $\sim t$	3. Steps 1 and 2 and Modus Tollens
4. $t \vee r$	4. Given
5. r	5. Steps 3 and 4 and Disjunctive Syllogism
6. $r \rightarrow s$	6. Given
7. s	7. Steps 5 and 6 and Modus Ponens

Page 583 · EXERCISES

1. (1) Given; (2) Step 1 and Double Negation; (3) Given; (4) Steps 2 and 3 and Modus Tollens

2. (1) Given; (2) Step 1 and Distributive Rule; (3) Step 2 and Simplification; (4) Step 3 and Commutative Rule; (5) Given; (6) Steps 4 and 5 and Disjunctive Syllogism

3.

Statements	Reasons
1. $a \wedge (b \wedge c)$	1. Given
2. $(a \wedge b) \wedge c$	2. Step 1 and Associative Rule
3. $c \wedge (a \wedge b)$	3. Step 2 and Commutative Rule
4. c	4. Step 3 and Simplification

4.

Statements	Reasons
1. $(p \wedge q) \rightarrow s$	1. Given
2. $\sim s$	2. Given
3. $\sim (p \wedge q)$	3. Steps 1 and 2 and Modus Tollens
4. $\sim p \vee \sim q$	4. Step 3 and DeMorgan's Rule

5.

Statements	Reasons
1. $p \vee (\sim q)$	1. Given
2. $(\sim q) \vee p$	2. Step 1 and Commutative Rule
3. q	3. Given
4. $\sim (\sim q)$	4. Step 3 and Double Negation
5. p	5. Steps 2 and 4 and Disjunctive Syllogism

6.

Statements	Reasons
1. $\sim q \rightarrow \sim p$	1. Given
2. $p \rightarrow q$	2. Step 1 and Contrapositive Rule
3. p	3. Given
4. q	4. Steps 2 and 3 and Modus Ponens
5. $q \rightarrow r$	5. Given
6. r	6. Steps 4 and 5 and Modus Ponens

7.

Statements	Reasons
1. $p \vee (q \wedge s)$	1. Given
2. $(p \vee q) \wedge (p \vee s)$	2. Step 1 and Distributive Rule
3. $(p \vee s) \wedge (p \vee q)$	3. Step 2 and Commutative Rule
4. $p \vee s$	4. Step 3 and Simplification

8.

Statements	Reasons
1. $t \vee (r \vee s)$	1. Given
2. $(r \vee s) \vee t$	2. Step 1 and Commutative Rule
3. $\sim r \wedge \sim s$	3. Given
4. $\sim (r \vee s)$	4. Step 3 and DeMorgan's Rule
5. t	5. Steps 2 and 4 and Disjunctive Syllogism

9. Given: $s \rightarrow w$; $\sim s \rightarrow p$; $\sim p$.   Prove: w.   Proof:

Statements	Reasons
1. $\sim s \rightarrow p$	1. Given
2. $\sim p$	2. Given
3. $\sim (\sim s)$	3. Steps 1 and 2 and Modus Tollens
4. s	4. Step 3 and Double Negation
5. $s \rightarrow w$	5. Given
6. w	6. Steps 4 and 5 and Modus Ponens

<u>10</u>. Given: e ∨ c; b ∨ m; b → s; m → ~ e; ~ s.   Prove: c.   Proof:

Statements	Reasons
1. b → s	1. Given
2. ~ s	2. Given
3. ~ b	3. Steps 1 and 2 and Modus Tollens
4. b ∨ m	4. Given
5. m	5. Steps 3 and 4 and Disjunctive Syllogism
6. m → ~ e	6. Given
7. ~ e	7. Steps 5 and 6 and Modus Ponens
8. e ∨ c	8. Given
9. c	9. Steps 7 and 8 and Disjunctive Syllogism

Page 585 · EXERCISES

<u>1</u>. p ∧ r

<u>2</u>. r ∨ s

<u>3</u>. s ∧ (t ∨ p)

<u>4</u>. (r ∧ p) ∨ (~ r ∧ q)

<u>5</u>. (t ∨ s) ∧ (~ t ∨ s)

<u>6</u>. (r ∨ s) ∨ ~ r

<u>7</u>.

$p \wedge {\sim} p$

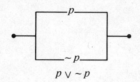

$p \vee {\sim} p$

Electricity can always pass through the circuit p ∨ ~ p and can never pass through the circuit p ∧ ~ p.

<u>8</u>.

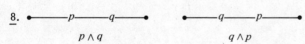

$p \wedge q$ $q \wedge p$

<u>9</u>.

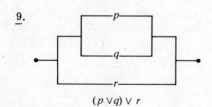

$(p \vee q) \vee r$

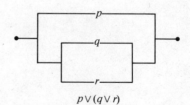

$p \vee (q \vee r)$

<u>10</u>.

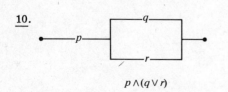

$p \wedge (q \vee r)$

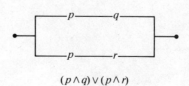

$(p \wedge q) \vee (p \wedge r)$

11.

p	q	~ q	p ∨ q	(p ∨ q) ∨ ~ q
T	T	F	T	T
T	F	T	T	T
F	T	F	T	T
F	F	T	F	T

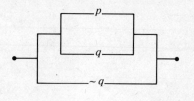

12.

p	q	~ q	p ∨ q	p ∨ ~ q	(p ∨ q) ∧ (p ∨ ~ q)
T	T	F	T	T	T
T	F	T	T	T	T
F	T	F	T	F	F
F	F	T	F	T	F

The circuit is equivalent to one which contains just switch p.

Appendix: Projections; Dihedral Angles

<u>A</u> <u>1</u>. yes   <u>2</u>. yes   <u>3</u>. yes   <u>4</u>. yes   <u>5</u>. no   <u>6</u>. no   <u>7</u>. yes   <u>8</u>. no

<u>B</u> <u>9</u>. yes   <u>10</u>. yes

<u>11</u>.
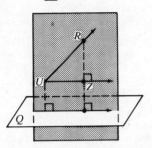

<u>12</u>.
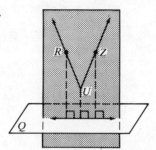

<u>13</u>.
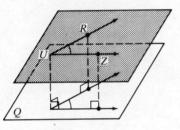

<u>14</u>.
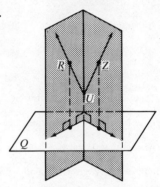

<u>C</u> <u>15</u>. 2 ∥ lines, a line, 2 points   <u>16</u>. a circle, a line segment, an ellipse

  <u>17</u>. an equilateral △, an isosceles △, a scalene △, a line segment

  <u>18</u>. a regular hexagon, a hexagon, a line segment

  <u>19</u>. a ▱, a rhombus, a rectangle, a square, a line segment

  <u>20</u>. an obtuse ∠, an acute ∠, a rt. ∠, a line, a ray

<u>A</u> <u>1</u>.
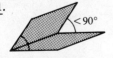

<u>2</u>.

<u>3</u>.

  <u>4</u>.
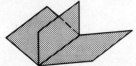

<u>B</u>   5. Two planes, X and Y, are ⊥ if a plane ∠ of the dihedral ∠ formed by X and Y

   is a rt. ∠.

   6. <u>a</u>, <u>b</u>.   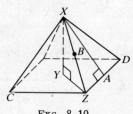   <u>c</u>. Y ⊥ X

                                                  <u>d</u>. contains the line, then the planes are ⊥.

   <u>7</u>. 1. If 2 ‖ planes are cut by a third plane, alt. int. dihedral ∡ are ≅.   2. If 2 ‖

   planes are cut by a third plane, same-side dihedral ∡ are supp.   3. If a plane is

   ⊥ to one of two ‖ planes, it is ⊥ to the other also.

   <u>8</u>. <u>a</u>. Answers will vary.   <u>b</u>. Draw the altitude, $\overline{XY}$, and draw $\overline{YZ}$.   △XYZ is a

   rt. △ with YZ = $3\sqrt{2}$ and XZ = 6, so △XYZ must be a 45°-45°-90° △.   Thus a

   lateral edge makes an ∠ of 45° with the base.

   <u>9</u>. <u>a</u>. Answers will vary.   <u>b</u>. Draw $\overline{XA}$ ⊥ $\overline{ZD}$ and

   $\overline{YA}$.   △XZD is an equilateral △ so XA = $3\sqrt{3}$.

   YA = 3 and cos ∠ XAY = $\dfrac{3}{3\sqrt{3}}$ ≈ 0.5774;

   m∠A ≈ 55.   The measure of the dihedral ∠

   formed by a lateral face and the base is ≈ 55.

   <u>10</u>. <u>a</u>. Answers will vary.   <u>b</u>. Draw $\overline{CB}$ and $\overline{DB}$,

   both ⊥ to $\overline{XZ}$.   △CBY and △DBY are ≅ rt. ∡ .   CY = $3\sqrt{2}$, CB = $3\sqrt{3}$, so

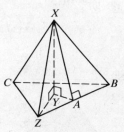

Exs. 8-10

   sin ∠ CBY = $\dfrac{3\sqrt{2}}{3\sqrt{3}}$ ≈ 0.8165 and m∠ B ≈ 54.7.   Then m∠ CBD ≈ 109.   ∠ CBD is a

   plane ∠ of dihedral ∠ C-XZ-D, so dihedral m∠ C-XZ-D ≈ 109.

   <u>11</u>. <u>a</u>. Answers will vary.   <u>b</u>. Draw $\overline{XY}$, the altitude

   of the pyramid.   The base is an equilateral △, so

   YZ = $2\sqrt{3}$.   Consider △XYZ: cos ∠XZY = $\dfrac{2\sqrt{3}}{6}$ ≈

   0.5774 and m∠XZY ≈ 55.

   <u>12</u>. <u>a</u>. Answers will vary.   <u>b</u>. Draw $\overline{XA}$ ⊥ $\overline{ZB}$.

   Consider △XAY.   cos A = $\dfrac{\sqrt{3}}{3\sqrt{3}}$ ≈ 0.3333 and

   m∠A ≈ 71.   ∠XAY is a plane ∠ of dihedral

   ∠X-BZ-C, so dihedral m∠X-BZ-C ≈ 71.

Exs. 11, 12

13. Suppose the △s shown are both plane △s of the given

dihedral ∠. All four rays are ⊥ to $\overline{ST}$. Then

the pair of rays in each plane are ‖. Choose A,

C, J and K so that $\overline{AJ}$ and $\overline{CK}$ are ‖ to $\overline{ST}$.

$\overline{AJ}$ ‖ $\overline{CK}$. Since AJEB and CKEB are ▱,

AJ = BE = CK, so AJKC is a ▱. Then AB = JE and BC = EK. Thus

△ABC ≅ △JEK, so ∠ABC ≅ ∠JEK.

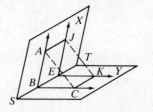

14. a. Consider △XAQ: cos 70° = $\frac{AQ}{10}$, AQ ≈ 3.42. Consider △XAR: cos 65° = $\frac{AR}{10}$,

AR ≈ 4.23; sin 65° = $\frac{XR}{10}$, XR ≈ 9.06. b. Consider △AQS, a rt. △ with

m∠QAS = 50: cos 50° ≈ $\frac{3.42}{AS}$, AS ≈ 5.32. Then RS = AS - AR ≈ 1.09. Now

consider △PRS, a rt. △ with m∠PSR = 40: tan 40° = $\frac{PR}{1.09}$, PR ≈ 0.92. Consider

rt. △PRX: PX = $\sqrt{(XR)^2 - (PR)^2}$ ≈ 9.01. Draw $\overline{AP}$. sin ∠PAX = $\frac{PX}{AX}$ ≈ $\frac{9.01}{10}$ ≈

0.90, m∠PAX ≈ 64. Since $\overline{AP}$ is the projection of $\overline{AX}$ into plane ABC, ∠PAX is

the ∠ of intersection of $\overrightarrow{AX}$ and plane ABC.

Appendix: Technical Drawing

Page 605 · EXERCISES

1.

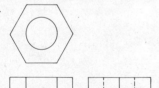

2.

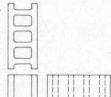

3.

4.